AN INTRODUCTION TO
SEQUENCES, SERIES, AND
IMPROPER INTEGRALS

The Mathesis Series

Kenneth O. May, Editor

Counterexamples in Analysis
Bernard R. Gelbaum and John M. H. Olmsted

Measure and the Integral
Henri Lebesgue

Lectures on Calculus
Edited by Kenneth O. May

Evolution of Mathematical Thought
Herbert Meschkowski

Ways of Thought of Great Mathematicians
Herbert Meschkowski

Numbers and Ideals
Abraham Robinson

An Introduction to Sequences, Series, and Improper Integrals
O. E. Stanaitis

AN INTRODUCTION TO SEQUENCES, SERIES, AND IMPROPER INTEGRALS

O. E. Stanaitis
St. Olaf College, Minnesota

Holden-Day, Inc.
San Francisco, Cambridge, London, Amsterdam

Library of Congress Catalog Card Number: 66-17896
Printed in the United States of America

PREFACE

This book is the result of experience the author has gained in teaching mathematics to undergraduates at the sophomore level and to high school teachers in National Science Foundation Summer Institutes.

To make the material readily accessible to the intended audience an effort has been made to give especially complete and detailed arguments, and to motivate and illustrate definitions, theorems and subtleties of proof with explicit numerical examples. Intuition and heuristics have been amply used, but rigor compatible with this level has been maintained throughout the text.

Although sequences, infinite series, and improper integrals are treated in textbooks on calculus and on infinite series—and there is no lack of good books— the beginner will have difficulty in finding a book that leads him on a lower level and in greater detail rapidly to the heart of the subject and to a deeper understanding of this topic which is so important in natural sciences today.

The primary objective of this book is to introduce the student to the fundamental concepts forming a firm basis for theory and applications. The author's experience, both as a student and as a teacher, has shown that if a student has had a good training in the fundamentals in mathematics he will have no difficulties in following the more difficult existence proofs and he will meet his future needs by his own further study, if necessary.

Some more difficult ideas which need repeating have been discussed repeatedly in a different setting. Some of the more general techniques which are essential for efficiency in proofs and in applications also have received special attention.

The first chapter deals at length with convergence of sequences, and it is deliberately elementary. To give the student a better intuitive feeling for the meaning of a limit, the neighborhood concept has been used. The concept of limit is basic in mathematics, and the beginner usually has some difficulty in mastering it. Because of this some teachers advocate replacing limits by ingenious artifices in high school mathematics. Our experience with summer institutes for high school students has shown that one can successfully teach limits on a high school level. It is firm belief of the author that whenever calculus is taught a good introductory section on limits should be mastered first.

Chapters 2 and 3 deal respectively with infinite series of positive and of more general terms. Theorems are stated in a form that is most likely to be useful in applications.

Chapter 4 gives an introduction to uniform convergence. Chapters 5 and 6 treat power series and Fouries series, respectively.

Chapter 7 deals with improper integrals. A prerequisite for this chapter is knowledge of the previous six chapters. The parallel between infinite series and improper integrals has been used to formulate the concept of convergence as well as the criteria of convergence of improper integrals. Because of the important role it plays in applications, the gamma function is introduced in section 7.12. A section on approximation of series concludes the chapter.

Hints are included in many of the exercises, and answers and hints to the odd-numbered ones are given at the end of the book.

I am indebted to my former teachers, colleagues and students for hints and help in preparing this book. Various parts of the manuscript were distributed to my classes in mimeographed form, and many improvements are due to their suggestions. In particular, my colleague Loren Larson read the manuscript and made suggestions in matters of exposition.

O. E. Stanaitis

Northfield, Minnesota, 1967

CONTENTS

AN INTRODUCTION TO
SEQUENCES, SERIES, AND
IMPROPER INTEGRALS

CHAPTER 1

PRELIMINARIES

The prerequisites for understanding the theory of infinite series are knowledge of inequalities, absolute value, and limits of sequences. Some of the more important properties and theorems of inequalities and absolute value are collected in this chapter, although many details have been omitted. It is suggested that the reader first review these preliminaries.

1.1 Inequalities

Let $a, b, c, \ldots$ be real numbers. The symbol $a \geq b$, or equivalently $b \leq a$, means that either $a > b$ or $a = b$. Whenever $a - b \geq 0$, we write $a \geq b$. The same basic relationship between a and b is stated by $b - a \leq 0$ or $b \leq a$.

1.1-1 Theorem. (a) If $a \geq b$, then $a + c \geq b + c$.

(b) If $a \geq b$, then $ac \geq bc$ if $c > 0$, and $ac \leq bc$ if $c < 0$.

(c) If $a \leq b$, $c \leq d$, then $a + c \leq b + d$.

(d) If $a \leq b$, $c \leq d$, and $b > 0$, $c > 0$, then $ac \leq bd$.

(e) If $a \leq b$, then $-b \leq -a$.

(f) If $a \leq b$ and $a > 0$, then $1/b \leq 1/a$.

(g) If $a \geq b$ and $b \geq 0$, then $a^2 \geq b^2$.

(h) $2ab \leq a^2 + b^2$; if p and q are positive, this inequality may be written in the form $2(pq)^{1/2} \leq p + q$.

(i) $(a_1 b_1 + a_2 b_2 + \cdots + a_n b_n)^2 \leq (a_1^2 + a_2^2 + \cdots + a_n^2)(b_1^2 + b_2^2 + \cdots + b_n^2)$.

(k) $(1 + h)^n > 1 + nh$ if $h > -1$ and n is an integer greater than 1.

(l) $(1 + h)^n > \dfrac{n(n - 1) \cdots (n - k + 1)}{k!} h^k$ if $h > 0$ and n is a positive integer.

(m) For $0 < x < 1$: $1 - x^p \leq (1 - x)p$ if $p > 1$ and $1 - x^p \geq (1 - x)p$ if $p < 1$.

It is not difficult to verify these inequalities. We prove some of them, while the others are left as exercises.

Proof. (a) If $a \geq b$, then $a - b \geq 0$. From the identity $a - b = a + c - (b + c)$ it follows that $a + c - (b + c) \geq 0$ which is equivalent to $a + c \geq b + c$.

(f) From $a \leq b$ and $a > 0$ it follows that $b > 0$ and, consequently, $1/ab > 0$. If the inequality is multiplied by $c = 1/ab$, by **1.1-1**(b) the statement $1/b \leq 1/a$ follows.

(g) $a \geq b$ and $b \geq 0$ implies $a - b \geq 0$ and $a + b \geq 0$, consequently, $(a - b)(a + b) \geq 0$ or $a^2 - b^2 \geq 0$. Hence, $a^2 \geq b^2$.

(h) Since the square of any real number is non-negative, it follows that $(a - b)^2 \geq 0$ or $a^2 - 2ab + b^2 \geq 0$, which is equivalent to $a^2 + b^2 \geq 2ab$. From $(a^{1/2} - b^{1/2})^2 \geq 0$, in the very same way it follows that $2(ab)^{1/2} \leq a + b$. Note that the equality sign holds only if $a = b$ and that $a^{1/2}$ and $b^{1/2}$ are defined only for $a \geq 0$, $b \geq 0$.

(i) First we note that the sum of the squares of real numbers is not negative. Consequently,

$$(a_1x + b_1)^2 + (a_2x + b_2)^2 + \cdots + (a_nx + b_n)^2 \geq 0$$

for all real a_i, b_i $(i = 1, 2, 3, \ldots, n)$, and x. Collecting of terms yields the quadratic expression in x

$$ax^2 + 2bx + c \geq 0 , \quad a = \sum_{i=1}^{n} a_i^2 , \quad b = \sum_{i=1}^{n} a_ib_i , \quad c = \sum_{i=1}^{n} b_i^2.$$

Put $x = -b/a$ to obtain $c - b^2/a \geq 0$. Multiplication by a $(a > 0)$ yields the desired inequality $b^2 \leq ac$, or

$$\left(\sum_{i=1}^{n} a_ib_i\right)^2 \leq \left(\sum_{i=1}^{n} a_i^2\right)\left(\sum_{i=1}^{n} b_i^2\right),$$

which is known as the Cauchy-Schwarz inequality.*

(k) Suppose the inequality is true for some integer $m > 1$, that is $(1 + h)^m > 1 + mh$ holds. If we multiply both sides of the inequality by the positive number $1 + h$ $(h > -1, h \neq 0)$, we obtain

$$(1 + h)^{m+1} > (1 + mh)(1 + h) = 1 + (m + 1)h + mh^2 .$$

If, on the right, the positive term mh^2 is omitted, the inequality $(1 + h)^{m+1} > 1 + (m + 1)h$ also holds. But this is our inequality for the index $n = m + 1$. It follows, therefore, that if the inequality holds for the index $n = m$, it also holds for the index $n = m + 1$. It is easily checked that the inequality holds for $m = 2$. But then it holds for

---

* Louis Cauchy (1789-1857), the father of modern analysis, exercised a great influence on the theory of infinite series, complex analysis, and differential equations.

$m + 1 = 3$, hence for $m = 4$, and so on. Consequently, it holds for every index $n > 1$. This is an example of a proof by mathematical induction, a type of proof often used.

(l) If the binomial expansion

$$(1 + h)^n = 1 + \binom{n}{1}h + \binom{n}{2}h^2 + \cdots + \binom{n}{k}h^k + \cdots + \binom{n}{n}h^n$$

is used, where n is a positive integer,

$$\binom{n}{k} = \frac{n(n - 1) \cdots (n - k + 1)}{k!}$$

and $k! = 1, 2, 3, \ldots, k$, the inequality follows immediately if $h > 0$. For $k = 1, 2$ we obtain the special cases

$$(1 + h)^n > nh \quad \text{and} \quad (1 + h)^n > \frac{1}{2}n(n - 1)h^2 \,,$$

respectively.

(m) By the mean value theorem $f(b) - f(a) = (b - a)f'(c)$, $a < c < b$. For $f(x) = x^p$, $b = 1$, $a = x < 1$, it follows that

$$1 - x^p = (1 - x)pc^{p-1} \,.$$

If we note that $0 < c^{p-1} < 1$ if $p > 1$ and $c^{p-1} > 1$ for $p < 1$, the statement follows immediately.

1.2 Absolute value

Inequalities containing absolute values of numbers are of importance in definitions and in proving of theorems. A collection of basic properties of absolute values of real numbers follows.

The absolute value of a real number a, denoted by $|a|$, is defined to be

$$|a| = a \quad \text{if} \quad a \geq 0$$
$$= -a \quad \text{if} \quad a < 0 \,.$$

1.2-1 Theorem. (a) $|a| = |-a|$.   (b) $|ab| = |a|\,|b|$.

(c) $\left|\dfrac{1}{a}\right| = \dfrac{1}{|a|}$.   (d) $\left|\dfrac{b}{a}\right| = \dfrac{|b|}{|a|}$ $(a \neq 0)$.   (e) $|a + b| \leq |a| + |b|$.

(f) $|a + b| \geq |a| - |b|$ and $|a + b| \geq ||a| - |b||$.

(g) The two relations $|x| \leq h$ $(h > 0)$ and $-h \leq x \leq h$ or $\pm x \leq h$ are equivalent. Similarly $|x - a| \leq h$ and $a - h \leq x \leq a + h$ or $\pm (x - a) \leq h$.

(h) $|a - b|$ is the distance between two points on the number line.

One way of proving the theorem is to verify the statements by considering all possible cases. As an example of this sort we consider the case (e) known as the triangle inequality.

Proof. (e) There are four cases to consider: (1) a and b both are positive. Since by definition $|a| = a$ and $|b| = b$, it follows that $a + b = |a| + |b|$. If we note that by definition $a + b = |a + b|$, it follows that $|a + b| = |a| + |b|$, that is, in this case the statement (e) is true.

(2) a and b both are negative. By definition $|a| = -a$ and $|b| = -b$. Addition yields $-(a + b) = |a| + |b|$. Since by definition $-(a + b) = |a + b|$, it follows that $|a + b| = |a| + |b|$, that is, the inequality (e) holds.

(3) $a = b = 0$. If we note that $|0| = 0$, it follows at once that $|a + b| = |a| + |b|$.

(4) $a \neq 0$, $b \neq 0$, and a and b are of opposite sign. Let us assume that a is positive. Then $a = |a|$ and $-b = |b|$. It follows that

$$a + b < a - b = |a| + |b| \quad \text{for} \quad a \geq |b| \, ,$$
$$-(a + b) < a - b = |a| + |b| \quad \text{for} \quad a < |b| \, .$$

By definition, $a + b = |a + b|$ for $a \geq |b|$ and $-(a + b) = |a + b|$ for $a < |b|$, consequently, $|a + b| < |a| + |b|$, that is, (e) holds.

Note that a strict inequality holds only if a and b are of opposite sign.

Another less intuitive proof of the same theorem is as follows. By definition, $\pm a \leq |a|$ and $\pm b \leq |b|$. If these two inequalities are added, it follows by **1.1-1**(c) that

$$\pm (a + b) \leq |a| + |b| \, .$$

Now apply **1.2-1**(g), (note that if, say, $\pm x \leq 5$, then $|x| \leq 5$) and **1.1-2** (e) follows.

Corollary. If in (e) b is replaced by $-b$ and **1.2-1**(a) is used, it follows that

$$|a + (-b)| = |a - b| \leq |a| + |-b| = |a| + |b| \, .$$

Hence,

$$|a - b| \leq |a| + |b| \, .$$

(f) If inequality (e) is applied to the sum $a = (a - b) + b$, it follows that $|a| \leq |a - b| + |b|$. If $-|b|$ is added to this inequality, it follows by **1.1-1**(a) that

$$|a| - |b| \leq |a - b|$$

holds. Now replace b by $-b$ and use $|-b| = |b|$, then the first part of

4

statement (f) $|a + b| \geq |a| - |b|$ follows. If the very same procedure is applied to the sum $b = (b - a) + a$, we obtain

$$|a + b| \geq |b| - |a| = -(|a| - |b|) .$$

The combination of the last two inequalities yields $\pm (|a| - |b|) \leq |a + b|$, which is equivalent to the second part of (f)

$$|a + b| \geq ||a| - |b|| .$$

Finally, we remark that the absolute value of a real number can be defined by a single equation. Since the positive root of a positive number is a positive number, it follows that

$$|a| = (a^2)^{1/2} .$$

From this definition it follows at once that $|a| = |-a|$ and $|a|^2 = a^2$. It is easy to prove (b). By definition, $|ab| = [(ab)^2]^{1/2} = (a^2b^2)^{1/2} = (a^2)^{1/2}(b^2)^{1/2}$. If $|a| = (a^2)^{1/2}$ and $|b| = (b)^{1/2}$ are substituted, the statement

$$|ab| = |a||b|$$

follows.

It is also easy to prove the triangle inequality. If we note that $|a|^2 = a^2$, $|b|^2 = b^2$, and $ab \leq |a||b|$, it follows that

$$|a + b| = [(a + b)^2]^{1/2} = (a^2 + 2ab + b^2)^{1/2} \leq (|a|^2 + 2|a||b| + |b|^2)^{1/2}$$
$$= [(|a| + |b|)^2]^{1/2} = |a| + |b| ,$$

that is,

$$|a + b| \leq |a| + |b| .$$

1.3 Neighborhood

If a and b are real numbers and $a < b$, then the set of numbers x such that $a < x < b$ forms an open interval, which is denoted by (a, b). In set notation

$$(a, b) = \{x | a < x < b\} ,$$

which reads: (a, b) is the set of all x such that $a < x < b$. If the end points a and b belong to the set, that is, if the inequality $a \leq x \leq b$ holds, we say that the interval is closed and denote it by $[a, b]$. If $a \leq x < b$ or $a < x \leq b$, then the intervals are neither closed nor open.

Every open interval containing the number c is called a neighborhood of c. Any neighborhood of c can be defined by the double inequality

$$c - k < x < c + h$$

where h and k denote positive numbers, that is by the set of all numbers between $c - k$ and $c + h$.

For proving of theorems the symmetric inequality

$$c - h < x < c + h$$

is often used and is written in the form

$$|x - c| < h .$$

If the familiar representation of points by numbers on a line is used, we may say that a symmetric neighborhood is an open interval containing the point c as the midpoint (Fig. 1).

If we have a point set in the plane, we define a neighborhood of a point with coordinates a and b denoted by (a, b) as a set of all points

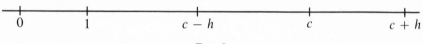

FIG. 1

(x, y) such that $|x - a| < h$ and $|y - b| < k$ $(h > 0, k > 0)$. Thus, the neighborhood of a point (a, b) in the plane is the set of all points inside a rectangle with center (a, b) and sides of length $2h$ and $2k$ (Fig. 2). If $h = k$, the neighborhood is the set of points inside a square.

Note that the notation (a, b) is also used for an open interval. It should be clear from the context whether (q, b) means an interval or a point in the plane.

Instead of a rectangular neighborhood, often a circular neighborhood is used, that is a set of all points (x, y) lying inside some circle with center at (a, b) and radius h. Thus for any positive number h the set of all (x, y) such that

$$(x - a)^2 + (y - b)^2 < h^2$$

is a circular neighborhood of the point (a, b).

The extension of the concept of a neighborhood to three or more dimensions of the Euclidean space causes no difficulty. The neighborhood of the point (a, b, c) may be defined by the inequalities

$$|x - a| < h , \quad |y - b| < k , \quad |z - c| < l , \quad (h > 0 , k > 0 , l > 0) ,$$

or by the spherical inequality

$$(x - a)^2 + (y - b)^2 + (z - c)^2 < r^2 .$$

In the case of four dimensions, we write

6

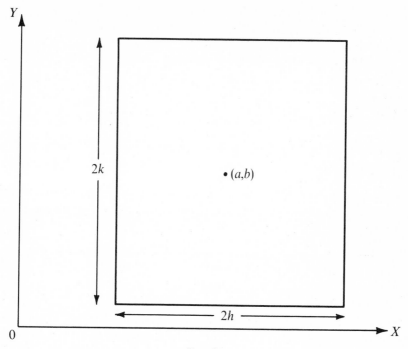

FIG. 2

$$|x - a| < h , \quad |y - b| < k , \quad |z - c| < l , \quad |w - d| < m$$

and still speak of a "spherical" neighborhood if the inequality

$$(x - a)^2 + (y - b)^2 + (z - c)^2 + (w - d)^2 < r^2$$

is given.

In applications one often needs to determine the neighborhoods of $a + b$, $a - b$, ab, a/b, that is, $|x + y - (a + b)| < h_1$, $|x - y - (a - b)| < h_2$, $|xy - ab| < h_3$, $|x/y - a/b| < h_4$, if the neighborhoods $|x - a| < h$ and $|y - b| < k$ of a and b are given. By simple algebraic manipulations of inequalities these neighborhoods can be found, that is, h_1, h_2, h_3, h_4 can be determined as functions of h and k. Since in most cases only rough estimates of these neighborhoods are needed, calculations can be simplified. First we show how accurate neighborhoods are found by working an example.

Example 1. Find the neighborhood of a/b if the neighborhoods of a and of b are given by $|x - a| < 1/2$ and $|y - b| < 1/3$, respectively, and $a = 2$, $b = 3$.

Solution. From the given neighborhood of $b = 3$

7

$$8/3 < y < 10/3$$

by **1.1-1**(f) we obtain for the reciprocal of y the inequality

$$3/10 < 1/y < 3/8 ,$$

which combined with the given neighborhood of $a = 2$

$$3/2 < x < 5/2$$

by **1.1-1**(b) yields

$$(1/y)x < (3/8)(5/2) = 15/16 , \quad (1/y)x > (3/10)(3/2) = 9/20 ,$$

whence

$$9/20 < (x/y) < 15/16 .$$

If to this inequality $- 2/3$ is added by **1.1-1**(a), the exact neighborhood of $2/3$

$$- 13/60 < x/y - 2/3 < 13/48$$

is obtained.

We remark that by somewhat shorter, though less intuitive and accurate, procedure a solution can be obtained as follows.

$$|x/y - 2/3| = \frac{|3x - 2y|}{3|y|} = \frac{|3x - 3 \cdot 2 + 3 \cdot 2 - 2y|}{3|y|} = \frac{|3(x-2) + 2(3 - y)|}{3|y|}$$

$$\leq \frac{3|x - 2| + 2|y - 3|}{3|y|} < \frac{3(1/2) + 2(1/3)}{3(8/3)} = 13/48 .$$

Note the trick of subtracting and adding of the product $3 \cdot 2$, **1.2-1** (d), (e), and (a), and the inequality $|y| < 8/3$ which have been used.

This example shows that the second solution leads to a symmetric neighborhood which, however, is larger, that is, less accurate than the result of the first solution.

1.3-1 Theorem. If $|x - a| < h$ and $|y - b| < k$, $(h > 0, \ k > 0)$, then
(a) $|x + y - (a + b)| < h + k$;   (b) $|x - y - (a - b)| < h + k$;
(c) $|xy - ab| < (|b| + k)h + |a|k$;
(d) $\left| \dfrac{x}{y} - \dfrac{a}{b} \right| < \dfrac{|b|h + |a|k}{|b|(|b| - k)}$, $b \neq 0$, $|b| - k > 0$.

We shall prove cases (b) and (c) and leave (a) and (d) as exercises.

Proof. (b) $|x - y - (a - b)| \leq |x - a| + |y - b| < h + k$ by **1.2-1** and by hypothesis. (c) $|xy - ab| = |xy - ay + ay - ab| = |y(x - a) + a(y - b)|$ $\leq |y||x - a| + |a||y - b|$ by **1.2-1**(b), (e). If for $|y|$, $|x - a|$, $|y - b|$, the larger values $|b| + k$, h, and k, respectively, are substituted, the statement follows.

Exercises 1.A

1. Prove properties **1.1-1**(b), (c), (d), and (e).
2. Prove that $a > b$ if $a^2 > b^2$ and $a > 0,\ b > 0$.
3. If $x < y$, prove that the arithmetic mean $(x + y)/2$ satisfies the inequality $x < (x + y)/2 < y$.
4. Prove that $a^2 + b^2 + c^2 \geq ab + bc + ac$. For what values of a, b, c does equality hold?
5. Find all real numbers, if any, which satisfy the following inequalities. Graph the solution set
   (a) $-7x - 5 < 4$ (b) $2x/(x + 4) < 1$
   (c) $x^2 + 3x + 1 \geq 0$ (d) $x + 1/x \geq 2 \quad x > 0$
   (e) $x + 1/x \leq -2 \quad x < 0$ (f) $x^2 + ax + a^2 > 0, \quad a \neq 0$.
6. If $a > b > 0$, prove that $a^3 - b^3 > (a - b)^3$.
7. Graph the solution sets of the inequalities
   (a) $|x| < 2$ (b) $|x| > 2$ (c) $|x - 1| < 3$
   (d) $|x - 2| \geq 3$ (e) $|2x/(4 + x)| \leq 1$
   (f) $|(x + 1)/(x + 2)| < 2$ (g) $|x + 1/x| \geq 2$
   (h) $|x - 1| - |x + 3| \leq 6$ (i) $|x - 1| + 2|x - 3| \geq 4$.
8. Graph the solution sets of
   (a) $|x + 1| = 2$ (b) $|2x + 1| = |3x|$ (c) $|2x| = 2|x|$
   (d) $|x - 4| \leq |x - 9|$.
9. Find a solution set, if any, for which both inequalities $|3x - 4| \leq 7$ and $|2 - 5x| < 3$ hold.
10. Prove properties **1.2-1**(c), (d), and (g).
11. If $|a| = |b|$, is $a = b$?
12. Prove the relations:
    (a) $|a + b + c| \leq |a| + |b| + |c|$ (b) $|abc| = |a||b||c|$.
13. Sketch the graphs of the following relations:
    (a) $y = |x|$ (b) $y = x/|x|$ if $x \neq 0$ and $y = 0$ if $x = 0$
    (c) $y = (|x|)^{1/2}$ (d) $|y| = |x|$ (e) $|x| + |y| = 1$ (f) $|x| + |y| < 1$.
14. Prove properties **1.3-1**(a) and (d).
15. Find exact neighborhoods of $a + b$, $a - b$, and ab if $|x - a| < 1/2$, $|y - b| < 1/3$ and $a = 2$, $b = 3$.
16. Find symmetric neighborhoods of $a + b$, $a - b$, a/b, and ab if $|x - a| < 1/100$, $|y - b| < 1/50$ and $a = -3$, $b = 1$.
17. The quantity x defined by $1/x = \frac{1}{2}(1/a + 1/b)$ is called the harmonic mean $(a > 0, b > 0)$. Prove that the geometric mean is not less than the harmonic mean, that is, $(ab)^{1/2} \geq x$. When does the equality sign hold?
18. If $x > 0$, $y > 0$ prove that $x^3 + y^3 \geq x^2 y + xy^2$.
19. Prove that $x/y + y/x \geq 2$ if $x > 0$, $y > 0$.
20. Graph the relation set of $|x| + |y| \leq 3$ if x and y are integers.

CHAPTER 2

THE CONCEPT OF THE LIMIT
OF A SEQUENCE

Mathematical analysis is based upon the concept of number, the concept of function, and the concept of limit. The notion of limit is one of the most important ideas in all mathematics. The concept of limit is found in all branches of mathematics. It is fundamental to the development of differential and integral calculus, topology, and infinite series.

Limits are often introduced through a consideration of infinite series. Yet one cannot build a precise theory of infinite series without first having an intelligent understanding of the limit of a sequence. Furthermore, the concept of the limit of a function can also be developed from the concept of the limit of a sequence so that ultimately the whole of mathematical analysis rests on the concept of the limit of a sequence.

First we shall consider some examples of sequences and then establish their fundamental properties.

2.1 Examples of sequences

Example 1. An infinite sequence denoted by $\{a_n\}$ with $a_n = 1/n$ is an endless succession of numbers

(a) $1, 1/2, 1/3, \ldots, 1/n, \ldots ,$

where for each positive integer k the kth number is obtained by taking the reciprocal of k. Another sequence $\{b_n\}$ with $b_n = 1/(n^3 - 6n^2 + 12n - 6)$ determines the array

(b) $1, 1/2, 1/3, 1/10, 1/29, \ldots, 1/(n^3 - 6n^2 + 12n - 6), \ldots .$

2.1-1 Definition. We define an infinite sequence as a function whose domain is the set of all positive integers.

Note that an infinite sequence is not defined if only a finite number of terms is given. For example,

$$1, 1/2, 1/3, \ldots ,$$

where the function is not given, does not determine uniquely a sequence, since there are many sequences having these first three terms in common. The sequences (a) and (b) are an example.

As n becomes larger and larger the terms a_n and b_n of the sequences (a) and (b) come closer and closer to zero. If we mark off a neighborhood of the point 0 on the number line as small as we please, then from a definite index n_0 onward all terms a_n will be contained in this neighborhood. If this is the case we say that as n increases, the terms a_n tend to 0, or that the sequence converges to 0, or that the sequence has a limit 0.

Consider the terms of sequence (a) plotted on the number line. The terms approach the point 0 as n increases in such a way that any neighborhood, no matter how small, contains all but a finite number of terms of the sequence (Fig. 3), in short, we say that the neighborhood contains **almost all** terms of the sequence.

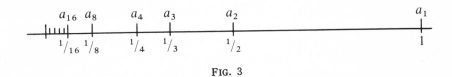

FIG. 3

Of course, a large enough neighborhood will contain all points of the sequence (a), for example, the neighborhood $|a_n| < 2$. But a smaller neighborhood, say, $|a_n| < 1/10$ contains all terms of the sequence with indices greater than 10, that is, the set $\{1/11, 1/12, 1/13, \ldots, 1/n, \ldots\}$. The first ten terms $1, 1/2, 1/3, \ldots, 1/10$ are outside the neighborhood. If the neighborhood is smaller, say, $|a_n| < 1/1000$, then obviously a larger number of terms will remain outside the neighborhood, in this case 1000. To show that for any neighborhood only a finite number of terms will be excluded, we choose the neighborhood

$$|a_n| < \varepsilon ,$$

where ε denotes any fixed positive number. Since in case (a)

$$|a_n| = 1/n < \varepsilon$$

for all $n > 1/\varepsilon$, we see that all terms with indices greater than $1/\varepsilon$ are inside the neighborhood. Since for any ε the number of terms with indices smaller than $1/\varepsilon$ is always finite, it follows that almost all terms

11

of the sequence are contained in any neighborhood, no matter how small.

If we denote the integer $[1/\varepsilon]$ by n_0, where the symbol $[x]$ means the greatest integer contained in x, we see that the terms

$$a_{n_0+1}, \ a_{n_0+2}, \ \ldots, a_n, \ \ldots$$

are inside the neighborhood. Consequently, only a finite number of terms are excluded.

This we express symbolically by writing

$$\lim_{n\to\infty} a_n = 0, \quad \text{or} \quad a_n \to 0 \quad \text{as} \quad n \to \infty, \quad \text{or} \quad a_n \to 0.$$

Since a sequence is defined as a function, it can be represented by points in a plane. Figure 4 represents the graph of the sequence (a). Note that the domain and the range of the function consist of isolated points. The graph indicates that the terms a_n of the sequence are steadily decreasing to 0, that is, they approach the n-axis as n increases.

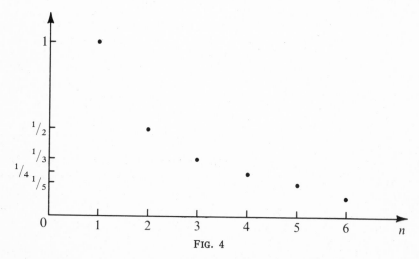

FIG. 4

Example 2. $\{a_n\}$, $a_n = (-1)^{n-1}/n$ is similar to the sequence (a) of Example 1. The terms

$$a_1 = 1, \ a_2 = -1/2, \ a_3 = 1/3, \ a_4 = -1/4, \ \ldots, \ a_n = (-1)^{n-1}/n$$

are alternately greater and smaller than 0. We say that the terms of the sequence oscillate about the point 0. That any neighborhood $|a_n| < \varepsilon$ contains almost all terms of the sequence can be shown exactly as in Example 1(a), since $|a_n| = 1/n$. It follows that $\lim_{n\to\infty} a_n = 0$.

Example 3. $\{a_n\}$, (a) $a_n = n/(n+1)$; (b) $a_n = (n^2 - 1)/(n^2 + n + 1)$. If we write the term a_n of the sequence (a) in the form

$$a_n = 1 - 1/(n+1) \quad \text{or} \quad a_n = 1/(1 + 1/n),$$

it is apparent that, as n increases, a_n approaches 1. Since

$$|a_n - 1| = 1/(n+1) < \varepsilon$$

for all $n + 1 > 1/\varepsilon$ or $n > [1/\varepsilon - 1] = n_0$, it follows that almost all terms of the sequence in case (a) are within any arbitrarily small neighborhood. This we express symbolically by writing $\lim\limits_{n \to \infty} a_n = 1$.

In case (b), by dividing the numerator and the denominator by n^2 we obtain

$$a_n = (1 - 1/n^2)/(1 + 1/n + 1/n^2).$$

As n increases, it is apparent that a_n approaches 1. To justify the equation $\lim\limits_{n \to \infty} a_n = 1$ we have to show that any neighborhood of 1 contains almost all terms of the sequence.

Since $2n - (n+2) > 0$ for all $n > 2$, it follows that $2n > n + 2$ if $n > 2$. It is obvious that $n^2 + n + 1 > n^2$ for all positive integers. If the numerator of a fraction is replaced by a larger number and the denominator by a smaller, the fraction increases. Thus,

$$|a_n - 1| = (n+2)/(n^2 + n + 1) < 2n/n^2 = 2/n.$$

If n is chosen such that $2/n < \varepsilon$ or $n > [2/\varepsilon] = n_0$, it follows that $|a_n - 1| < \varepsilon$, that is, the neighborhood of 1 includes all terms with indices $n > n_0$. Consequently, there are at most a finite number of terms outside the neighborhood determined by ε.

Note that for the proof accuracy is irrelevant. The point in the proof is to show that the neighborhood contains all but a finite number of terms at most. Therefore, there is no need to solve the inequality $(n+2)/(n^2 + n + 1) < \varepsilon$ accurately. Of course, by solving it we can obtain a smaller value for n_0, that is, a more accurate result than by the above method, but this requires more effort and yields an awkward expression for n_0.

Example 4. $\{a_n\}$, $a_n = (-1)^{n-1}n/(n+1)$. In the sequence

$$a_1 = 1/2, \ a_2 = -2/3, \ a_3 = 3/4, \ a_4 = -4/5, \ a_5 = 5/6, \ \ldots, \ a_{2n}$$
$$= -2n/(n+1), \ a_{2n+1} = (2n+1)/(2a+2), \ \ldots,$$

the terms with odd indices are to the right and terms with even indices are to the left of 0. There are no points of the sequence on the number line between $a_2 = -2/3$ and $a_1 = 1/2$ (see Fig. 5). Terms with odd

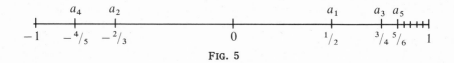

FIG. 5

indices $a_1, a_3, a_5, \ldots, a_{2k+1}, \ldots$, are approaching 1 while terms with even indices are approaching -1. There is no number c such that the neighborhood $|a_n - c| < \varepsilon$ of c includes almost all the terms of the sequence, when ε is small enough, say, $\varepsilon < 1$, we say that the sequence has no limit, or that the sequence is divergent.

Example 5. $\{a_n\}$, $a_n = b^n$ where b denotes any real fixed number. We consider six cases.

(a) $0 < b < 1$. We put $b = 1/(1+h)$, $h > 0$. By **1.1-1** (l) the inequality $(1+h)^n > nh$ holds and it follows that

$$|a_n| = 1/(1+h)^n < 1/nh < \varepsilon$$

holds for all $n > n_0 = [1/\varepsilon h]$, that is, any neighborhood of 0 contains almost all terms of the sequence. Thus, $\lim\limits_{n\to\infty} b^n = 0$.

(b) $b = c$, where $c = 1$ or $c = 0$. In this case all the terms of the sequence are equal, that is, $a_1 = a_2 = a_3 = \cdots = a_n = \cdots = c$. It is easy to see that every neighborhood of c contains all the terms of the sequence. Consequently,

$$\lim\limits_{n\to\infty} a_n = c .$$

(c) $b > 1$. If we put again $b = 1 + h$ and use the same inequality as in case (a), we obtain

$$a_n = (1 + h)^n > nh .$$

The last inequality shows that for fixed h (h depends only on b, not on n) the terms a_n of the sequence are steadily increasing as n increases. We see that no matter how large a number M we may choose, b^n can be made larger than M if only n is large enough. We say that $a_n = b^n$ is increasing beyond all bounds, the sequence is divergent, and we write

$$\lim\limits_{n\to\infty} a_n = \lim\limits_{n\to\infty} b^n = \infty .$$

Note that ∞ is not a real number.

(d) $b = -1$. In this case the terms of the sequence are

$$-1, 1, -1, \ldots, -1, 1, \ldots ,$$

and there is no number c such that every neighborhood $|a_n - c| < \varepsilon$ of c contains almost all terms of the sequence if we choose $\varepsilon < 1$. We say that the sequence has no limit, or that the sequence diverges.

(e) $-1 < b < 0$. This case is similar to the case (a). If we note that $|a_n| = |b|^n$, we obtain exactly the same neighborhood as in case (a). Consequently,

$$\lim_{n \to \infty} b^n = 0 .$$

(f) $b < -1$. This case is similar to the case (c). If we note that $|a_n| = |b|^n$ it follows that the absolute value of the terms of the sequence are increasing beyond all bounds. The alternating character of the divergent sequence is indicated by writing

$$\lim_{n \to \infty} b^n = \pm \infty .$$

Example 6. $\{a_n\}$, (a) $a_n = b^{1/n}$ where b denotes any fixed positive number. The equation $\log a_n = (\log b)/n$ shows that $\log a_n$ approaches 0 as n increases. Consequently, a_n tends to 1.

To show that for every $\varepsilon > 0$ there exists a number n_0 such that all terms a_n with indices n larger than n_0 are in the neighboorhood $|a_n - 1| < \varepsilon$ we proceed as follows: If $b > 1$, then $a_n > 1$, and we put $b^{1/n} = 1 + h_n$, $h_n > 0$. By **1.1-1**(1) $b = (1 + h_n)^n > n h_n$, whence $h_n < b/n$. Thus

$$|a_n - 1| = |b^{1/n} - 1| = h_n < b/n .$$

It follows that $|a_n - 1| < \varepsilon$ if $b/n < \varepsilon$ or $n > b/\varepsilon$. If $[b/\varepsilon] = n_0$, then $|a_n - 1| < \varepsilon$ whenever $n > n_0$. Hence, $\lim_{n \to \infty} b^{1/n} = 1$.

If $b < 1$, then $a_n < 1$, and we put $b^{1/n} = 1/(1 + h_n)$, where $h_n > 0$. Hence, $b = 1/(1 + h_n)^n < 1/n h_n$, since the denominator is replaced by a smaller number $n h_n$. Thus, $h_n < 1/bn$ and

$$|a_n - 1| = |b^{1/n} - 1| = |1/(1 + h_n) - 1| = |h_n/(1 + h_n)| < h_n < 1/bn .$$

Hence, we conclude that $|a_n - 1| < \varepsilon$ if $1/bn < \varepsilon$ or $n > 1/b\varepsilon$. If we denote $[1/b\varepsilon]$ by n_0, then all terms with indices $n > n_0$ are in the neighborhood of 1, and $\lim_{n \to \infty} b^{1/n} = 1$ follows.

The case $b = 1$ is trivial, since $a_n = 1$ for all n. Consequently, any neighborhood of 1 contains all terms of the sequence, and it follows that $\lim_{n \to \infty} 1^{1/n} = 1$.

(b) $a_n = n^{1/n}$. If we consider $\log a_n = (\log n)/n$, it is apparent that $\log a_n$ approaches 0 as n increases. This indicates that a_n approaches 1 as n increases.

To prove that the limit of the sequence is 1 we put $n^{1/n} = 1 + h_n$ where $h_n > 0$ for $n > 1$. Hence, by **1.1-1**(1) we obtain

15

$$n = (1 + h_n)^n > [n(n - 1)/2]h_n^2 \, ,$$

whence $h_n < [2/(n - 1)]^{1/2}$ follows. The neighborhood

$$|a_n - 1| = |n^{1/n} - 1| = h_n < [2/(n - 1)]^{1/2} < \varepsilon$$

contains all terms a_n of the sequence with indices larger than $n_0 = [1 + (2/\varepsilon^2)]$. This proves that $\lim\limits_{n \to \infty} n^{1/n} = 1$.

Example 7. $\{a_n\}$, $a_n = (n + 1)^{1/2} - n^{1/2}$. If the term a_n is put in the form

$$a_n = [(n + 1)^{1/2} - n^{1/2}]\frac{(n + 1)^{1/2} + n^{1/2}}{(n + 1)^{1/2} + n^{1/2}} = \frac{1}{(n + 1)^{1/2} + n^{1/2}} < 1/2n^{1/2} \, ,$$

then it is obvious that a_n approaches 0 as $n \to \infty$.

From the above inequality $|a_n| < 1/2n^{1/n}$ follows that $|a_n| < \varepsilon$ if $1/2n^{1/2} < \varepsilon$ for $n > n_0 = [1/(4\varepsilon^2)]$. That means that every neighborhood of 0 includes almost all terms of the sequence. Consequently,

$$\lim\limits_{n \leftarrow \infty} [(n + 1)^{1/2} - n^{1/2}] = 0 \, .$$

Example 8. $\{a_n\}$, $a_n = 1 + q + q^2 + \cdots + q^{n-1}$. The terms of the sequence are geometric series which play an important role in the theory of infinite series. a_n is called a partial sum of the infinite series

$$1 + q + q^2 + \cdots + q^{n-1} + \cdots \, .$$

If a_n has a limit as $n \to \infty$, we say that the infinite series is convergent and has a "sum" which is defined to be the $\lim\limits_{n \to \infty} a_n$.

From the easily calculated relation $a_n - a_n q = 1 - q^n$ it follows that

$$a_n = (1 - q^n)/(1 - q) = 1/(1 - q) - q^n/(1 - q) \, , \quad q \neq 1 \, .$$

Since $\lim\limits_{n \to \infty} q^n = 0$ if $|q| < 1$ [Example 5(a) and (e)], it follows that

$$\lim\limits_{n \to \infty} a_n = 1/(1 - q) \, .$$

Thus, the "sum" of the infinite series is $1/(1 - q)$ if $|q| < 1$.

If $q = 1$, then $a_n = n$ and $\lim\limits_{n \to \infty} a_n = \infty$, that is, the sequence diverges.

If $q = -1$, then $a_1 = 1$, $a_2 = 0$, $a_3 = 1$, $a_4 = 0$, ..., $2_{2k} = 0$, $a_{2k+1} = 1$, ... That is, the sequence oscillates between 0 and 1, and there is no number c such that a neighborhood of c includes almost all terms of the sequence if ε is small enough, say, $\varepsilon < 1/2$. Consequently, the sequence is divergent.

If $|q| > 1$, we have a case similar to Examples 5 (c) and (f). Since $\lim\limits_{n \to \infty} |q|^n = \infty$, the sequence is divergent.

16

Thus, by definition the infinite series is divergent and has no "sum" if $|q| \geq 1$.

Example 9. $\{a_n\}$, $a_n = 1/(n^2 + 1)^{1/2} + 1/(n^2 + 2)^{1/2} + \cdots + 1/(n^2 + n)^{1/2}$. Note that the term a_n of the sequence is a sum of n numbers. As n increases, each number of the series tends to 0. One might assume that the limit of the sequence is also 0. This is not always the case and sequences of this sort must be treated with care. To evaluate the limit of the sequence we proceed as follows.

First we note that $1/(n^2 + 1)^{1/2}$ is the largest and $1/(n^2 + n)^{1/2}$ the smallest number of the series (why?). If all numbers of the series are replaced by the largest number, then the new series is clearly larger than a_n. Similarly, if all numbers are replaced by the smallest number, then the new series is evidently smaller than a_n. Thus,

$$\frac{1}{(n^2 + n)^{1/2}} + \frac{1}{(n^2 + n)^{1/2}} + \cdots + \frac{1}{(n^2 + n)^{1/2}} < a_n < \frac{1}{(n^2 + 1)^{1/2}}$$
$$+ \frac{1}{(n^2 + 1)^{1/2}} + \cdots + \frac{1}{(n^2 + 1)^{1/2}} , \quad n > 1 .$$

If we note further that the series has n terms, we write the inequality in the form

$$n \cdot 1/(n^2 + n)^{1/2} < a_n < n \cdot 1/(n^2 + 1)^{1/2} ,$$

or

$$1/(1 + 1/n)^{1/2} < a_n < 1/(1 + 1/n^2)^{1/2} .$$

This shows that the left-hand side and the right-hand side of the inequality approach 1 as n increases. Since a_n is between them, we conclude that a_n also approaches 1.

This squeeze method is often useful in evaluating limits of sequences. The result of this example is stated in the following theorem.

2.1-2 Theorem. If two convergent sequences $\{b_n\}$ and $\{c_n\}$ having the same limit can be found such that $c_n \leq a_n \leq b_n$ holds for every n, then the sequence $\{a_n\}$ also converges and has the same limit.

Proof. It is given that $\lim_{n \to \infty} b_n = \lim_{n \to \infty} c_n = d$ exists. This means that there exist numbers n_1 and n_2 such that the neighborhoods

$$|b_n - d| < \varepsilon \quad \text{and} \quad |c_n - d| < \varepsilon$$

contain all terms of the sequences with indices larger than n_1 and n_2, respectively. We denote the larger of n_1 and n_2 by n_0. Then the neighborhood of d contains all terms b_n and c_n with indices greater than n_0.

Since $c_n \le a_n \le b_n$, it follows that the neighborhood of d contains all but a finite number of terms of the sequence. This means that $\lim\limits_{n \to \infty} a_n = d$.

Example 10. $\{a_n\}$, $a_n = 1/1 \cdot 2 + 1/2 \cdot 3 + 1/3 \cdot 4 + \cdots + 1/n(n+1)$. First note that $1/k(k+1) = 1/k - 1/(k+1)$. Consequently,

$$a_1 = 1 - 1/2 , \qquad a_2 = 1/1 \cdot 2 + 1/2 \cdot 3 = (1 - 1/2) + (1/2 - 1/3) = 1 - 1/3 ,$$
$$a_3 = 1/1 \cdot 2 + 1/2 \cdot 3 + 1/3 \cdot 4 = (1 - 1/2) + (1/2 - 1/3) + (1/3 - 1/4)$$
$$= 1 - 1/4, \ldots ,$$
$$a_n = (1 - 1/2) + (1/2 - 1/3) + \cdots + [1/(n-1) - 1/n] + [1/n - 1/(n+1)]$$
$$= 1 - 1/(n+1) .$$

The simplified series

$$a_n = 1 - 1/(n+1)$$

is exactly Example 3. Therefore,

$$\lim_{n \to \infty} a_n = \lim_{n \to \infty} [1/1 \cdot 2 + 1/2 \cdot 3 + 1/3 \cdot 4 + \cdots + 1/n(n+1)] = 1 .$$

Example 11. $\{a_n\}$, (a) $a_n = 1 + 1/2 + 1/3 + \cdots + 1/n$; (b) $a_n = 1 + 1/2^p + 1/3^p + \cdots + 1/n^p$, $p < 1$. To show that the series (a) is divergent we arrange a_n into the following groups.

$$a_n = (1 + 1/2) + (1/3 + 1/4) + (1/5 + 1/6 + 1/7 + 1/8) + (1/9 + \cdots + 1/16)$$
$$+ (1/17 + \cdots + 1/32) + \cdots + (1/(2^{m-1} + 1) + \cdots + 1/2^m) ,$$

where the first term in each group is a power of 2, and $n = 2^m$. If all terms in each group are replaced by the smallest terms, the obvious inequality

$$a_n > (1/2 + 1/2) + (1/4 + 1/4) + (1/8 + 1/8 + 1/8 + 1/8) + (1/16 + \cdots$$
$$+ 1/16) + \cdots + (1/2^m + \cdots + 1/2^m)$$

follows. There are m groups and each group, except the first, is equal to 1/2. Consequently,

$$a_n > 1 + (m - 1)/2 = (m + 1)/2 .$$

By choosing n large enough we can form as many groups as we please, that is, a_n can be made larger than any finite number N. This means that $\lim\limits_{n \to \infty} a_n = \infty$.

Case (b) is a generalization of a_n. If, for example, $p = 1/2$, we obtain the special series

$$a_n = 1 + 1/2^{1/2} + 1/3^{1/2} + \cdots + 1/n^{1/2} .$$

For $p = 1$ we obtain case (a).

If we note that for $p < 1$ the inequalities

$$1/2^p > 1/2, \ 1/3^p > 1/3, \ \ldots, \ 1/n^p > 1/n, \ \ldots$$

hold (do the inequalities hold for $p > 1$?), it follows that

$$a_n = 1/2^p + 1/3^p + \cdots + 1/n^p > (m + 1)/2$$

also. This means that $\lim_{n \to \infty} a_n = \infty$.

The series (b) is called harmonic series. It diverges for $p \leq 1$.

Exercises 2.A

1. Graph some terms of the following sequences on the number line and in the plane. Indicate limits, if any, suggested by the graph. $\{a_n\}$:
   (a) $a_n = (n + 1)/n$,
   (b) $a_n = (n^2 + n - 1)/(3n^2 + 1)$,
   (c) $a_n = (n + 1)/(n^2 + 1)$,
   (d) $a_n = (n^2 + 1)/(n + 2)$,
   (e) $a_n = 1 + (-1)^n 1/n$,
   (f) $a_n = 1 - (-1)^n n/(n + 1)$,
   (g) $a_n = 1/1 \cdot 3 + 1/2 \cdot 4 + \cdots + 1/n(n + 2)$,
   (h) $a_n = 1/n^2 + 1/(n + 1)^2 + \cdots + 1/(n + n)^2$,
   (i) $a_n = 1/(n + 1) + 1/(n + 2) + \cdots + 1/(n + n)$.
2. Show that $a_n = (2n^2 + n - 1)/(3n^2 + 1)$ approaches $2/3$ as n increases. Find n_0 such that for $n > n_0$ almost all terms a_n are in the neighborhood $|a_n - 2/3| < \varepsilon$ if
   (a) $\varepsilon = 0.1$, (b) $\varepsilon = 0.01$, (c) $\varepsilon = 5/333$, (d) $\varepsilon = 0.000001$.
3. $a_n = (n + 1)/n$. Determine the smallest neighborhood such that $|a_n - 1| \leq \varepsilon$ contains all terms from a_{31} onward.
4. Given two sequences $\{a_n\}$, $a_n = (2n + 1)/n$ and $\{b_n\}$, $b_n = (2n^2 - 1)/(n^2 + 1)$. Find n_1 such that for all $n > n_1$ the inequality $|a_n - 2| < 0.01$ holds. Then determine n_2 such that for all $n > n_2$ the inequality $|b_n - 2| < 0.01$ holds. Finally determine n_0 such that for $n > n_0$ all terms of both sequences with indices greater than n_0 are contained in the neighborhood of 2. Could $n_0 = 10$, $n_0 = 100$, $n_0 = 10^6$ be chosen?
5. $a_n = (n^2 + 1)/n$. Find n_0 such that for all $n > n_0$ the value of a_n exceeds 10^6.
   Find limits, if any, of the following sequences $\{a_n\}$:
6. $a_n = (6n^3 + 2n + 1)/(n^3 + n^2 + 1)$.
7. $a_n = (n^5 + 3n + 1)/(n^6 + 7n^2 + 2)$.
8. $a_n = (n^6 + 3n + 1)/(n^5 + 7n^2 + 2)$.
9. $a_n = (a_0 n^k + a_1 n^{k+1} + \cdots + a_k)/(b_0 n^k + b_1 n^{k-1} + \cdots + b_k)$, where k is a positive integer, a_i, b_i ($i = 0, 1, 2, \ldots, k$) are given constants, and $b_0 \neq 0$.
10. $a_n = [(n + 2)^{1/2} - (n + 1)^{1/2}]n^{1/2}$.
11. $a_n = [(n + a)(n + b)]^{1/2} - n$, $a > 0$, $b > 0$.
12. $a_n = a^{k/n}$, $a > 0$, k an integer.
13. $a_n = n^{2/n}$.

14. $a_n = (3^n + 2^n)^{1/n}$. Hint: $3 < a_n < 3(1 + 1)^{1/n}$.
15. $a_n = (a^n + b^n)^{1/n}$, $a > 0$, $b > 0$.
16. $a_n = 1/n^2 + 2/n^2 + \cdots + n/n^2$. Hint: use $1 + 2 + 3 + \cdots + n = n(n + 1)/2$.
17. $a_n = 3/1^2 \cdot 2^2 + 5/2^2 \cdot 3^2 + \cdots + (2n + 1)/n^2(n + 1)^2$. Hint: $(2k+1)/k^2(k+1)^2$ $= 1/k^2 - 1/(k + 1)^2$.
18. $a_n = 1/1 \cdot 3 + 1/2 \cdot 4 + \cdots + 1/n(n + 2)$.
19. $a_n = 1/c(c + 1) + 1/(c + 1)(c + 2) + \cdots + 1/(c + n)(c + n + 1)$, $c > 0$.
20. $a_n = 1/1 \cdot 2 \cdot 3 + 1/2 \cdot 3 \cdot 4 + \cdots + 1/n(n + 1)(n + 2)$.
21. $a_n = 1/(n^2 + 1)^{1/2} + 1/(n^2 + 2)^{1/2} + \cdots + 1/(n^2 + 100)^{1/2}$.
22. $a_n = 1/2 + 1/2^2 + \cdots + 1/2^n$.
23. $a_n = 1 - 1/3 + 1/3^2 - + \cdots + (-1)^{n-1}1/3^{n-1}$.
24. $a_n = 1 - 1 + 1 - + \cdots + (-1)^{n-1}$.
25. $a_n = (-1)^n + (-1)^{n-1}$.
26. $a_n = 1/10 + 6/10^2 + 6/10^3 + \cdots + 6/10^{n+1}$.
27. $a_n = 0.433\overset{n}{\overline{3}} \cdots 3$.
28. $a_n = (-1)^n + (-1)^{n-1}(1 + 1/n)$.
29. $a_n = 1 + (-1)^n 1/n + (-1)^n n/(2n + 1)$.
30. $a_n = n!/n^n$. Hint: $n!/n^n = k/n$, $k < 1$.
31. $a_n = (n + 1)^{1/3} - n^{1/3}$. Hint: $a - b = (a^{1/3} - b^{1/3})[a^{2/3} + (ab)^{1/3} + b^{2/3}]$.
32. $a_1 = 2^{1/2}$, $a_2 = [2(2)^{1/2}]^{1/2}$, $a_3 = \{2[2(2)^{1/2}]^{1/2}\}^{1/2}, \ldots$. Hint: $a_1 = 2^{1/2}$, $a_2 = 2^{1/2+1/2^2}, \ldots$.
33. $a_n = [1 - (1 - 1/n)^4]/[1 - (1 - 1/n)^3]$.
34. $a_n = 1^2/n^3 + 2^2/n^3 + \cdots + a^2/n^3$. Hint: use $1^2 + 2^2 + 3^2 + \cdots + n^2$ $= [n(n + 1)(2n + 1)]/6$.
35. $a_n = 1/(n + 1)^{1/2} + 1/(n + 2)^{1/2} + \cdots + 1/(n + n)^{1/2}$.
36. $a_n = n/2^n$.
37. $a_n = 10^n/n!$.

2.2 Definition of convergence of a sequence

2.2-1 First Definition. If an infinite sequence $\{a_n\}$ of numbers is given and there exists a number a such that every neighborhood of a, no matter how small, contains all but a finite number of terms, then the number a is called the limit of the sequence, symbolically, $\lim_{n \to \infty} a_n = a$.

Note that in the definition it is assumed that the number a is known. To prove that a is the limit of the sequence $\{a_n\}$ we have to show that for any given $\varepsilon > 0$ there exists a number n_0 such that for all $n > n_0$ the terms of the sequence are in the neighborhood

$$|a_n - a| < \varepsilon .$$

We proceed by discussing an example. $\{a_n\}$, $a_n = (n + 1)/n = 1 + 1/n$. It is apparent that in this case $a = 1$. We have to prove that 1 is the limit of the sequence, that is, that

$$|a_n - 1| < \varepsilon$$

for all $n > n_0$. What is n_0?

From the relation

$$|a_n - 1| = |1 + 1/n - 1| = 1/n < \varepsilon$$

it follows that $|a_n - 1| < \varepsilon$ if $1/n < \varepsilon$ or $n > [1/\varepsilon] = n_0$. This shows that for every positive number ε there always exists a number $n_0 = [1/\varepsilon]$ such that all terms with indices larger than n_0 are in the neighborhood of $a = 1$. Consequently, only a finite number of terms a_n with indices smaller than n_0 or equal to n_0 are outside the neighborhood.

If, for example, $\varepsilon = 0.01$, then $n_0 = 100$, and $a_{101}, a_{102}, \ldots, a_n, \ldots$ are in the neighborhood $|a_n - 1| < 0.01$, while the terms $a_1, a_2, \ldots, a_{100}$ are outside. For $\varepsilon = 0.000001$ all terms with indices larger than $n_0 = 1\,000\,000$ are in the neighborhood $|a_n - 1| < 0.000001$, and $a_1, a_2, \ldots, a_{1\,000\,000}$ (a million terms) are outside the neighborhood. We see that a larger and larger number of terms will remain outside the neighborhood as smaller and smaller values of ε are chosen. However, their number is always finite, since the number of indices smaller than any number $n_0 = [1/\varepsilon]$ is always finite.

Note that the trivial case in which all the terms of the sequence are equal is included in the definition. If $a_1 = a_2 = \cdots = a_n = \cdots = c$, then any neighborhood of c contains all terms of the sequence and, consequently, $\lim\limits_{n \to \infty} a_n = c$.

If the value of a, the limit of the sequence, is not known, the test for convergence by the above definition fails. And yet the most important sequences in analysis are those sequences which define new numbers, that is, numbers which are not known in advance. As a first example of this sort, we mention the sequence

$$\{a_n\}, \; a_n = 1 + 1/1! + 1/2! + \cdots + 1/n! \, ,$$

which defines one of the most important numbers in analysis. The terms of the sequence

$$a_1 = 1 + 1/1! = 2 \, , \qquad a_2 = 1 + 1/1! + 1/2! = 5/2 \, ,$$
$$a_3 = 1 + 1/1! + 1/2! + 1/3! = 8/3, \, \ldots$$

are rational numbers, but the limit of the sequence is an irrational number denoted by e. The number e is the base for natural logarithms and it is of great theoretical value.

Thus, it is of great importance to know whether a sequence is convergent without knowing its limit in advance. An answer to this problem is Cauchy's condition which allows us to speak of the limit of a sequence without any further information about the limit itself.

2.2-2 Definition. Convergence of a sequence (Cauchy's criterion). An infinite sequence $\{a_n\}$ of numbers a_n is convergent if for any positive number ε, a number n_0 can always be found such that for every $n > n_0$ all terms with indices $n + k$, $k \geq 1$ are contained in the neighborhood of a_n, that is,

$$|a_{n+k} - a_n| < \varepsilon .$$

If we put $n + k = m$, the inequality takes the form

$$|a_m - a_n| < \varepsilon .$$

In words, if for any $\varepsilon > 0$, there exists a number n_0 such that the inequality holds whenever m and n are larger than n_0, then the sequence has a limit.

We may also say that a sequence is convergent if for any neighborhood of a term a_p there exists a number n_0 such that if n, m, p are larger than n_0, then all but a finite number of terms of the sequence are contained in the neighborhood of a_p.

Cauchy's criterion is intuitively obvious if the terms of a sequence are represented on the number line. It requires that terms with large indices are close to one another in such a way that the neighborhood of any one of these terms, no matter how small, contains all of the other terms if $n > n_0$.

To illustrate the point we proceed with the sequence

$$\{a_n\}, \, a_n = 1 + 1/1! + 1/2! + \cdots + 1/n! ,$$

which defines the number e. It follows that

$$|a_{n+k} - a_n| = 1/(n + 1)! + 1/(n + 2)! + \cdots + 1/(n + k)!$$
$$= 1/(n + 1)! \cdot [1 + 1/(n + 2) + \cdots + 1/(n + 2)(n + 3)\cdots(n + k)] .$$

If $n + 2, n + 3, \ldots, n + k$, are replaced by the smaller number $n + 1$, the fractions in parentheses are increased, and the inequality

$$|a_{n+k} - a_n| < 1/(n + 1)! \cdot [1 + 1/(n + 1) + 1/(n + 1)^2 + \cdots + 1/(n + 1)^{k-1}]$$

follows. If we note that parentheses contain a geometric series [see Example 8 for $q = 1/(n +)$], we obtain

$$|a_{n+k} - a_n| < \frac{1}{(n + 1)!} \, \frac{1 - 1/(n + 1)^k}{1 - 1/(n + 1)} < \frac{1}{(n + 1)!} \, \frac{1}{1 - 1/(n + 1)} = \frac{1}{n!n} .$$

Hence, $|a_{n+k} - a_n| < \varepsilon$ for all $k \geq 1$ if $1/n!n < \varepsilon$ or $n!n > [1/\varepsilon]$.

If, for example, $\varepsilon = 0.01$, the Cauchy's criterion is satisfied for all $n > n_0 = 4$ and $k \geq 1$; if $\varepsilon = 10^{-6}$, then $n > n_0 = 8$. We see that for any given ε we can determine a definite number n_0 such that the inequality holds for all $n > n_0$ and $k \geq 1$. This proves that the above sequence has a limit.

By trial we obtained $n_0 = 4$ and $n_0 = 8$ for $\varepsilon = 10^{-2}$ and $\varepsilon = 10^{-6}$, respectively. But for the proof of convergence, accuracy is irrelevant. All that matters here is to show that for a certain n_0 and $n > n_0$ the inequality holds.

Therefore, we may proceed by simplifying the right-hand side of the inequality still more as follows.

$$|a_{n+k} - a_n| < 1/n!n < 1/n < \varepsilon .$$

Hence, we obtain n_0 explicitly as a function of ε, namely $n_0 = [1/\varepsilon]$. If $\varepsilon = 10^{-2}$, it follows that $n_0 = 100$. Although n_0 in this case is considerably larger than 4, the inequality $|a_{n+k} - a_n| < 10^{-2}$ holds for all $n > n_0 = 100$ and all $k \geq 1$, and this is the point in the proof.

It is easy to see that if a sequence $\{a_n\}$ has a limit, then Cauchy's convergence criterion is always satisfied.

If $\lim_{n\to\infty} a_n = a$, then there exists a number n_0 such that $|a_n - a| < \varepsilon/2$ for all $n > n_0$. Since $n + k > n > n_0$, the inequality $|a_{n+k} - a| < \varepsilon/2$ holds also. By the triangle inequality

$$|a_{n+k} - a_n| = |(a_{n+k} - a) + (a - a_n)| < |a_{n+k} - a| + |a_n - a| < \varepsilon/2 + \varepsilon/2 = \varepsilon$$

and Cauchy's criterion follows. The converse can also be proved.

2.3 Bounds.

If there is a number A such that $a_n \leq A$ for all n, we say that A is an upper bound of the sequence $\{a_n\}$.

Similarly, if there is a number B such that all terms a_n of a sequence $\{a_n\}$ satisfy the inequality $a_n \geq B$, then B is called a lower bound of the sequence. For example, the sequence $\{a_n\}$, $a_n = (-1)^{n-1} n/(n + 1)$ (see 2.1, Example 4) has many upper bounds: $1, 3/2, 2^{1/2}, 10, \dots$. Similarly, $-1, -1.2, -3^{1/2}, -10, \dots$ are lower bounds.

If M is an upper bound and if there is no smaller number which is also an upper bound of $\{a_n\}$, then M is called the least upper bound. For example, the least upper bound of the above sequence is 1.

If there is no number which is larger than N and is also a lower bound of $\{a_n\}$, then N is called the greatest lower bound. In our example the greatest lower bound is -1.

A sequence which has an upper and a lower bound is called bounded.

It is apparent that a bounded sequence cannot have more than one least upper bound and one largest lower bound if they exist. Their existence we state as an axiom.

2.3-1 Axiom. Every bounded sequence possesses a least upper bound and a greatest lower bound.

2.3-2 Theorem. Every convergent sequence is bounded.

Proof. Since the sequence has a limit a, by definition of a limit the inequality $|a_n - a| < \varepsilon$ holds for all $n > n_0$. Choose $\varepsilon = 1$ (any other value for ε, say, 1/2, 2, ... would work as well).

This means that outside the neighborhood $|a_n - a| < 1$ there is a finite number of terms with indices smaller than or equal to n_0. Since every finite set of numbers

$$|a_1 - a|, \; |a_2 - a|, \; \ldots, \; |a_{n_0} - a|$$

has a largest term which we denote by A, it follows that $|a_n - a| < A + 1$ for $n = 1, 2, \ldots, n_0$. But $|a_n - a| < 1$ for all $n > n_0$. Consequently, $|a_n - a| < A + 1$ for all n. This means that

$$a - A - 1 < a_n < a + A + 1 \,.$$

This completes the proof.

If a sequence is not bounded, then the absolute value $|a_n|$ of its terms increases beyond all bounds, and the sequence is divergent. Symbolically, either $\lim\limits_{n \to \infty} a_n = \infty$ or $\lim\limits_{n \to \infty} a_n = -\infty$, or $\lim\limits_{n \to \infty} a_n = \pm \infty$ if the sequence is alternating.

Note that not every bounded sequence is convergent [see Examples 4 and 5(d)].

2.4 Monotonic sequences

If the terms of a sequence $\{a_n\}$ are such that $a_n \le a_{n+1}$ for all n, we say the sequence is monotonically increasing, symbolically, $\{a_n\!\uparrow\}$. Similarly, if $a_n \ge a_{n+1}$ for all n, we speak of a monotonically decreasing sequence, symbolically $\{a_n\!\downarrow\}$.

If $a_n < a_{n+1}$ or $a_n > a_{n+1}$ for all n, we speak of strictly monotonic sequences. Often monotonic sequences are called nondecreasing sequences if $a_n \le a_{n+1}$ and nonincreasing sequences if $a_n \ge a_{n+1}$.

Examples 3, 8, 9, 10 are strictly increasing and Examples 1 and 7 are strictly decreasing sequences (see 2.1).

The sequence $\{a_n\}$, $a_n = [n^{1/2}]$ ($a_1 = a_2 = a_3 = 1$, $a_4 = a_5 = a_6 = a_7 = a_8 = 2$, $a_9 = a_{10} = \cdots = a_{15} = 3$, ...) is an example of a nondecreasing sequence.

If $\{a_n\}$, $a_n = c_1 + c_2 + \cdots + c_n$ and $c_k > 0$ ($k = 1, 2, 3, \ldots, n$), then the sequence is always strictly increasing, since $a_{n+1} - a_n = c_{n+1} > 0$, whence $a_{n+1} > a_n$ follows.

The first three terms of the sequence $\{a_n\}$, $a_n = n^2/2^n$, $a_1 = 1/2$, $a_2 = 1$, $a_3 = 9/8$, are strictly increasing; however, the sequence is not monotonic. It is easily seen that

$$a_n - a_{n+1} = [(n-1)^2 - 2]/2^{n+1}$$

is negative for $n = 1, 2$ and positive for $n \geq 3$, that is, the sequence first increases then decreases. This may be easily checked by writing further terms: $a_4 = 1$, $a_5 = 25/32$, $\ldots$.

To prove that a sequence is monotonic sometimes requires somewhat more effort. As an example we consider the sequence $\{a_n\}$, $a_n = (1 + 1/n)^n$.

The binominal expansion [1.1-1 (l) for $h = 1/n$] yields

$$a_n = 1 + n\frac{1}{n} + \frac{n(n-1)}{1 \cdot 2}\bigg/n^2 + \frac{n(n-1)(n-2)}{1 \cdot 2 \cdot 3}\bigg/n^3 + \cdots$$

$$+ \frac{n(n-1)(n-2)\cdots(n-n+1)}{1 \cdot 2 \cdot 3 \cdots n}\bigg/n^n$$

$$= 1 + 1 + \frac{1}{2!}\Big(1 - \frac{1}{n}\Big) + \frac{1}{3!}\Big(1 - \frac{1}{n}\Big)\Big(1 - \frac{2}{n}\Big) + \cdots$$

$$+ \frac{1}{n!}\Big(1 - \frac{1}{n}\Big)\Big(1 - \frac{2}{n}\Big)\cdots\Big(1 - \frac{n-1}{n}\Big).$$

If n is replaced by $n + 1$, it follows that

$$a_{n+1} = 1 + 1 + \frac{1}{2!}\Big(1 - \frac{1}{n+1}\Big) + \frac{1}{3!}\Big(1 - \frac{1}{n+1}\Big)\Big(1 - \frac{2}{n+1}\Big) + \cdots$$

$$+ \frac{1}{(n+1)!}\Big(1 - \frac{1}{n+1}\Big)\Big(1 - \frac{2}{n+1}\Big)\cdots\Big(1 - \frac{n}{n+1}\Big).$$

If we compare the series a_n and a_{n+1} term by term, we see that each term of a_{n+1} after the first two terms (which are equal) is larger than the corresponding term of a_n $\Big[$ why is $\frac{1}{2!}\Big(1 - \frac{1}{n+1}\Big) > \frac{1}{2!}\Big(1 - \frac{1}{n}\Big)$, $\frac{1}{3!}\Big(1 - \frac{1}{n+1}\Big)\Big(1 - \frac{2}{n+1}\Big) > \frac{1}{3!}\Big(1 - \frac{1}{n}\Big)\Big(1 - \frac{2}{n}\Big)$? $\Big]$ and, in addition, a_{n+1} has one more positive term. Thus, certainly, $a_{n+1} > a_n$ for all n. This proves that the sequence is strictly increasing.

If a sequence $\{a_n\}$ and a specified number a are given, then by the first definition of convergence of a sequence we can decide whether a is the limit. The second definition (Cauchy's criterion) enables us by intrinsic characteristics of the sequence itself to recognize whether the sequence is convergent. The decision in either case often involves tedious work in estimating the magnitude of $|a_n - a|$ or $|a_{n+k} - a_n|$ as n is large. Often it is simpler to prove the existence of a limit of a sequence if the sequence is monotonic. It is easy to prove the following theorem.

2.4-1 Theorem. If a monotonic sequence is bounded, then it has a limit.

Proof. Let $\{a_n\uparrow\}$ be bounded. Then by **2.3-1** the sequence has a least upper bound A. We prove that $\lim_{n\to\infty} a_n = A$.

Since $a_n \leq A$ for all n, it follows that no term of the sequence in the neighborhood $|a_n - A| < \varepsilon$ is to the right of A. There is, however, at least one term of the sequence in the neighborhood to the left of A, since otherwise we would have $a_n \leq A - \varepsilon$ for all n, so that not A but $A - \varepsilon$ would be an upper bound—a contradiction to the hypotheses. Let us denote this term which is in the neighborhood by a_{n_0}. Then all terms with indices $n > n_0$ are also in the neighborhood of A, since the sequence is monotonically increasing, that is, $a_n \geq a_{n_0}$ if $n > n_0$. Since there are only a finite number of terms with indices $n \leq n_0$, it follows that the neighborhood of A contains all but a finite number of terms at most. By definition, this means that $\lim_{n\to\infty} a_n = A$.

For monotonically decreasing sequences the proof follows the very same lines, and it is left to the reader.

To illustrate the point we consider the sequence $\{a_n\}$, $a_n = 1 + 1/1! + 1/2! + \cdots + 1/n!$. Since $a_{n+1} - a_n = 1/(n+1)! > 0$, it follows that the sequence is strictly increasing. If we note that

$$1/3! < 1/2^2,\ 1/4! < 1/2^3,\ \ldots,\ 1/n! < 1/2^{n-1},\quad \text{for}\quad n \geq 3,$$

it follows that

$$a_n \leq 1 + 1 + 1/2 + 1/2^2 + \cdots + 1/2^{n-1} = 1 + \frac{1 - (1/2^n)}{1 - (1/2)} < 1 + \frac{1}{1 - (1/2)} = 3.$$

Thus, we have shown that the sequence is monotonically increasing and bounded from above. Note that there is no need to show that a sequence has a lower bound if it is monotonically increasing, since its lower bound is always a_1. Similarly, a_1 is the upper bound if the sequence is monotonically decreasing. Consequently, by **2.4-1**, the above sequence is convergent.

Next we show that the sequence $\{b_n\}$, $b_n = (1 + 1/n)^n$ is also convergent. We have already seen that $\{b_n\}$ is monotonically increasing and its terms can be written in the form

$$(2.4)\qquad b_n = 1 + 1 + \frac{1}{2!}\left(1 - \frac{1}{n}\right) + \cdots$$
$$+ \frac{1}{m!}\left(1 - \frac{1}{n}\right)\left(1 - \frac{2}{n}\right)\cdots\left(1 - \frac{m-1}{n}\right) + \cdots$$
$$+ \frac{1}{n!}\left(1 - \frac{1}{n}\right)\cdots\left(1 - \frac{n-1}{n}\right).$$

If we compare b_n with $a_n = 1 + 1 + 1/2! + 1/3! + \cdots + 1/n!$, we see that the terms of b_n for $n \geq 3$ are smaller than the corresponding terms of a_n (the first two terms are equal). Therefore, $b_n \leq a_n \leq 3$. Thus, we have shown that $\{b_n\}$ is monotonic and bounded. Consequently, by **2.4-1** it has a limit.

As an instructive example of operation with limits we prove further that $\lim_{n \to \infty} a_n = \lim_{n \to \infty} b_n$.

If, for $m > n$, the terms of the series

$$b_m = 1 + 1 + \frac{1}{2!}\left(1 - \frac{1}{m}\right) + \frac{1}{3!}\left(1 - \frac{1}{m}\right)\left(1 - \frac{2}{m}\right) + \cdots$$
$$+ \frac{1}{n!}\left(1 - \frac{1}{m}\right)\left(1 - \frac{2}{m}\right) \cdots \left(1 - \frac{n-1}{m}\right)$$
$$+ \frac{1}{(n+1)!}\left(1 - \frac{1}{m}\right) \cdots \left(1 - \frac{n}{m}\right) + \cdots + \frac{1}{m!}\left(1 - \frac{1}{m}\right) \cdots \left(1 - \frac{m-1}{m}\right)$$

from the term

$$\frac{1}{(n+1)!}\left(1 - \frac{1}{m}\right)\left(1 - \frac{2}{m}\right) \cdots \left(1 - \frac{n}{m}\right)$$

on are omitted, the inequality

$$b_m > 1 + 1 + \frac{1}{2!}\left(1 - \frac{1}{m}\right) + \frac{1}{3!}\left(1 - \frac{1}{m}\right)\left(1 - \frac{2}{m}\right) + \cdots$$
$$+ \frac{1}{n!}\left(1 - \frac{1}{m}\right)\left(1 - \frac{2}{m}\right) \cdots \left(1 - \frac{n-1}{m}\right)$$

follows. If n is fixed, that is, if the number of terms of the series is finite, and m increases beyond all bounds, it follows that

$$\lim_{n \to \infty} b = b \geq 1 + 1 + 1/2! + 1/3! + \cdots + 1/n! = a_n$$

since $\lim_{n \to \infty} b_m = b$ exists and

$$\frac{1}{k!}\left(1 - \frac{1}{m}\right)\left(1 - \frac{2}{m}\right) \cdots \left(1 - \frac{k-1}{m}\right) \to \frac{1}{k!}$$

as $m \to \infty$ for $k = 2, 3, \ldots, n$.

Combining $b_n \leq a_n$ and $b \geq a_n$, we obtain the inequality $b_n \leq a_n \leq b$ which holds for all n. Since a_n and b_n have limits a and b, respectively, the "squeeze" method yields $a = b$. Thus we have proved that

$$\lim_{n \to \infty}\left(1 + \frac{1}{n}\right)^n = \lim_{n \to \infty}\left(1 + \frac{1}{1!} + \frac{1}{2!} + \cdots + \frac{1}{n!}\right) = e .$$

Note that passing to the limit as $m \to \infty$ does not yield a strict inequality. It is worth while to remember a general rule: if $\lim_{n\to\infty} a_n = a$ and $\lim_{n\to\infty} b_n = b$ exist, and, in addition, the inequality $a_n > b_n$ holds for every n, then $a \geq b$. That the equality has to be added can be easily verified by the example $a_n = 1/n$, $b_n = 1/2n$ where $a = b = 0$.

2.5 Calculation of the number e

Since, by the definition of a limit, the inequality $|a_n - e| < \varepsilon$ holds for ε as small as we please if n is chosen large enough, we can approximate e as accurately as we wish by $a_n = 1 + 1/1! + 1/2! + \cdots + 1/n!$. Also, since $\lim_{n\to\infty} a_{n+k} = e$, it follows from the inequality $|a_{n+k} - a_n| < 1/n!n$ (see 2.2) which holds for all $k \geq 1$ that

$$|e - a_n| \leq 1/n!n \ .$$

This inequality shows that if e is approximated by a_n, that is, $e \approx a_n$, then the error of the approximation is less than or equal to $1/n!n$. Since a_n is strictly increasing and e is its least upper bound, it follows that

$$a_n < e \leq a_n + 1/n!n \ .$$

If, for example, $n = 9$, then the error of the approximation

$$e \approx a_9 = 1 + 1 + \frac{1}{2!} + \frac{1}{3!} + \frac{1}{4!} + \frac{1}{5!} + \frac{1}{6!} + \frac{1}{7!} + \frac{1}{8!} + \frac{1}{9!}$$

is less than 10^{-6}. Evaluation of a_9 correct to six decimals yields the inequality

$$2.718281 < e < 2.718282 \ ,$$

which already gives us a good idea of the value of the number e.

2.6 Limit theorems for sequences

Calculating of limits can be considerably simplified if rational operations and passage to the limit are interchanged. In other words, we first perform a passage to the limit and then a rational operation, or we first perform a rational operation and then pass to the limit. That for certain sequences such interchange leads to different results is shown by the following example.

$$\{a_n\}, a_n = (-1)^{n-1}n/(n+1) \qquad \{b_n\}, b_n = (-1)^n \ .$$

It is easily seen that

$$\lim_{n\to\infty} (a_n + b_n) = \lim_{n\to\infty} (-1)^n/(n+1) = 0 .$$

However,

$$\lim_{n\to\infty} a_n + \lim_{n\to\infty} b_n$$

does not exist, since $\lim_{n\to\infty} a_n$ and $\lim_{n\to\infty} b_n$ do not exist [see Examples 4 and 5 (d)]. Consequently,

$$\lim_{n\to\infty} (a_n + b_n) \neq \lim_{n\to\infty} a_n + \lim_{n\to\infty} b_n .$$

Similarly, it is easily verified that

$$\lim_{n\to\infty} (a_n b_n) \neq \lim_{n\to\infty} a_n \lim_{n\to\infty} b_n , \quad \lim_{n\to\infty} (a_n/b_n) \neq \lim_{n\to\infty} a_n/\lim_{n\to\infty} b_n .$$

2.6-1 Theorem. If $\lim_{n\to\infty} a_n = a$ and $\lim_{n\to\infty} b_n = a$ exist, then

(a) $\lim_{n\to\infty} (a_n \pm b_n) = \lim_{n\to\infty} a_n \pm \lim_{n\to\infty} b_n ,$ (b) $\lim_{n\to\infty} a_n b_n = \lim_{n\to\infty} a_n \lim_{n\to\infty} b_n ,$

(c) $\lim_{n\to\infty} a_n/b_n = \lim_{n\to\infty} a_n/\lim_{n\to\infty} b_n ,$ provided $\lim_{n\to\infty} b_n = b \neq 0.$

The proof of these rules is simple. As an example we prove case (b) and leave the reader to establish the other statements for himself.

Proof (b). Since $\lim_{n\to\infty} a_n = a$ and $\lim_{n\to\infty} b_n = b$ exist, it follows that for any $\varepsilon > 0$ and $n' > 0$ we can choose n_0 so large that when $n > n_0$

$$|a_n - a| < \varepsilon/n' \quad \text{and} \quad |b_n - b| < \varepsilon/n'$$

hold. The proof of the theorem is completed if we establish the inequality

$$|a_n b_n - ab| < \varepsilon$$

for $n > n_0$. Without loss of generality we may assume that $\varepsilon/n' < 1$. If we put $x = a_n$, $y = b_n$, $k = h = \varepsilon/n'$, $n' = |b| + 1 + |a|$ in **1.3-1** (e), it follows that

$$|a_n b_n - ab| < (|b| + \varepsilon/n') \cdot (\varepsilon/n') + |a| \cdot \varepsilon/n' < (|b| + |a| + 1) \cdot \varepsilon/n' = \varepsilon .$$

Another proof without use of 1.3-1(e) is also simple.

$$|a_n b_n - ab| = |(a_n b_n - ab_n) + (ab_n - ab)| \leq |b_n||a_n - a| + |a||b_n - b|$$
$$< (|b_n| + |a|)\varepsilon/n' .$$

If we note that $|b_n| = |(b_n - b) + b| \leq |b_n - b| + |b| < 1 + |b|$ for $n > n_0$, it follows that

$$|a_n b_n - ab| < (|a| + |b| + 1)\varepsilon/n' ,$$

29

and for $n' = |a| + |b| + 1$ the statement follows.

Corollary. If $a_n = c$, then $\lim\limits_{n\to\infty} a_n = c$ and **2.6-1**(b) yields $\lim\limits_{n\to\infty} cb_n = c \lim\limits_{n\to\infty} b_n$, that is, if a sequence $\{b_n\}$ is convergent, then the sequence $\{cb_n\}$ also converges and $\lim\limits_{n\to\infty} cb_n = cb$.

Example 12. $\{a_n\}$, $a_n = [1 - (1 - 1/n)^3]/[1 - (1 - 1/n)^2]$. Since the limit of the denominator is 0 as $n \to \infty$, **2.6-1**(c) cannot be applied. However, it is easily seen that a_n can be rewritten in the form

$$a_n = \left(3 - \frac{3}{n} + \frac{1}{n^2}\right)\Big/\left(2 - \frac{1}{n}\right),$$

and it follows that

$$\lim_{n\to\infty} a_n = \frac{\lim\limits_{n\to\infty}(3 - 3/n + 1/n^2)}{\lim\limits_{n\to\infty}(2 - 1/n)} = \frac{3}{2}.$$

Note that **2.6-1** holds for any finite number of sequences. For example, if $\lim\limits_{n\to\infty} a_n = a$, $\lim\limits_{n\to\infty} b_n = b$, and $\lim\limits_{n\to\infty} c_n = c$, then

$$\lim_{n\to\infty}(a_n b_n c_n) = \lim_{n\to\infty} a_n \lim_{n\to\infty} b_n \lim_{n\to\infty} c_n = abc.$$

If we write $\lim\limits_{n\to\infty}(a_n b_n c_n) = \lim\limits_{n\to\infty}(a_n b_n) \lim\limits_{n\to\infty} c_n$, by **2.6-1**(b) the statement follows.

The generalization can easily be proved by induction.

2.6-2 Theorem. If a sequence $\{a_n\}$ converges, then its limit is unique.

Proof. Assume that there is another limit a' and that $a' \neq a$. Then if follows that both neighborhoods

$$|a_n - a| < \varepsilon \quad \text{and} \quad |a_n - a'| < \varepsilon$$

contain all but a finite number of terms of the sequence $\{a_n\}$. Choose $\varepsilon < \frac{1}{2}|a - a'|$. Then the neighborhoods of a and of a' have no point in common and yet each contains infinitely many terms. It follows that outside each neighborhood there are infinitely many terms of $\{a_n\}$, consequently, neither a nor a' are limits of the sequence. This contradicts the hypothesis. Therefore, if a sequence is convergent, there exists only one limit.

2.6-3 Theorem. If $\lim\limits_{n\to\infty} a_n = a$, then the sequence $\{b_n\}$ of arithmetic means

$$b_n = (a_1 + a_2 + \cdots + a_n)/n$$

also converges to a.

Proof. We have to show that for every $\varepsilon > 0$ there exists a number n_0 such that all terms b_n with indices greater than n_0 are in the neighborhood

$$|b_n - a| < \varepsilon .$$

Since $\lim\limits_{k \to \infty} a_k = a$, we certainly can choose k so large that $|a_{k+1} - a| < \varepsilon/2$, $|a_{k+2} - a| < \varepsilon/2, \cdots, |a_n - a| < \varepsilon/2$. Then,

$$
\begin{aligned}
|b_n - a| &\leq \left| \frac{(a_1-a)+(a_2-a)+\cdots+(a_k-a)}{n} \right| + \left| \frac{(a_{k+1}-a)+(a_{k+2}-a)+\cdots+(a_n-a)}{n} \right| \\
&\leq \left| \frac{(a_1-a)+(a_2-a)+\cdots+(a_k-a)}{n} \right| + \frac{|a_{k+1}-a|+|a_{k+2}-a|+\cdots+|a_n-a|}{n} \\
&< \left| \frac{(a_1-a)+(a_2-a)+\cdots+(a_k-a)}{n} \right| + \frac{n-k}{n} \frac{\varepsilon}{2} .
\end{aligned}
$$

For a fixed k the numerator of the first fraction on the right is a finite number, and we choose n_0 such that for $n > n_0$ the first fraction is less than $\varepsilon/2$. Since $(n - k)/n < 1$, it follows that

$$|b_n - a| < \varepsilon/2 + \varepsilon/2 = \varepsilon ,$$

whenever $n > n_0$. This completes the proof.

Note the technique of the proof. Many theorems involving limits are proved by considering separately two or more parts of an expression.

Example 13. $\lim\limits_{n \to \infty} (1 + 1/2 + 1/3 + \cdots + 1/n)/n = 0$ because $\lim\limits_{n \to \infty} 1/n = 0$.

Example 14. $\lim\limits_{n \to \infty} (1 + 2^{1/2} + 3^{1/3} + \cdots + n^{1/n})/n = 1$ because $\lim\limits_{n \to \infty} n^{1/n} = 1$.

One may wonder whether the inverse of **2.6-3** holds. That is, does $\lim\limits_{n \to \infty} a_n = a$ exist if $\lim\limits_{n \to \infty} (a_1 + a_2 + \cdots + a_n)/n = A$ exists?

That this is not always the case is shown by the example $\{a_n\}$, $a_n = 1 - 1 + 1 - 1 + \cdots + (-1)^{n-1}$. The terms of the sequence of arithmetic means are easily calculated

$$b_1 = 1, \; b_2 = \frac{1}{2}, \; b_3 = \frac{2}{3}, \; b_4 = \frac{1}{2}, \; \ldots, \; b_{2k} = \frac{1}{2}, \; b_{2k+1} = \frac{k+1}{2k+1}, \; \ldots .$$

Hence, $\lim\limits_{n \to \infty} b_n = 1/2$ exists, but $\lim\limits_{n \to \infty} a_n$ does not exist. (See Example 8 for $q = -1$.)

2.6-4 Theorem. If $\{a_n\}$, $a_n > 0$ and $\lim\limits_{n \to \infty} a_n/a_{n-1} = b$ exists, then $\lim\limits_{n \to \infty} a_n^{1/n} = b$.

Proof. If the identity

$$(a_n)^{1/n} = \left(\frac{a_1}{1} \cdot \frac{a_2}{a_1} \cdot \frac{a_3}{a_2} \cdots \frac{a_n}{a_{n-1}}\right)^{1/n}$$

is written in the form

$$\log (a_n)^{1/n} = (\log a_1/1 + \log a_2/a_1 + \cdots + \log a_n/a_{n-1})/n \ ,$$

2.6-3 yields

$$\lim_{n \to \infty} \log (a_n)^{1/n} = \lim_{n \to \infty} \log a_n/a_{n-1} = \log b \ . \quad \text{Thus, } \lim_{n \to \infty} (a_n)^{1/n} = b \ .$$

(We assume here that $\log x$ is continuous for $x > 0$.)

Does the inverse of **2.6-3** hold? That is, if $\lim_{n \to \infty} (a_n)^{1/n} = b$ exists, does $\lim_{n \to \infty} a_n/a_{-1}$ exist? That this is not the case is shown by the example $\{a_n\}$, $a_{2k-1} = 1/k$, $a_{2k} = 1/2k$ (that is, $a_1 = 1$, $a_2 = 1/2$, $a_3 = 1/2$, $a_4 = 1/4$, $a_5 = 1/3$, $a_6 = 1/6$, ...). It is easily seen that $\lim_{n \to \infty} (a_n)^{1/n} = 1$ (see Example 6). However, $\lim_{n \to \infty} a_n/a_{n-1}$ does not exist.

2.7 Sequences defined recursively

In many applications, the first few terms of a sequence are given and thereafter each term depends by a given law on the immediately preceding term.

Example 15. $\{a_n\}$, $a_n = \frac{1}{2}(a_{n-1} + A/a_{n-1})$, where A is any positive number and $a_1 > A^{1/2}$ is a first approximation of $A^{1/2}$. This is the familiar sequence used in high school algebra for approximation of $A^{1/2}$.

If, say, $A = 3$ and $a_1 = 2 > 3^{1/2}$ is chosen, then $a_1 = 2$, $a_2 = \frac{1}{2}\left(2 + \frac{3}{2}\right)$ $= \frac{7}{4}$, $a_3 = \frac{1}{2}\left(\frac{7}{4} + \frac{3}{7/4}\right) = \frac{97}{56}$, $a_4 = \frac{1}{2}\left(\frac{97}{56} + \frac{3}{97/56}\right) = \frac{18817}{10864}$, ...

In order to prove that $\lim_{n \to \infty} a_n = A^{1/2}$ we proceed as follows. First note that A, $A^{1/2}$, and $a_1 > A^{1/2}$ are positive numbers. From $a_2 = \frac{1}{2}(a_1 + A/a_1)$, $a_3 = \frac{1}{2}(a_2 + A/a_2)$, ..., it follows that $a_2 > 0$, $a_3 > 0$, ..., $a_n > 0$,.... From the relation

$$a_n - A^{1/2} = \frac{1}{2} \frac{a_{n-1}^2 - 2a_{n-1}(A)^{1/2} + A}{a_{n-1}} = \frac{(a_{n-1} - A^{1/2})^2}{2a_{n-1}}$$

it follows that $a_n - A^{1/2} \geq 0$ or $a_n \geq A^{1/2}$. Consequently, by **1.1-1(g)** it follows that $a_n^2 \geq A$ for $n \geq 2$ and $a_{n-1}^2 \geq A$ for $n \geq 3$.

If we note further that

$$a_{n-1} - a_n = \frac{a_{n-1}^2 - A}{2a_{n-1}} \geq 0 \, ,$$

it follows that $a_{n-1} \geq a_n$. Consequently, the sequence is monotonically decreasing and bounded $(a_n \geq A^{1/2})$. By **2.4-1** it follows that $\lim\limits_{n \to \infty} a_n = a$ exists and is positive. Since $\lim\limits_{n \to \infty} a_n = \lim\limits_{n \to \infty} a_{n-1} = a$, we have

$$\lim_{n \to \infty} a_n = \frac{1}{2}\left(\lim_{n \to \infty} a_{n-1} + \frac{A}{\lim\limits_{n \to \infty} a_{n-1}} \right)$$

or

$$a = \frac{1}{2}\left(a + \frac{A}{a} \right) ,$$

whence $a = A^{1/2}$ follows. This completes the proof.

If the relations

$$a_n - A^{1/2} = \frac{(a_{n-1} - A^{1/2})^2}{2a_{n-1}} , \quad a_n + A^{1/2} = \frac{(a_{n-1} + A^{1/2})^2}{2a_{n-1}}$$

are written down for $n = 2, 3, \ldots, k$ and then consecutive substitutions are made, the relation

$$\frac{a_k - A^{1/2}}{a_k + A^{1/2}} = \left(\frac{a_1 - A^{1/2}}{a_1 + A^{1/2}} \right)^{2^{k-1}}$$

is obtained by induction. If $R_k = a_k - A^{1/2}$ is the error of the approximation $A^{1/2} \approx a_k$, then it follows that

$$R_k = \left(\frac{a_1 - A^{1/2}}{a_1 + A^{1/2}} \right)^{2^{k-1}} (a_k + A^{1/2}) .$$

In the case of $3^{1/2} \approx a_4 = 18817/10864$ we have

$$R_4 = \left(\frac{2 - 3^{1/2}}{2 + 3^{1/2}} \right)^8 (a_4 + 3^{1/2}) < \left(\frac{0 \cdot 3}{3 \cdot 72} \right)^8 \cdot (4) < 10^{-8} \, ,$$

which shows that already $3^{1/2} \approx a_4$ yields an approximation with an error less than 10^{-8}.

Example 16. Given $a > b > 0$, $a_1 = \frac{1}{2}(a + b)$, $b_1 = (ab)^{1/2}$. If a_n and b_n are determined by the equations

$$a_n = \tfrac{1}{2}(a_{n-1} + b_{n-1}), \quad b_n = (a_{n-1}b_{n-1})^{1/2}, \quad n = 2, 3, 4, \ldots ,$$

prove that (a) $\{a_n\}$ is monotonically decreasing; (b) $\{b_n\}$ is monotonically increasing; (c) both sequences possess limits; (d) the limits are equal.

Solution. From $a_n - b_n = \frac{1}{2}[(a_{n-1})^{1/2} - (b_{n-1})^{1/2}]^2 > 0$ it follows by induction that $a_n > b_n$ for $n = 1, 2, 3, \ldots$. Similarly, from the relations

$$a_{n-1} - a_n = \frac{1}{2}(a_{n-1} - b_{n-1}) \quad \text{and} \quad b_n - b_{n-1} = (b_{n-1})^{1/2}[(a_{n-1})^{1/2} - (b_{n-1})^{1/2}]$$

the statements (a) and (b) follow immediately.

Since $\{b_n\}$ is a monotonically increasing sequence and $a_n > b_n$, it follows that $a_n > b$, that is, $\{a_n\}$ is bounded. Similarly, since $\{a_n\}$ is a monotonically decreasing sequence and $b_n < a_n$, it follows that $b_n < a$, that is, b_n is bounded. Hence, by **2.4-1** it follows that $\lim_{n \to \infty} a_n = A$ and $\lim_{n \to \infty} b_n = B$ exist. Finally, by **2.6-1(a)** it follows that

$$\lim_{n \to \infty} a_n = \frac{1}{2}\left(\lim_{n \to \infty} a_{n-1} + \lim_{n \leftarrow \infty} b_{n-1}\right),$$

or

$$A = \frac{1}{2}(A + B),$$

whence it follows that $A = B$, and this is statement (d).

Example 17. If $a_{n+1} = \frac{1}{2}(a_n + b_n)$, $b_{n+1} = (a_{n+1}b_n)^{1/2}$, $a_n > 0$, $b_n > 0$, show that $\{a_n\}$ and $\{b_n\}$ are monotonic and converge to the same limit. Evaluate the common limit if $a_1 = \cos\theta$, $b_1 = 1$.

Solution. Assume $b_1 > a_1$. If $a_1 = b_1$, then $a_n = b_n = a_1$, that is, $\lim_{n \to \infty} a_n = \lim_{n \to \infty} b_n = a_1$. The case $a_1 > b_1$ is similar to the case $b_1 > a_1$.

From the relations

$$a_{n+1} - b_n = \frac{1}{2}(a_n - b_n), \quad a_{n+1} - a_n = \frac{1}{2}(b_n - a_n), \quad b_{n+1} - b_n$$
$$= (b_n)^{1/2}[(a_{n+1})^{1/2} - (a_n)^{1/2}]$$

it follows easily, as in Example 16, that $\{a_n\}$ is monotonically increasing and bounded by b_1, and that $\{b_n\}$ is monotonically decreasing and bounded by a_1 ($b_n > a_1$). By **2.4-1** it follows that $\lim_{n \to \infty} a_n = a$ and $\lim_{n \to \infty} b_n = b$ exist. Then from

$$\lim_{n \to \infty} a_{n+1} = \frac{1}{2}\left(\lim_{n \to \infty} a_n + \lim_{n \to \infty} b_n\right),$$

or

$$a = \frac{1}{2}(a + b),$$

it follows that $a = b$.

Note that the common limit can be approximated by a_n, or b_n, for any initial positive values a_1 and b_1. Since one sequence approaches its limit from above and the other sequence tends to its limit from below, the difference $(b_n - a_n)$ represents the error of the approximation $a \approx a_n$ or $a \approx b_n$.

Sometimes for special initial values the limit can be found in closed form. Such, for example, is the case if $a_1 = \cos\theta$, $b_1 = 1$ $(0 < \theta < \pi/2)$.

The equations

$$a_n = \cos\theta/2 \cos\theta/2^2 \cdots \cos\theta/2^{n-2} \cos^2\theta/2^{n-1},$$
$$b_n = \cos\theta/2 \cos\theta/2^2 \cdots \cos\theta/2^{n-2} \cos\theta/2^{n-1}$$

are easily calculated and proved by induction. If we note that

$$2\sin\theta/2^{k-1} \cos\theta/2^{k-1} = \sin\theta/2^{k-2}, \quad k = n, n-1, \ldots, 2,$$

it follows that

$$2^{n-1}\sin\theta/2^{n-1}b_n = \sin\theta.$$

If the familiar equation $\lim_{x \to 0}(\sin\theta x)/x = \theta$ with $x = 1/2^{n-1}$ is used, it follows that

$$\lim_{n \gets \infty} \frac{\sin\theta/2^{n-1}}{1/2^{n-1}} b_n = \theta b = \sin\theta,$$

or

$$b = (\sin\theta)/\theta.$$

Exercises 2.B

1. Using Cauchy's criterion of convergence show that $\{a_n\}$ converges:
   (a) $a_n = 1 + 1/2^2 + 1/3^2 + \cdots + 1/n^2$ [Hint: $1/k^2 < 1/(k-1)k = 1/(k-1) - 1/k)$].
   (b) $a_n = 1/n^2 + 2/n^2 + \cdots + n/n^2$ (Hint: first simplify).
   (c) $a_n = 1/2! - 1/3! + 1/4! - \cdots + (-1)^{n+1}/(n+1)!$.
   (d) $a_n = (n+1)/n$.
2. Show that the sequence $\{a_n\}$ is monotonic and bounded. In order to make sure the notation is understood, write a few terms of the sequence for $n = 1, 2, 3, \ldots$.
   (a) $a_n = 1/(n+1) + 1/(n+2) + \cdots + 1/(n+n)$.
   (b) $a_n = \dfrac{1 \cdot 3 \cdot 5 \cdots (2n-1)}{2 \cdot 4 \cdot 6 \cdots 2n}$ $\left(\text{Hint: } a_{n+1} = \dfrac{2n+1}{2n+2}a_n\right)$.
   (c) $a_n = \dfrac{2 \cdot 4 \cdots 2n}{1 \cdot 3 \cdots (2n-1)} \cdot \dfrac{1}{n^2}$.
3. Prove that $\{a_n\}$, $a_n = 1 + 1/2^2 + 1/3^2 + \cdots + 1/n^2$ is convergent, first

by Cauchy's criterion, then by showing that the sequence is monotonic and bounded. Compare the methods and decide which of them is simpler to apply in this case.

4. From Cauchy's criterion of convergence obtain an approximation of the limit of $\{a_n\}$, $a_n = 1 + 1/2^2 + 1/3^2 + \cdots + 1/n^2$, if the error is to be less than 0.1. How many terms of the series are to be added if the error of the approximation is to be less than 0.001?

5. Prove that the sequence $\{a_n\}$, $a_n = 1 + 1/2^p + 1/3^p + \cdots + 1/n^p$ converges if $p > 1$. (Hint: to show that a_n is bounded use $1/2^p + 1/3^p < 1/2^p + 1/2^p = 1/2^{p-1}$, $1/4^p + 1/5^p + 1/6^p + 1/7^p < 4/4^p = (1/2^{p-1})^2, \ldots$.)

6. Determine whether $\{a_n\}$ converges or diverges.
   (a) $a_n = \ln 1/2 + \ln 2/3 + \cdots + \ln n/(n+1)$.
   (b) $a_n = 1 + 1/3 + 1/5 + \cdots + 1/(2n-1)$.
   (c) $a_n = 1 + e^{-1} + e^{-2} + \cdots + e^{-(n-1)}$.
   (d) $a_n = (2^{1/2} - 1) + (3^{1/2} - 2^{1/2}) + \cdots + [(n+1)^{1/2} - n^{1/2}]$.
   (e) $a_n = 1/(1 + 1^3) + 2/(1 + 2^3) + 3/(1 + 3^3) + \cdots + n/(1 + n^3)$.

7. If p is a fixed positive integer show that $\{a_n\}$, $a_n = 1/(n+1) + 1/(n+2) + \cdots + 1/(n + np)$ has a limit.

8. If $a > b > 0$, $a_1 = \frac{1}{2}(a + b)$, $b_1 = 2ab/(a + b)$, and $a_n = \frac{1}{2}(a_{n-1} + b_{n-1})$, $b_n = (2a_{n-1}b_{n-1})/(a_{n-1} + b_{n-1})$, show that $\{a_n\}$ and $\{b_n\}$ converge to the same limit $(ab)^{1/2}$ called the Arithmetic-Harmonic Mean.

9. If $a_{n+2} = (a_{n+1}a_n)^{1/2}$ and $a_n > 0$, show that the sequences $\{a_{2n-1}\}$ and $\{a_{2n}\}$ are monotonic, one increasing, the other decreasing, and that $\lim_{n\to\infty} a_n = (a_1 a_2^2)^{1/3}$.

10. If $a_{n+2} = \frac{1}{2}(a_{n+1} + a_n)$, $a_n > 0$, show that the sequences $\{a_{2n+1}\}$ and $\{a_{2n}\}$ are both monotonic, one increasing, the other decreasing, and that $\lim_{n\to\infty} a_n = \frac{1}{3}(a_1 + 2a_2)$.

11. If $a_n = b/(1 + a_{n-1})$, $a_n > 0$, $b > 0$, prove that $\{a_n\}$ has a limit which is the positive root of the equation $x^2 + x = b$.

12. If the sequence $\{a_n\}$ is monotonic, prove that the sequence $\{b_n\}$, $b_n = (a_1 + a_2 + \cdots + a_n)/n$, of arithmetic means is also monotonic in the same sense, that is, if $\{a_n \uparrow\}$, then $\{b_n \uparrow\}$, if $\{a_n \downarrow\}$, then $\{b_n \downarrow\}$.

13. If $a_n > 0$ and $\lim_{n\to\infty} a_n = a \neq 0$, then $\lim_{n\to\infty} c_n = \lim_{n\to\infty} (a_1 a_2 \cdots a_n)^{1/n} = a$.

14. Prove that $\lim_{n\to\infty} (n^n/n!)^{1/n} = e$.

2.8 Evaluation of sequences by integrals

It follows from the definition of the definite integral that

$$\int_a^b f(x)\, dx = \lim_{n\to\infty} h \sum_{i=1}^n f(a + ih), \quad h = \frac{b - a}{n}.$$

That is, the limit of the sequence $\{S_n\}$, $S_n = h \sum_{i=1}^n f(a + ih)$ can be reduced to evaluation of a definite integral. It follows that if the integral exists, then the limit of the sequence exists also. We have seen how a limit of a convergent sequence can be approximated by the sequence itself (see 2.5), but often it is easier to evaluate the corresponding definite integral which leads to a more convenient or desirable closed form.

Example 18. $\{a_n\}$, $a_n = 1/(n + 1) + 1/(n + 2) + \cdots + 1/(n + n)$. If we put a_n in the form

$$a_n = \frac{1}{n}\left(\frac{1}{1 + 1/n} + \frac{1}{1 + 2/n} + \cdots + \frac{1}{1 + n/n}\right) = h \sum_{i=1}^{n} \frac{1}{1 + ih}, \quad h = \frac{1}{n}$$

and note that for $a = 1$ from $b = a + nh = 1 + 1 = 2$ follows, we obtain

$$\lim_{n \to \infty} a_n = \int_1^2 \frac{dx}{x} = \ln 2 .$$

Note that one may choose $a = 0$, $f(x) = 1/(1 + x)$, then $b = 0 + nh = 1$ and obtain

$$\lim_{n \to \infty} a_n = \int_0^1 \frac{dx}{1 + x} = \ln 2 .$$

The following technique may lead to a different form which often is simpler to evaluate.

If we note that

$$a_{k+1} - a_k = \frac{1}{(2k + 1)(2k + 2)}$$

and add them for $k = 1, 2, 3, \ldots, n - 1$, we obtain

$$a_n = \frac{1}{1 \cdot 2} + \frac{1}{3 \cdot 4} + \cdots + \frac{1}{(2n - 1)2n} = 1 - \frac{1}{2} + \frac{1}{3} - \cdots$$

$$+ \frac{1}{2n - 1} - \frac{1}{2n} .$$

Thus,

$$\lim_{n \to \infty}\left(\frac{1}{1 \cdot 2} + \frac{1}{3 \cdot 4} + \cdots + \frac{1}{(2n - 1)2n}\right) = \lim_{n \leftarrow \infty}\left(1 - \frac{1}{2} + \frac{1}{3} - \frac{1}{4} + \cdots\right.$$

$$\left. + \frac{1}{2n - 1} - \frac{1}{2n}\right) = \ln 2 .$$

Example 19. $\{a_n\}$, $a_n = 1/n^{1/2}(1 + 1/2^{1/2} + \cdots + 1/n^{1/2})$. If we write

$$a_n = \frac{1}{n}\left(\frac{1}{(1/n)^{1/2}} + \frac{1}{(2/n)^{1/2}} + \cdots + \frac{1}{(n/n)^{1/2}}\right) = h \sum_{i=1}^{n} \frac{1}{(ih)^{1/2}}, \quad h = \frac{1}{n},$$

then for $a = 0$, $b = a + nh = 1$, $f(x) = 1/x^{1/2}$ it follows that

$$\lim_{n \to \infty} a_n = \int_0^1 \frac{dx}{x^{1/2}} = 2 .$$

Example 20. $\{a_n\}$, $a_n \sum_{k=1}^n n/(n^2 + k^2)$. It is easily seen that

$$\lim_{n \to \infty} \sum_{k=1}^n \frac{n}{n^2 + k^2} = \lim_{n \to \infty} h \sum_{k=1}^n \frac{1}{1 + (kh)^2} = \int_0^1 \frac{dx}{1 + x^2} = \frac{\pi}{4} , \quad h = \frac{1}{n} .$$

However, $\lim_{n \leftarrow \infty} \sum_{k=1}^{n^2} n/(n^2 + k^2)$ cannot be deduced at once from the definition of the integral.

If we write $a_n = \sum_{x=1}^{n^2} f(x)$, $f(x) = n/(n^2 + x^2)$ is a monotonically decreasing function on the interval $[1, n^2]$. Comparing the area bounded by the curve $f(x)$, the ordinates $f(1)$ and $f(n^2)$, and the x-axis with the corresponding areas formed by the sums of inscribed and circumscribed rectangles, respectively, we obtain the inequalities (Fig. 6)

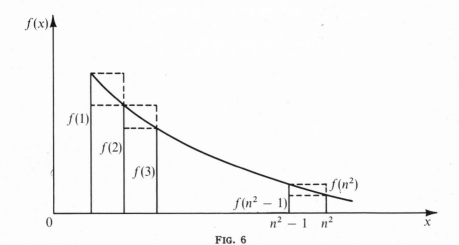

FIG. 6

$$\sum_{k=2}^{n^2} f(x) < \int_1^{n^2} f(x)\, dx , \quad \sum_{k=1}^{n^2-1} f(x) > \int_1^{n^2} f(x)\, dx ,$$

whence the inequality

$$\int_1^{n^2} f(x)\, dx + f(n^2) < \sum_{k=1}^{n^2} f(x) < \int_1^{n^2} f(x)\, dx + f(1)$$

follows. Since $\int_1^{n^2} f(x)\, dx = \arctan n - \arctan 1/n$, it follows that

38

$$\arctan n - \arctan \frac{1}{n} + \frac{1}{n+n^3} < a_n < \arctan n - \arctan \frac{1}{n} + \frac{1}{n^2+1} \, .$$

The "squeeze" method (2.1-2), as $n \to \infty$, yields $\lim\limits_{n\to\infty} a_n = \pi/2$.

Exercises 2.C

Evaluate the limits of $\{a_n\}$ by definite integrals.

1. $a_n = n[1/(n+1)^2 + 1/(n+2)^2 + \cdots + 1/(n+n)^2]$.

2. $a_n = n^2[1/(n^2+1^2)^2 + 2/(n^2+2^2)^2 + \cdots + n/(n^2+n^2)^2]$.

3. $a_n = \dfrac{1}{n}\left(1 + \sec^2 \dfrac{\pi}{4n} + \sec^2 \dfrac{2\pi}{4n} + \cdots + \sec^2 \dfrac{n\pi}{4n}\right)$.

4. $a_n = 1/n^2 + 2/n^2 + \cdots + n/n^2$.

5. $a_n = 1/(n+1) + 1/(n+2) + \cdots + 1/(n+pn)$, p a positive integer.

6. $a_n = (1^p + 2^p + \cdots + n^p)/n^{p+1}$.

7. $a_n = n/(n^2+1^2) + n/(n^2+2^2) + \cdots + n/(n^2+n^2)$.

8. $a_n = 1/(n^2-1^2)^{1/2} + 1/(n^2-2^2)^{1/2} + \cdots + 1/[n^2-(n-1)^2]^{1/2}$.

9. $a_n = n^2 \sum\limits_{k=1}^{n^p} \dfrac{k}{(k^2+n^2)^2}$ (p integer ≥ 2).

10. $a_n = \sum\limits_{k=1}^{pn} \dfrac{1}{(k^2+n^2)^{1/2}}$ (p integer ≥ 1).

11. $a_n = 2 \sum\limits_{k=1}^{pn} \dfrac{1}{2n+2k-1}$ (p integer ≥ 1).

CHAPTER 3

SERIES OF POSITIVE TERMS

3.1 Infinite series

Let a sequence $\{a_n\}$ of numbers be given, then the following symbols

$$a_1 + a_2 + a_3 + \cdots + a_n + \cdots, \quad \sum_{k=1}^{\infty} a_k$$

are used to denote an infinite series.

Note that the letter k used in $\sum_{k=1}^{\infty} a_k$ is a "dummy" variable and may be replaced by any other letter or symbol, that is, $\sum_{p=1}^{\infty} a_p$ is identical with $\sum_{k=1}^{\infty} a_k$. Furthermore, the symbol of an infinite series has in itself no meaning whatever, for addition of an infinite number of terms is meaningless. Speaking of a sum in any sense previously in use for a finite number of terms might lead to a misunderstanding. For example, if the number of terms is finite, the sum of these terms has under all circumstances a definite value; however, the "sum" of an infinite series might depend on the order in which the numbers are added.

3.1-1 Definition. An infinite series

$$a_1 + a_2 + a_3 + \cdots + a_n + \cdots, \quad \text{or} \quad \sum_{m=1}^{\infty} a_m,$$

where $\{a_m\}$ is a given sequence of numbers, is a sequence $\{S_n\}$,

$$S_n = a_1 + a_2 + a_3 + \cdots + a_n.$$

The number S_n is called the nth partial sum and a_n is called the nth term of the infinite series. If $\{S_n\}$ has a limit S, we say that the infinite series converges. The number S is called the sum of the infinite series and we write

$$S = \sum_{m=1}^{\infty} a_m \, ,$$

using the same symbol $\sum_{m=1}^{\infty} a_m$ to denote both the series and its sum, and letting the context distinguish between these meanings. But it should be clearly understood that S is the limit of a sequence of sums, and it is not obtained simply by addition of terms.

If $\{S_n\}$ does not converge, the infinite series is said to diverge.

If $\sum_{n=1}^{\infty} a_n$ is given, the sequence of partial sums $\{S_n\}$, $S_n = a_1 + a_2 + \cdots + a_n$ can be found. Conversely, we can write the infinite series

$$S_1 + (S_2 - S_1) + (S_3 - S_2) + \cdots + (S_n - S_{n-1}) + \cdots = \sum_{n=1}^{\infty} a_n$$

if $\{S_n\}$ is given. For example, $\{S_n\}$, $S_n = n/(n+1)$ is the sequence of partial sums of the infinite series

$$\frac{1}{2} + \left(\frac{2}{3} - \frac{1}{2} \right) + \cdots + \left(\frac{n}{n+1} - \frac{n-1}{n} \right) + \cdots ,$$

or

$$\frac{1}{1 \cdot 2} + \frac{1}{2 \cdot 3} + \cdots + \frac{1}{n(n+1)} + \cdots .$$

Since $\lim_{n \to \infty} S_n = \lim_{n \to \infty} [n/(n+1)] = 1$, it follows that the series $\sum_{n=1}^{\infty} 1/n(n+1)$ converges and has a sum equal to 1.

A series of the form $\sum_{n=1}^{\infty} (\alpha_n - \alpha_{n+1})$ is known as a telescopic series. If $\{\alpha_n\}$ converges to α, then from $S_n = (\alpha_1 - \alpha_2) + (\alpha_2 - \alpha_3) + \cdots + (\alpha_n - \alpha_{n+1}) = \alpha_1 - \alpha_{n+1}$ it follows that $\lim_{n \to \infty} S_n = \alpha_1 - \alpha$, that is, the series $\sum_{n=1}^{\infty} (\alpha_n - \alpha_{n+1})$ converges to $\alpha_1 - \alpha$, and we write $\sum_{n=1}^{\infty} (\alpha_n - \alpha_{n+1}) = \alpha_1 - \alpha$.

For example, if $\alpha_n = n^2/(n^2 + 1)$, then $\alpha_n - \alpha_{n+1} = -(2n+1)/\{(n^2 + 1)[(n+1)^2 + 1]\}$ and

$$-\sum_{n=1}^{\infty} \frac{2n+1}{(n^2+1)[(n+1)^2+1]} = \frac{1}{1^2+1} - 1 = -\frac{1}{2} .$$

Hence,

$$\sum_{n=1}^{\infty} \frac{2n+1}{(n^2+1)[(n+1)^2+1]} = \frac{1}{2} .$$

3.2 Examples of infinite series

By **3.1-1** we obtain from sequences considered in § 2.1 the following infinite series.

Example 1. $\sum_{n=0}^{\infty} q^n = 1/(1-q)$, $|q| < 1$ (Example 8 of Chapter 2). That is, the infinite series converges if $|q| < 1$ and has a sum $1/(1-q)$, and diverges otherwise (if $|q| \geq 1$). It is called the geometric series and plays an important role in the theory and applications of infinite series.

Example 2. The series $\sum_{n=1}^{\infty} 1/n^p$, $p \leq 1$ (Example 11 of Chapter 2) diverges.

Example 3. $\sum_{n=0}^{\infty} 1/n! = e$, $(0! = 1)$ (Section 2.5).

Example 4. The infinite series $\sum_{n=1}^{\infty} 1/(2n-1)2n = \sum_{n=1}^{\infty} (-1)^{n-1}/n = \log 2$ (Example 18 of Chapter 2).

3.3 Tests of convergence

A necessary and sufficient condition for convergence of an infinite series is easily obtained if Cauchy's convergence criterion is applied to the sequence of partial sums $\{S_n\}$, $S_n = a_1 + a_2 + \cdots + a_n$. This leads to the following theorem.

3.3-1 Theorem. The series $\sum_{n=1}^{\infty} a_n$ converges if and only if for every $\varepsilon > 0$ there exists an integer $n_0(\varepsilon)$ such that $n > n_0(\varepsilon)$ implies

$$|S_{n+k} - S_n| = |a_{n+1} + a_{n+2} + \cdots + a_{n+k}| < \varepsilon$$

for $k = 1, 2, 3, \ldots$.

Proof. If we note that $S_{n+k} - S_n = a_{n+1} + a_{n+2} + \cdots + a_{n+k}$, Cauchy's criterion (**2.2-2**) immediately yields the statement.

Corollary. For $k = 1$ it follows that $|a_{n+1}| < \varepsilon$ for all $n > n_0(\varepsilon)$ if the series is convergent. This means that $\lim_{n\to\infty} a_n = 0$. In words, if an infinite series converges, then its nth term approaches zero as n increases beyond all bounds.

That $\lim_{n\to\infty} a_n = 0$ is not sufficient for convergence of a series is easily shown by the following example. Cauchy's condition cannot be satisfied for the series $\sum_{n=1}^{\infty} a_n$ where $a_n = 1/n$ and $\varepsilon \leq 1/2$. For if we choose $n = 2^m$ and $k = 2^m$, then

$$a_{n+1} + a_{n+2} + \cdots + a_{n+k} = \frac{1}{2^m + 1} + \frac{1}{2^m + 2} + \cdots$$

$$+ \frac{1}{2^m + 2^m} \geq \frac{2^m}{2^m + 2^m} = \frac{1}{2}.$$

Thus, though $\lim_{n\to\infty} a_n = \lim_{n\to\infty} 1/n = 0$, the series diverges. (See also Example 11 of Chapter 2.)

Theorem **3.3-1** is of a general nature and yields a necessary and sufficient condition for convergence of infinite series. However, one does not always succeed in obtaining an explicit expression for $|a_{n+1} + a_{n+2} + \cdots + a_{n+k}|$ as a function of n, which in most cases is essential for proving Cauchy's inequality. On the other hand, in many cases the calculations are tedious, although possible, and the inequality is hard to prove.

There are necessary as well as sufficient conditions which are simple to apply and cover series of importance for practical purposes. Unless otherwise specified, the following tests of convergence will be of special nature or will apply only to a specified class of series.

3.4 Series of positive terms

In the following we assume that the terms of the series $\sum_{n=1}^{\infty} a_n$ are non-negative, that is, $a_k \geq 0$, $k = 1, 2, \ldots$. We have already seen that sequences $\{S_n\}$, $S_n = a_1 + a_2 + \cdots + a_n$ of this kind are monotonically increasing, and it is easy to prove the following theorem.

3.4-1 Theorem. A series $\sum_{n=1}^{\infty} a_n$, $a_n \geq 0$ is convergent if and only if the sequence $\{S_n\}$, $S_n = a_1 + a_2 + \cdots + a_n$ of partial sums is bounded.

Proof. Since $S_{n+1} - S_n = a_{n+1} \geq 0$ it follows that $S_{n+1} \geq S_n$. That is, the sequence of partial sums is monotonically increasing. If $\{S_n\}$ is bounded by **2.4-1**, it has a limit. On the other hand, if $\{S_n\}$ is not bounded, then $\lim_{n \to \infty} S_n = \infty$. By **3.1-1**, this means that the series $\sum_{n=1}^{\infty} a_n$ is convergent if the sequence of partial sums is bounded, and it is divergent if the sequence of partial sums is not bounded.

Example 5. The series $\sum_{n=1}^{\infty} 1/n(n + 1)$ is convergent, since

$$S_n = \frac{1}{1 \cdot 2} + \frac{1}{2 \cdot 3} + \cdots + \frac{1}{n(n + 1)} = 1 - \frac{1}{n + 1} < 1$$

is bounded. (See Example 10, Chapter 2.)

Example 6. The series $\sum_{n=1}^{\infty} 1/n^p$, $p \leq 1$ is divergent, since $S_n = 1 + 1/2^p + 1/3^p + \cdots + 1/n^p$ can be made larger than any finite number by choosing n large enough, that is, the sequence of partial sums is not bounded. (See Example 11, Chapter 2.)

Note that if the sequence of partial sums is bounded, but the condition $a_n > 0$ for all n is not satisfied, the series might diverge. For example, the series $1 - 1 + 1 - 1 + 1 - \cdots (- 1)^{n-1} + \cdots$ has partial sums $S_n = 1$ if n is odd and $S_n = 0$ if n is even, that is, these partial sums are bounded. Since $\lim_{n \to \infty} S_n$ does not exist, the series is divergent

(3.1-1). That the series is divergent follows also from the Corollary 3.1-1, since $\lim_{n \to \infty} a_n = \lim_{n \to \infty} (-1)^{n-1} \neq 0$.

3.4-2 Theorem (Comparison test). If $a_n \geq 0$ and $b_n \geq 0$ for $n = 1, 2, \ldots$ and if there exists a positive integer n_0 such that for all $n > n_0$ the inequality $a_n \leq b_n$ holds, then convergence of the series $\sum_{n=1}^{\infty} b_n$ implies convergence of the series $\sum_{n=1}^{\infty} a_n$, and divergence of $\sum_{n=1}^{\infty} a_n$ implies divergence of $\sum_{n=1}^{\infty} b_n$.

Proof. If we note that $\sum_{i=1}^{n_0} a_i$ and $\sum_{i=1}^{n_0} b_i$ are fixed constants independent of n, it follows from

$$S_n = \sum_{i=1}^{n_0} a_i + \sum_{i=n_0+1}^{n} a_i, \quad \sigma_n = \sum_{i=1}^{n_0} b_i + \sum_{i=n_0+1}^{n} b_i, \text{ and } a_n \leq b_n \text{ for } n > n_0, \text{ that}$$

$$S_n \leq \sum_{i=1}^{n_0} a_i + \sum_{i=n_0+1}^{n} b_i, \quad \sigma_n \geq \sum_{i=1}^{n_0} b_i + \sum_{i=n_0+1}^{n} a_i,$$

that is, if σ_n is bounded, so is S_n, and if S_n is not bounded, neither is σ_n. By **3.4-1** this completes the proof.

Example 7. If $b_n = 1/[n(n+1)]$, $a_n = 1/(n+1)^2$, then $a_n < b_n$ for all n, and convergence of $\sum_{n=1}^{\infty} 1/[n(n+1)]$ (see Example 5) implies convergence of $\sum_{n=1}^{\infty} 1/(n+1)^2$.

Example 8. If $a_n = 1/n$ and $b_n = 1/(n)^{1/2}$, then $a_n < b_n$ for all $n \geq 2$. Since $\sum_{n=1}^{\infty} 1/n$ is divergent, it follows that $\sum_{n=1}^{\infty} 1/(n)^{1/2}$ diverges (see Example 2).

3.4-3 Theorem (Limit comparison test). If $a_n > 0$, $b_n > 0$ and $\lim_{n \to \infty} a_n/b_n = c \neq 0$, then either both series $\sum_{n=1}^{\infty} a_n$ and $\sum_{n=1}^{\infty} b_n$ converge, or both series diverge.

Proof. Since $a_n/b_n \to c \neq 0$, there exists an integer n_0 such that for all $n > n_0$ the ratio is contained in the neighborhood $c/2 < a_n/b_n < 3c/2$ [$\varepsilon = c/2$ is of no significance for the proof, any other neighborhood, say $|a_n/b_n - c| < c/3$ would serve as well]. Hence,

$$b_n < (2/c)a_n \text{ and } a_n < (3c/2)b_n \text{ for all } n > n_0.$$

If **3.4-2** is applied to the first and second inequalities, the statement follows.

Example 9. If $a_n = 1/[n(n+1)]$ and $b_n = n^4/(n^6+3)$, then $\lim_{n \to \infty} a_n/b_n = 1$. Since $\sum_{n=1}^{\infty} 1/[n(n+1)]$ converges, so does $\sum_{n=1}^{\infty} n^4/(n^6+3)$.

Example 10. If $a_n = 1/(2n-1)$ and $b_n = 1/n$, then $\lim_{n \to \infty} a_n/b_n = 1/2$.

Since $\sum_{n=1}^{\infty} 1/n$ diverges, the series $\sum_{n=1}^{\infty} 1/(2n-1)$ also diverges.

Note that if $\lim_{n \to \infty} a_n/b_n = 0$, then we can only conclude that convergence of $\sum_{n=1}^{\infty} b_n$ implies convergence of $\sum_{n=1}^{\infty} a_n$, and divergence of $\sum_{n=1}^{\infty} a_n$ implies divergence of $\sum_{n=1}^{\infty} b_n$. (Why?)

To use comparison tests effectively one must have at his disposal some examples of series of known behaviour. Some of the most useful series for comparison are the geometric and harmonic series.

3.4-4 Theorem (Root test). The series $\sum_{n=1}^{\infty} a_n$, $a_n \geq 0$ is convergent if there exists an integer k_0 such that $(a_k)^{1/k} \leq q < 1$, whenever $k > k_0$; if $(a_k)^{1/k} \geq 1$ for infinitely many k, the series diverges.

Proof. From the condition $(a_k)^{1/k} \leq q$, $k > k_0$ follows that

$$a_{k_0+1} \leq q^{k_0+1}, \quad a_{k_0+2} \leq q^{k_0+2}, \cdots, a_n \leq q^n, \cdots.$$

Since the geometric series $\sum_{n=k_0+1}^{\infty} q^n$ converges for $q < 1$, it follows by **3.4-2** that $\sum_{n=1}^{\infty} a_n$ converges.

If $(a_k)^{1/k} \geq 1$ for infinitely many k, then $a_k \geq 1$ for infinitely many k, and, consequently, $\lim_{k \to \infty} a_k \neq 0$. By the Corollary of **3.3-1** the series diverges.

Corollary 1. If $\lim_{k \to \infty} (a_k)^{1/k} = b$, the series $\sum_{n=1}^{\infty} a_n$ converges if $b < 1$ and diverges if $b > 1$.

Proof. From the definition of a limit of a sequence follows that $(a_k)^{1/k}$ is contained in the neighborhood $b - \varepsilon < (a_k)^{1/k} < b + \varepsilon$ for all $k > k_0$. If $b < 1$ choose $\varepsilon = (1-b)/2$, then $(a_k)^{1/k} < b + \varepsilon = (b+1)/2 = q < 1$ for $k > k_0$. If $b > 1$ choose $\varepsilon = (b-1)/2$, then $(a_k)^{1/k} > b - \varepsilon = (b+1)/2 = q > 1$ for $k > k_0$. Thus, the conditions of **3.4-4** are satisfied and the statement follows.

Corollary 2. The error R_{k_0} of the approximation $S \approx S_{k_0}$ is less than $q^{k_0+1}/(1-q)$.

The statement follows from the inequality

$$R_{k_0} = \sum_{i=k_0+1}^{\infty} a_i < \frac{q^{k_0+1}}{1-q}.$$

Example 11. Let $a_n = n/2^n$. Since $\lim_{n \to \infty} a_n^{1/n} = \lim_{n \to \infty} n^{1/n}/2 = 1/2$ [$n^{1/n} \to 1$ by Example 6(b) of 2.1], it follows that $\sum_{n=1}^{\infty} n/2^n$ converges.

Example 12. Let us consider the series $\sum_{n=1}^{\infty} a_n$ where $a_{2k-1} = 1/2^k$, $a_{2k} = 1/3^k$, that is,

$$1/2 + 1/3 + 1/2^2 + 1/3^2 + 1/2^3 + 1/3^3 + \cdots + 1/2^n + 1/3^n + \cdots.$$

Since $\lim_{n\to\infty} (1/2^n)^{1/(2n-1)} = 1/2^{1/2}$ and $\lim_{n\to\infty} (1/3^n)^{1/2n} = 1/3^{1/2}$, it follows that the limit of $a_n^{1/n}$ as $n \to \infty$ does not exist. However, it is easily seen that the inequality $a_k^{1/k} < 1/2^{1/2} + \varepsilon$ can be satisfied for $\varepsilon > 0$ if $k > k_0(\varepsilon)$. If we choose $\varepsilon = (1 - 1/2^{1/2})/2$ it follows that the inequality $(a_k)^{1/k} < [1 + 1/(2)^{1/2}]/2 = q < 1$ holds for all $k > k_0$. Consequently, the series converges by Theorem 2.5.

3.4-5 Theorem (Ratio test). The series $\sum_{n=1}^{\infty} a_n$, $a_n > 0$ is convergent if there exists an integer k_0 such that $a_{k+1}/a_k \leq q < 1$, whenever $k > k_0$; if $a_{k+1}/a_k \geq q > 1$, whenever $k > k_0$, the series diverges.

Proof. From the inequality $a_{k+1}/a_k \leq q$ follows that $a_{k_0+1} \leq a_{k_0}q$, $a_{k_0+2} \leq a_{k_0+1}q \leq a_{k_0}q^2, \cdots, a_n \leq a_{k_0}q^{n-k_0-1}$. Consequently,

$$S_n \leq \sum_{i=1}^{k_0} a_i + a_{k_0}q(1 + q + q^2 + \cdots + q^{n-k_0-2}) .$$

Since the first sum is a constant and the second sum is the familiar geometric series which converges, it follows that S_n is bounded, and, consequently, by **3.4-1** the series converges.

If $q > 1$, the divergence of the series follows immediately if we note that $a_{k+1} > qa_k$ implies $a_{k+1} > a_k$ for all $k > k_0$, that is, the sequence $\{a_k\}$ is monotonically increasing. It follows that $\lim_{n\to\infty} a_n \neq 0$, consequently, by the Corollary **3.3-1** the series diverges.

Corollary. If $\lim_{n\to\infty} a_{n+1}/a_n = b$ exists, the series $\sum_{n=1}^{\infty} a_n$ converges if $b < 1$ and diverges if $b > 1$.

The proof is the same as that of Corollary 1 of **3.4-4**.

Consider the series of Example 11. Since $\lim_{n\to\infty} a_{n+1}/a_n = \lim (n + 1)/2n = 1/2 < 1$, it follows that the series $\sum_{n=1}^{\infty} n/2^n$ converges by the ratio test.

For the series of Example 12 the ratio test is inconclusive, since $a_{2n+1}/a_{2n} = \frac{1}{2}(3/2)^n > 1$ and $a_{2n}/a_{2n-1} = (2/3)^n < 1$, that is, there is no number n_0 such that $a_{n+1}/a_n < 1$ or $a_{n+1}/a_n > 1$ for all $n > n_0$. Note that $\lim_{n\to\infty} a_{n+1}/a_n$ does not exist either.

Remarks on 3.4-4 and 3.4-5. The root and the ratio tests are most commonly used in practice. The ratio test is frequently easier to apply than the root test, however, the root test has wider scope. This is a consequence of **2.6-4**, that is, whenever the ratio test shows convergence, the root test does, too; whenever the root test is inconclusive, the ratio test is, too. This is illustrated by Example 12 where the ratio test fails and the root test shows convergence. In Example 11 the ratio test shows convergence and so does the root test.

If $\lim_{n\to\infty} (a_n)^{1/n} = \lim_{n\to\infty} a_{n+1}/a_n = 1$, neither test gives any information.

To show this we consider the series $\sum_{n=1}^{\infty} 1/n$, $\sum_{n=1}^{\infty} 1/n^2$. In each of these we have $\lim_{n \to \infty} a_{n+1}/a_n = \lim_{n \to \infty} a_n^{1/n} = 1$, but the first diverges (see Example to Corollary of **3.3-1**), the second converges (**3.4-2**, Example 7).

Warning! The inequalities $a_n^{1/n} < 1$, $a_{n+1}/a_n < 1$, for all n, are not sufficient for convergence. If $a_n = 1/n$, then it is apparent that $(1/n)^{1/n} < 1$, $n/(n+1) < 1$ holds for all $n > 1$, but the series $\sum_{n=1}^{\infty} 1/n$ is divergent. For convergence it is essential that $a_n^{1/n} \leq q < 1$, $a_{n+1}/a_n \leq q < 1$, where q is a definite number less than 1.

3.5 Series of positive monotonically decreasing terms

In many cases the ratio and root tests fail and it is extremely difficult to devise an appropriate test series for the comparison test. If the terms of a series are monotonically decreasing, then the following theorem due to Cauchy is of particular interest. The striking feature of this theorem is that a rather "small" subsequence of $\{a_n\}$ determines the convergence or divergence of $\sum_{n=1}^{\infty} a_n$.

3.5-1 Theorem. If $\{a_k \downarrow\}$, $a_k > 0$, then the series $\sum_{n=1}^{\infty} a_n$ and $\sum_{n=1}^{\infty} 2^{n-1} a_{2^{n-1}}$ both converge or diverge together.

Proof. We consider the partial sums

$$S_n = a_1 + a_2 + \cdots + a_n,$$
$$\sigma_k = a_1 + 2 a_2 + \cdots + 2^k a_{2^k}.$$

For $n < 2^k$ we have

$$S_n \leq a_1 + (a_2 + a_3) + \cdots + (a_{2^k} + \cdots + a_{2^{k+1}-1})$$
$$\leq a_1 + 2 a_2 + \cdots + 2^k a_{2^k} = \sigma_k,$$

since by hypothesis $a_1 \geq a_2 \geq a_3 \geq \cdots \geq a_n \geq a_{n+1} \geq \cdots \geq 0$. Hence, $S_n \leq \sigma_k$. On the other hand, if $n > 2^k$, we obtain

$$S_n \geq a_1 + a_2 + (a_3 + a_4) + \cdots + (a_{2^{k-1}+1} + \cdots + a_{2^k})$$
$$\geq \frac{1}{2} a_1 + a_2 + 2 a_4 + \cdots + 2^{k-1} a_{2^k} = \frac{1}{2} \sigma_k$$

so that $2 S_n \geq \sigma_k$.

From these inequalities it follows that $\{S_n\}$ and $\{\sigma_k\}$ are either both bounded or both unbounded. Consequently, by **3.4-1** either both series converge or both series diverge.

Note that **3.5-1**, which is also called Condensation Theorem, does not state that both series converge to the same limit.

Example 13. Consider the series $\sum_{n=1}^{\infty} 1/n^p$. Since

$$\sigma_k = 1 + \frac{2 \cdot 1}{2^p} + \frac{2^2 \cdot 1}{(2^2)^p} + \cdots + \frac{2^k \cdot 1}{(2^k)^p} = 1 + \frac{1}{2^{p-1}} + \frac{1}{(2^{p-1})^2} + \cdots + \frac{1}{(2^{p-1})^k}$$

is a geometric series [see Example 8 of Chapter 2 for $q = 1/(2^{p-1})$] which converges only if $1/(2^{p-1}) < 1$, that is $p > 1$, and diverges for $1/(2^{p-1}) \geq 1$, that is, $p \leq 1$, it follows by **3.5-1** that $\sum_{n=1}^{\infty} 1/n^p$ converges if $p > 1$ and diverges if $p \leq 1$.

Example 14. Let $a_n = 1/(n \ln n)$, where $\ln A = \log_e A$. If one compares the series $\sum_{n=2}^{\infty} 1/(n \ln n)$ with $\sum_{n=2}^{\infty} 1/n$ it is apparent that the terms of the first series from the second term on are smaller than the corresponding terms of the second series. Since $\sum_{n=1}^{\infty} 1/n^p$ converges for $p = 1 + \varepsilon$, no matter how small $\varepsilon > 0$ is, one might conjecture that the series $\sum_{n=2}^{\infty} 1/(n \ln n)$ converges. However, it is easily calculated that

$$\sigma_k = \frac{1}{\ln 2}\left(1 + \frac{1}{2} + \frac{1}{3} + \cdots + \frac{1}{k}\right),$$

which diverges. Consequently, $\sum_{n=2}^{\infty} 1/(n \ln n)$ diverges.

3.5-2 Theorem. If $\{a_k \downarrow\}$, $a_k > 0$, and $\sum_{n=1}^{\infty} a_n$ converges, then $\lim_{k \to \infty} k a_k = 0$.

Proof. If $\sum_{n=1}^{\infty} a_n$ converges, so also does $\sum_{n=0}^{\infty} 2^n a_{2^n}$. Consequently, by the Corollary to **3.3-1**, $\lim_{n \to \infty} 2^n a_{2^n} = 0$. Now, if $2^n \leq k < 2^{n+1}$, then $a_k \leq a_{2^n}$ and

$$k a_k < 2^{n+1} a_{2^n} = 2^n a_{2^n} + 2^n a_{2^n} \to 0 \quad \text{as} \quad n \to \infty.$$

Hence, $\lim_{k \to \infty} k a_k = 0$.

Example 15. If $a_n = 1/n^{1+1/n}$, then $n a_n = 1/n^{1/n}$, and $\lim_{n \to \infty} n a_n = 1 \neq 0$. Consequently, $\sum_{n=1}^{\infty} 1/n^{1+1/n}$ diverges.

Note that the condition $\lim_{n \to \infty} n a_n = 0$ is necessary but not sufficient. This is easily demonstrated by the series $\sum_{n=2}^{\infty} 1/(n \ln n)$. Here $\lim_{n \to \infty} n a_n = \lim_{n \to \infty} 1/\ln n = 0$ and yet the series diverges (Example 14).

3.5-3 Theorem (Cauchy's integral test). If $\{a_n \downarrow\}$, $a_n > 0$, and if $f(x)$ is a positive, continuous, and monotonically decreasing function defined for $x \geq 1$ such that $f(k) = a_k$, $k = 1, 2, 3, \ldots$, then

$$\sum_{n=1}^{\infty} a_n \quad \text{and} \quad \int_{1}^{\infty} f(x)\, dx$$

converge and diverge together.

Proof. Figure 7 represents $f(x)$ and the values $f(1) = a_1$, $f(2) = a_2$, $f(3) = a_3$, ... , $f(n-1) = a_{n-1}$, $f(n) = a_n$, $f(n+1) = a_{n+1}$.

Each term a_k represents the area of a rectangle of width 1 and height a_k. For example, a_1 represents the area of the rectangle $1\,ad\,2$ containing the arc ab of $f(x)$, a_2 represents the area of the rectangle $2\,bk\,3$ containing the arc bc, and so on. On the other hand, one can interpret a_2 as representing the area of the rectangle $1\,fb\,2$ below the arc ab. If one compares the rectangular areas represented by a_1 and a_2 with the area bounded by the arc ab and ordinates a_1 and a_2, the obvious inequality

$$a_1 > \int_1^2 f(x)\,dx > a_2$$

follows. If we consider the partial sums

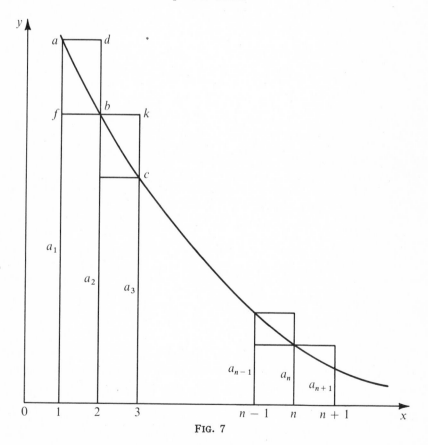

FIG. 7

49

$$S_n = a_1 + a_2 + \cdots + a_n \,, \quad S_{n+1} - a_1 = a_2 + a_3 + \cdots + a_n + a_{n+1}$$

as representing the circumscribed and the inscribed rectangular areas and compare these areas with the corresponding area bounded by the arc of the curve $y = f(x)$ and the ordinates a_1 and a_{n+1}, the inequality

$$S_{n+1} - a_1 < \int_1^{n+1} f(x)\, dx < S_n$$

follows immediately. Assume that $\lim\limits_{n\to\infty} \int_1^{n+1} f(x)\, dx = \int_1^{\infty} f(x)\, dx$ exists.

Since $S_{n+1} - a_1 < \int_1^{\infty} f(x)\, dx$, it follows that the partial sums S_{n+1} are bounded and, consequently, by **3.4-1** the infinite series $\sum_{n=1}^{\infty} a_n$ converges. If $\int_1^{\infty} f(x)\, dx$ does not exist, then $\lim\limits_{n\to\infty} \int_1^{n+1} f(x)\, dx = \infty$. From $S_n > \int_1^{n+1} f(x)\, dx$ it follows that S_n is not bounded. Consequently, by **3.4-1** the series diverges. This completes the proof.

Example 16. $\sum_{n=1}^{\infty} 1/n^p$. Since $f(x) = 1/x^p$ and

$$\int_1^{n+1} f(x)\, dx = \int_1^{n+1} \frac{dx}{x^p} = \frac{1}{1-p}\left(\frac{1}{(n+1)^{p-1}} - 1\right) \quad \text{if} \quad p \neq 1 \,,$$
$$= \ln(n+1) \quad \text{for} \quad p = 1 \,,$$

it follows that $\int_1^{\infty} dx/x^p$ is finite only if $p > 1$ and $\lim\limits_{n\to\infty} \int_1^{n+1} dx/x^p = \infty$ otherwise. Consequently the harmonic series converges if $p > 1$ and diverges if $p \leq 1$.

Note that for $f(x) > 0$ the sequence $\left\{\int_1^n f(x)\, dx\right\}$ is monotonically increasing. It follows that $\int_1^{\infty} f(x)\, dx$ exists if $\int_1^n f(x)\, dx$ is bounded (**2.4-1**). Thus, it follows that $\sum_{k=1}^{\infty} f(k)$ converges if $\int_1^n f(x)\, dx$ is bounded. This is of importance, since it is far from easy to evaluate, say the integral $\int_1^n (x^2 - x)/(x^4 + 2)\, dx$, but it requires little effort to find an upper bound, namely, $\int_1^n (x^2 - x)/(x^4 + 2)\, dx < \int_1^n x^2/x^4\, dx = \int_1^n 1/x^2\, dx = 1 - (1/n) < 1$, which proves that $\sum_{n=1}^{\infty} (n^2 - n)/(n^4 + 2)$ converges.

Example 17. Approximate the series $S = \sum_{k=1}^{\infty} 1/k^2$ by its partial sums $S_n = \sum_{k=1}^{n} 1/k^2$. Determine n such that the error $R_n = S - S_n$ of the·approximation is less than $\varepsilon > 0$.

Solution. By standard method (see Section 2.5) we obtain that

$$R_n = \sum_{k=n+1}^{\infty} \frac{1}{k^2} < \sum_{k=n+1}^{\infty} \frac{1}{(k-1)k} = \sum_{k=n+1}^{\infty} \left(\frac{1}{k-1} - \frac{1}{k} \right) = \frac{1}{n} .$$

If $R_n < \varepsilon$, then $n \geq [1/\varepsilon]$. That is, if, say, $\varepsilon = 10^{-6}$, then a million terms are to be added. This is practically not feasible; we say the series is slowly convergent.

We obtain a better approximation if we proceed as follows.

If, in Figure 7, instead of a_1 we start with a_{n+1} and proceed in comparing inscribed and circumscribed areas in exactly the same way as in **3.5-3**, we obtain for $R_n = \sum_{x=n+1}^{\infty} f(x)$ the inequality

$$R_n - a_{n+1} < \int_{n+1}^{\infty} f(x)\,dx < R_n .$$

If we combine it with $S = S_n + R_n$, it follows that

$$S_n + \int_{n+1}^{\infty} f(x)\,dx < S < S_n + \int_{n+1}^{\infty} f(x)\,dx + a_{n+1} .$$

Hence, it follows that the error of the approximation $S \approx S_n + \int_{n+1}^{\infty} f(x)\,dx$ is less than a_{n+1}.

Since in our special case $f(x) = 1/x^2$ and $\int_{n+1}^{\infty} dx/x^2 = 1/(n+1)$, it follows that the error of the approximation

$$S \approx 1 + \frac{1}{2^2} + \frac{1}{3^2} + \cdots + \frac{1}{n^2} + \frac{1}{n+1}$$

is less than $1/(n+1)^2$. If $\varepsilon = 10^{-6}$, then $n \geq 10^3$, that is, only 1000 terms are to be added, a remarkable improvement over the standard method.

This method of upper and lower estimates of the remainder can be refined to become an efficient tool for approximation of slowly convergent series (see Section 8.13).

Example 18. If a function $f(x)$ satisfies the conditions of **3.5-3**, the sequence $d_n = S_n - \int_1^n f(x)\,dx$ has a $\lim_{n \to \infty} d_n = d$ and $0 < d < f(1)$.

Proof. A glance at Figure 7 shows that

$$S_n - \int_1^n f(x)\,dx > f(1) - \int_1^2 f(x)\,dx > 0 \quad \text{and} \quad S_n - f(1) < \int_1^n f(x)\,dx$$

$\left(\text{note that } S_n - \int_1^{n+1} f(x)\,dx < S_n - \int_1^n f(x)\,dx \right).$ Hence,

$$0 < f(1) - \int_1^2 f(x)\,dx < d_n < f(1) \, .$$

Furthermore,

$$d_{n+1} - d_n = (S_{n+1} - S_n) - \left(\int_1^{n+1} f(x)\,dx - \int_1^n f(x)\,dx \right)$$

$$= f(n+1) - \int_n^{n+1} f(x)\,dx < 0 \, ,$$

since $f(x) > f(n+1)$ on $n \le x < n + 1$.

These two inequalities show that d_n is a monotonically decreasing sequence and is bounded below by a positive number. Consequently, the statement follows by **2.4-1**.

A special case $f(x) = 1/x$ yields the sequence

$$d_n = 1 + \frac{1}{2} + \frac{1}{3} + \cdots + \frac{1}{n} - \log n$$

and $1 - \log 2 < d_n < 1$, $n > 1$. The relation

$$S_n = 1 + \frac{1}{2} + \frac{1}{3} + \cdots + \frac{1}{n} = \log n + d_n$$

indicates the rate at which the harmonic series diverges to ∞. If both sides of the last equality are divided by n, passage to the limit as $n \to \infty$ yields $\lim_{n \to \infty} \log n/n = 0$, since $\lim_{n \to \infty} d_n/n = 0$ and $\lim_{n \to \infty} S_n/n = 0$ (see **2.6-3**).

It is not known whether d, the so-called Euler's[*] constant, is a rational number. The first few digits of d are

$$d = 0.5772156649 \ldots .$$

Raabe's test. In case $\lim_{n \to \infty} (a_n)^{1/n} = 1$, the root and ratio tests fail. Thus, for example, they are inconclusive for the series

$$\sum_{n=1}^{\infty} \frac{1 \cdot 3 \cdot 5 \cdots (2n-1)}{4 \cdot 6 \cdot 8 \cdots (2n+2)} \, .$$

We can easily obtain a sharper test if instead of the geometric series we use the harmonic series $\sum_{n=1}^{\infty} 1/n^p$ as comparison series (see **3.4-4** and **3.4-5**).

---

[*] Leonhard Euler (1707–1783), Swiss mathematician, contributed to almost all branches of mathematics. He published important books on algebra and calculus which contain numerous results of his own research work.

3.5-4 Theorem (Raabe's test). The series $\sum_{n=1}^{\infty} a_n$, $a_n > 0$ converges if there exists an integer n_0 such that

$$\frac{a_{n+1}}{a_n} \leq 1 - \frac{p}{n}$$

for $n \geq n_0$ and $p > 1$, and the series diverges if

$$\frac{a_{n+1}}{a_n} \geq 1 - \frac{1}{n}$$

for $n \geq n_0$. In particular, if

$$\lim_{n \to \infty} n\left(1 - \frac{a_{n+1}}{a_n}\right) = m$$

exists, the series converges if $m > 1$ and diverges if $m < 1$. For $m = 1$ the test is inconclusive.

Proof. First we show that $\sum_{n=1}^{\infty} a_n$ converges if

$$\frac{a_{n+1}}{a_n} < \frac{1/n^p}{1/(n-1)^p} = \frac{(n-1)^p}{n^p} = \left(1 - \frac{1}{n}\right)^p \quad \text{for} \quad n > n_0, \; p > 1 \,.$$

If the inequalities

$$a_{n_0+1} < \frac{(n_0-1)^p}{n_0^p} a_{n_0}, \quad a_{n_0+2} < \frac{n_0^p}{(n_0+1)^p} a_{n_0+1} < \frac{(n_0-1)^p}{(n_0+1)^p} a_{n_0}, \; \dots,$$

$$a_{n+1} < \frac{(n_0-1)^p}{n^p} a_{n0}$$

are added and $(n_0 - 1)^p a_{n_0} = k$, it follows that

$$\sum_{i=n_0+1}^{n+1} a_i < k \sum_{k=n_0}^{n} \frac{1}{k^p} \,.$$

From the relation

$$S_n = \sum_{i=1}^{n_0} a_i + \sum_{i=n_0+1}^{n+1} a_i < \sum_{i=1}^{n_0} a_i + k \sum_{k=n_0}^{n} \frac{1}{k^p}$$

it follows that the partial sums of the series are bounded, since $\sum_{i=1}^{n_0} a_i$ is a constant independent of n and $\sum_{k=n_0}^{\infty} 1/k^p$ converges. By **3.4-1** the series converges.

If we use the harmonic series for $p = 1$ as a comparison series, we obtain in the very same way that $\sum_{n=1}^{\infty} a_n$ diverges if $a_{n+1}/a_n \geq 1 - (1/n)$.

If we put $x = 1 - (1/n)$ for $p > 1$ in the inequality **1.1-1** (m), it follows that

$$\left(1 - \frac{1}{n}\right)^{p} > 1 - \frac{p}{n}.$$

Hence, the inequality $a_{n+1}/a_n < (1 - 1/n)^p$ holds whenever $a_{n+1}/a_n \leq 1 - p/n$ is satisfied. This completes the first part of the proof.

If $\lim_{n \to \infty} n(1 - a_{n+1}/a_n) = m$ exists, then for any $\varepsilon > 0$ there exists an integer n_0 such that for $n \geq n_0$ the inequality

$$\left| n\left(1 - \frac{a_{n+1}}{a_n}\right) - m \right| < \varepsilon$$

holds. Hence,

$$\frac{a_{n+1}}{a_n} < 1 - \frac{m - \varepsilon}{n} \quad \text{for} \quad n > n_0.$$

If $m > 1$, choose $\varepsilon = (m - 1)/2$. Then $a_{n+1}/a_n < 1 - p/n$, $p = (m + 1)/2 > 1$, that is, the series $\sum_{n=1}^{\infty} a_n$ converges. If $m < 1$, the same inequality yields

$$\frac{a_{n+1}}{a_n} > 1 - \frac{m + \varepsilon}{n}, \quad n > n_0.$$

Choose $\varepsilon = (1 - m)/2$. Then $a_{n+1}/a_n > 1 - p/n$, $p = (m + 1)/2 < 1$, and consequently $a_{n+1}/a_n \geq 1 - 1/n$ for $n > n_0$, that is, the series diverges.

If $m = 1$, the series may converge or diverge, that is, the criterion is inconclusive.

Example 19. $\sum_{n=1}^{\infty} \dfrac{1 \cdot 3 \cdot 5 \cdots (2n - 1)}{4 \cdot 6 \cdot 8 \cdots (2n + 2)}$. Since $\lim_{n \to \infty} \dfrac{a_{n+1}}{a_n} = 1$, the ratio test fails. The root test $\lim_{n \to \infty} (a_n)^{1/n} = 1$ is also inconclusive (see **3.4-4** and **3.4-5**).

It is easily seen that $\lim_{n \to \infty} n(1 - a_{n+1}/a_n) = \lim_{n \to \infty} 3n/(2n + 2) = 3/2 > 1$; the series converges by Raabe's test.

Example 20. $\sum_{n=2}^{\infty} 1/(n \log n)$. If we put $n(1 - a_{n+1}/a_n)$ in the form

$$n\left(1 - \frac{a_{n+1}}{a_n}\right) = \frac{n}{n + 1}\left|\frac{\log(1 + 1/n)^n}{\log(1 + n)} + 1\right|,$$

it follows that $\lim_{n \to \infty} n(1 - a_{n+1}/a_n) = 1$. Raabe's test is inconclusive. The series diverges (see **3.5-1** and Example 14).

Example 21. $\sum_{n=2}^{\infty} 1/[n(\log n)^2]$. From

$$n\left(1 - \frac{a_{n+1}}{a_n}\right) = \frac{n}{n + 1} + \frac{n[\log(n + 1) + \log n]\log(1 + 1/n)^n}{(n + 1)[\log(n + 1)]^2}$$

follows that $\lim\limits_{n \to \infty} n(1 - a_{n+1}/a_n) = 1$, that is, Raabe's test fails.

Since $\int_2^\infty \dfrac{dx}{x(\log x)^2} = \dfrac{1}{\log 2}$ exists, the series converges by **3.5-3**.

3.6 Remarks on comparison tests

The root and the ratio tests have been obtained by comparing series with the geometric series $\sum_{n=1}^\infty q^{n-1}$. Similarly, using as comparison the harmonic series $\sum_{n=1}^\infty 1/n^p$ we deduced Raabe's test.

These tests are sufficient conditions only and some or all may therefore fail in special cases. Of course, we may obtain more tests of this kind and their success will depend on the choice of the comparison series.

We say that the series $S = \sum_{n=1}^\infty a_n$ converges more rapidly than the series $T = \sum_{n=1}^\infty b_n$ if an approximation of the sum S to some degree of accuracy by $S_n = \sum_{i=1}^n a_i$ requires fewer terms than an approximation of T. For example, if $a_n = 1/2^{n-1}$ and $b_n = 1/n^2$, the error of the approximation is less than 0.01, then

$$S = S_8 = 1 + \frac{1}{2} + \frac{1}{2^2} + \cdots + \frac{1}{2^7}$$

requires addition of 8 terms, whereas the approximation

$$T \approx T_{100} = 1 + \frac{1}{2^2} + \frac{1}{3^3} + \cdots + \frac{1}{100^2}$$

requires addition of 100 terms (see **3.5-3**, Example 17).

It follows that $\sum_{n=1}^\infty 1/2^{n-1}$ converges more rapidly than the series $\sum_{n=1}^\infty 1/n^2$.

If we consider the ratio

$$\frac{a_n}{b_n} = \frac{n^2}{2^n} < n^2 \Big/ \binom{n}{3} = \frac{6\,n}{(n-1)(n-2)}$$

$\left[\text{note that } 2^n = (1+1)^n > \binom{n}{3}, \; \textbf{1.1-1} \; (l) \text{ for } h = 1\right]$, it follows that $\lim\limits_{n \to \infty} a_n/b_n = 0$. This leads us to a more precise definition.

3.6-1 Definition. If $S = \sum_{n=1}^\infty a_n$ and $T = \sum_{n=1}^\infty b_n$ are two convergent series of positive terms and if $\lim\limits_{n \to \infty} a_n/b_n = 0$, then S is called more rapidly convergent than T.

Similarly, if $G = \sum_{n=1}^\infty c_n$ and $H = \sum_{n=1}^\infty d_n$ are two divergent series of positive terms and if $\lim\limits_{n \to \infty} c_n/d_n = 0$, then the series G diverges less rapidly than H.

For example, if $a_n = q^n$, $0 < q < 1$ and $b_n = 1/n^p$, $p > 1$, then it is easily seen that $\lim_{n \to \infty} a_n/b_n = \lim_{n \to \infty} n^p q^n = 0$, that is, the geometric series converges more rapidly than the harmonic series. If $c_n = 1/n^p$, $p \le 1$ and $d_n = q^n$, $q > 1$, then $\lim_{n \to \infty} c_n/d_n = \lim_{n \to \infty} 1/(n^p q^n) = 0$, that is, the geometric series diverges more rapidly than the harmonic series.

We have seen that a less rapidly convergent series has led to Raabe's test which is a more refined test than the root and the ratio tests. In many cases where the root and the ratio tests fail Raabe's test is conclusive. The question arises whether there exists a least rapidly convergent series. If such a series existed we would be led to a never failing test for we could use it for obtaining a test.

In order to clarify the question of existence of such a series let us consider the harmonic series

$$T_1 = \sum_{n=1}^{\infty} \frac{1}{n^{p_1}}, \quad T_2 = \sum_{n=1}^{\infty} \frac{1}{n^{p_2}}, \quad T_3 = \sum_{n=1}^{\infty} \frac{1}{n^{p_3}}, \quad T_4 = \sum_{n=1}^{\infty} \frac{1}{n^{p_4}},$$

where $p_1 > p_2 > 1 > p_3 > p_4$. It is apparent that T_2 converges less rapidly than T_1 and that T_3 diverges less rapidly than T_4. In particular, $T = \sum_{n=1}^{\infty} 1/n$ diverges less rapidly than any harmonic series $\sum_{n=1}^{\infty} 1/n^p$ with $p < 1$, that is, among the harmonic series there exists a least rapidly divergent series. However, such a series does not exist if we consider the set of all divergent series. To show this we prove the following theorem.

3.6-2 Theorem. If $G = \sum_{n=1}^{\infty} c_n$ is a divergent series of positive terms, then the series $H = \sum_{n=1}^{\infty} d_n$, where $d_1 = 1$, $d_{n+1} = (G_{n+1})^{1/2} - (G_n)^{1/2}$, and G_n is the nth partial sum of G, is less rapidly divergent than G.

Proof. Since $H_n = 1 - (G_1)^{1/2} + (G_n)^{1/2}$, it follows that $\lim_{n \to \infty} H_n = \infty$ (note that $\lim_{n \to \infty} G_n = \infty$ by hypothesis), that is, H diverges. If we note that $c_n = G_n - G_{n-1}$, it follows that

$$\lim_{n \to \infty} d_n/c_n = \lim_{n \to \infty} [((G_n)^{1/2} - (G_{n-1})^{1/2})/(G_n - G_{n-1})]$$
$$= \lim_{n \to \infty} 1/[(G_n)^{1/2} + (G_{n-1})^{1/2}] = 0 .$$

Consequently, by definition H diverges less rapidly than G. Thus, we have shown that to every divergent series there exists another less rapidly divergent series.

3.6-3 Theorem. If $S = \sum_{n=1}^{\infty} a_n$ is a convergent series of positive terms, then the series $T = \sum_{n=1}^{\infty} c_n$, where $c_1 = 1$, $c_n = (z_{n-1})^{1/2} - (z_n)^{1/2}$ and $z_n = \lim_{k \to \infty} (S_{n+k} - S_n)$ converges less rapidly than S.

Proof. First we note that from Cauchy's convergence criterion

$$|S_{n+k} - S_n| = |a_{n+1} + a_{n+2} + \cdots + a_{n+k}| < \varepsilon \quad n > n_0, \quad k = 1, 2, \ldots$$

it follows that $\lim_{n\to\infty} z_n = 0$. Consequently,

$$\lim_{n\to\infty} T_n = \lim_{n\to\infty} (1 + (z_1)^{1/2} - (z_n)^{1/2}) = 1 + (z_1)^{1/2}$$

exists, and it follows that T converges. Since

$$\lim_{n\to\infty} a_n/c_n = \lim_{n\to\infty} [(z_{n-1} - z_n)/((z_{n-1})^{1/2} - (z_n)^{1/2})] = \lim_{n\to\infty} ((z_{n-1})^{1/2} + (z_n)^{1/2}) = 0 ,$$

it follows that the series T converges less rapidly than S.

Theorems **3.6-2** and **3.6-3** imply that there is no comparison test which is conclusive for all series of positive terms. Thus every convergence test, no matter how refined it may be, will surely fail for some series.

Though convergence criteria given in Chapter 3 are conclusive for series of practical importance, nevertheless, we have before us a theoretical challenge, and this makes the theory of infinite series so interesting.

Exercises 3. A

In Exercises 1–9 find the sum of the infinite series $\sum_{n=1}^{\infty} a_n$ by evaluating the limit of partial sums, if it exists.

1. $a_n = 1/[n(n + 2)]$.
2. $a_n = 1/[(2n - 1)(2n + 1)]$.
3. $a_n = (2n + 1)/[n^2(n + 1)^2]$.
4. $a_n = 1/[(c + n)(c + n - 1)], c > 0$.
5. $a_n = 1/[n(n + 1)(n + 2)]$.
6. $a_n = 1/3^n$.
7. $a_n = (- 1)^n$.
8. $a_n = 2^{n-1}/3^n$.
9. $a_n = (- 1)^{n-1}/4^n$.

In each of Exercises 10–15 write the infinite series $\sum_{n=1}^{\infty} a_n$ where the sequence of partial sums $\{S_n\}$ is given and tell whether the series is convergent or divergent, and if convergent, find its sum.

10. $S_n = 2 - 1/2^{n-1}$.
11. $S_n = n/(2n + 1)$.
12. $S_n = \log(n + 1)$.
13. $S_n = n^2/(n^2 + 1)$.
14. $S_{2n-1} = 1, S_{2n} = 0$.
15. $S_n = \log(1 + 1/n)$.

In Exercises 16–19 prove convergence or divergence of the infinite series $\sum_{n=1}^{\infty} a_n$ by using **3.3-1**.

16. $a_n = 1/n^2$.
17. $a_n = \log(1 + 1/n)$.
18. $a_n = 1/|n(n + 1)|$.
19. $a_n = 1/(2n - 1)$.

In Exercises 20–27 test the infinite series $\sum_{n=1}^{\infty} a_n$ for convergence or divergence using **3.4-2**. Examples given in the text may be used as comparison.

20. $a_n = 1/n^{1/2}$.

21. $a_n = 1/[1 \cdot 3 \cdots (2n - 1)]$.

22. $a_n = (n + 1)/n!$.

23. $a_n = 1/n^n$.

24. $a_n = 1/2^n + 1/3^n$.

25. $a_n = 1/[n^2 \log(n + 1)]$.

26. $a_n = \cos(1/n)/n^2$.

27. $a_n = n/(n^3 + 1)$.

In Exercises 28–35 establish convergence or divergence of the series $\sum_{n=1}^{\infty} a_n$ by **3.4-3**.

28. $a_n = 1/(2n - 1)$.

29. $a_n = n/[(n + 1)2^n]$.

30. $a_n = (2n + 1)/(n^2 + n)$.

31. $a_n = n^2/(n^3 + 1)$.

32. $a_n = n^{(1-n)/n}$.

33. $a_n = (n + 1)^n/n^{2n}$.

34. $a_n = n/[(4n - 3)(4n - 1)]$.

35. $a_n = (n^2 + n + 1)/(n^4 + 3n + 5)$.

In Exercises 36–43 test convergence or divergence of the series $\sum_{n=1}^{\infty} a_n$ by the root or the ratio tests.

36. $a_n = 1/n!$.

37. $a_n = n^2/2^n$.

38. $a_n = n!/3^{n+1}$.

39. $a_n = e^{-n^2}$.

40. $a_n = 1/(\log n)^n$.

41. $a_n = (n + 1)/(2^n n)$.

42. $a_n = n^n/n!$.

43. $a_{2n-1} = 1/2^n$, $a_{2n} = 1/2^{n-1}$.

In Exercises 44–47 establish convergence or divergence by **3.5-1**. Also use **3.5-2** where it is conclusive.

44. $a_n = 1/[n(\log n)^p]$.

45. $a_n = 1/[n \cdot \log n \cdot \log(\log n)]$.

46. $a_n = [\log(\log n)]/n^2$.

47. $a_n = (\log n)/\{n[\log(\log n)]^2\}$. [Hint: after reduction use the series of the text: $\sum_{n=1}^{\infty} 1/n^p$ and $\sum_{n=1}^{\infty} 1/(n \log n)$.]

Test the series 48–54 for convergence or divergence by **3.5-3**.

48. $a_n = 1/[n(\log n)^p]$.

49. $a_n = 1/\{n \log n[\log(\log n)]^2\}$.

50. $a_n = (\log n)/n^2$.

51. $a_n = 1/(n + 1)^3$.

52. $a_n = n/(n^2 + 3)$.

53. $a_n = (\log n)/n$.

54. $a_n = (\log n)/n^2$.

By using the method of upper and lower estimates of the remainder approximate the following series (see **3.5-3**, Example 17).

55. $\sum_{n=1}^{\infty} 1/n^4$, error less than 10^{-4}.

56. $\sum_{n=1}^{\infty} 1/n^2$. How many terms are to be added if the error of the approximation is to be less than 10^{-3}?

57. $\sum_{n=2}^{\infty} 1/[n(\log n)^2]$. How many terms of the series are to be added if the error of the approximation is less than 10^{-2}? (Do not compute the sum of the series 56 and 57.)

58. $\sum_{n=1}^{\infty} 1/n^3$, error less than 10^{-3}.

In Exercises 59–62 test the series $\sum_{n=1}^{\infty} a_n$ for convergence or divergence by Raabe's test.

59. $a_n = n/(n^2 + 1)$.

60. $a_n = \dfrac{1 \cdot 3 \cdots (2n - 1)}{2 \cdot 4 \cdots 2n}$.

61. $a_n = \dfrac{2 \cdot 4 \cdots 2n}{5 \cdot 7 \cdots (2n + 3)}$.

62. $a_n = \dfrac{1 \cdot 3 \cdots (2n - 1)}{2 \cdot 4 \cdots 2n} \cdot \dfrac{1}{2n + 1}$.

Test for convergence or divergence by any test.

63. $a_n = 1/n^{1/2}$.

64. $a_n = 1/(\log n)^2$.

65. $a_n = n(\frac{3}{4})^n$.

66. $a_n = \dfrac{2 \cdot 4 \cdots (2n)}{4 \cdot 7 \cdots (3n+1)}$.

67. $a_n = n^{n-1}/[3^{n-1}(n-1)!]$.

68. $a_n = (3n+1)/(n^2+n)$.

69. $a_n = [(n+1)^{1/2} - n^{1/2}]/n$.

70. $a_n = \dfrac{1}{n} \log \left[\dfrac{(n+1)^2}{n(n+2)} \right]$.

71. $a_n = (1+n^2)^{1/2} - n$.

72. $a_n = [n^{1/n} - 1]^n$.

73. $a_n = 1/n^{3/2}n$.

74. $a_n = n^{1/2}/(n^2-4)$, $n = 3, 4, \ldots$.

75. $a_n = (1 + \sin n)/n^2$.

76. $a_n = 1/[n(n+1)(n+2)]^{1/2}$.

77. $a_n = \sin^2[\pi(n+1/n)]$.

78. $a_1 = 1$, $S_1 = 1$, $a_{n+1} = 1/S_n$, that is, $S = 1 + 1 + 1/2 + 2/5 + 10/29 + \cdots$.

79. $\sum\limits_{n=1}^{\infty} \dfrac{a_n}{n!}$, $0 \le a_n \le n-1$.

80. $a_n = \left[\dfrac{n+1}{2n+1} \right]^n$.

81. $a_n = \dfrac{1 \cdot 3 \cdots (2n-1)}{2 \cdot 4 \cdots (2n+2)}$.

82. $a_n = (n!)^2/(2n)!$.

83. $a_n = 3^n n!/n^n$.

84. $a_n = \dfrac{2 \cdot 5 \cdot 8 \cdots (2n-1)}{3^n n!}$.

85. $a_n = \dfrac{\log(n+1) - \log n}{(\log n)^2}$.

86. $a_n = \dfrac{1 \cdot 2 \cdot 3 \cdots n}{(\alpha+1)(\alpha+2)\cdots(\alpha+n)}$.

87. $a_n = \dfrac{(1+\alpha)(2+\alpha)\cdots(n+\alpha)}{(1+\beta)(2+\beta)\cdots(n+\beta)}$.

88. $a_n = \dfrac{(a+1)(2a+1)\cdots(na+1)}{(b+1)(2b+1)\cdots(nb+1)}$.

Prove the following statements.

89. $\sum_{n=1}^{\infty} a_n$, $a_n > 0$ diverges if $\lim\limits_{n \to \infty} n a_n = d \neq 0$ exists.

90. If $\sum_{n=1}^{\infty} a_n$, $a_n > 0$ converges, then $\sum_{n=1}^{\infty} a_n^2$ also converges.

91. If $\sum_{n=1}^{\infty} a_n^2$ and $\sum_{n=1}^{\infty} b_n^2$ converge, then $\sum_{n=1}^{\infty} a_n b_n$ also converges.

92. If $\sum_{n=1}^{\infty} a_n^2$ converges, then so does $\sum_{n=1}^{\infty} a_n/n$.

93. If $\sum_{n=1}^{\infty} a_n$, $a_n > 0$ converges, then so does $\sum_{n=1}^{\infty} (a_n a_{n+1})^{1/2}$. If $\sum_{n=1}^{\infty} (a_n a_{n+1})^{1/2}$ converges, does the series $\sum_{n=1}^{\infty} a_n$ converge? (Hint: Consider the series
$1 + 1/2^3 + 1/3 + 1/4^3 + 1/5 + 1/6^3 + \cdots + 1/(2n-1) + 1/(2n)^3 + \cdots$.)

94. If $\sum_{n=1}^{\infty} a_n$, $a_n > 0$ diverges, then $\sum\limits_{n=1}^{\infty} \left[\dfrac{a_n}{(1+a_1)(1+a_2)\cdots(1+a_n)} \right]$ converges to its sum 1.

95. If $\sum_{n=1}^{\infty} a_n$, $a_n > 0$ converges, then so does $\sum_{n=1}^{\infty} [(a_n)^{1/2}/(n)^{(1+\alpha)/2}]$ for $\alpha > 0$.

96. If $\sum_{n=1}^{\infty} a_n$ converges, and $a_{n+1} < a_n$ with $\lim\limits_{n \to \infty} a_n = 0$, then $\sum_{n=1}^{\infty} (a_n - a_{n+1})$ also converges.

97. If $\sum_{n=1}^{\infty} a_n$ converges, and $S_n = a_1 + a_2 + \cdots + a_n$, then
$$\lim_{n \to \infty} \frac{S_1 + S_2 + \cdots + S_n}{n} = \sum_{n=1}^{\infty} a_n .$$

CHAPTER 4

SERIES WITH VARIABLE SIGNS

We next consider series whose terms are not restricted to be positive, that is, series of terms in which infinitely many are positive and infinitely many are negative. One of the simplest examples of this sort is the alternating series

$$\sum_{n=1}^{\infty} \frac{(-1)^{n-1}}{n} = 1 - \frac{1}{2} + \frac{1}{3} - \frac{1}{4} + \cdots + \frac{1}{2n-1} - \frac{1}{2n} + \cdots.$$

We have already seen that $\lim_{n \to \infty} S_{2n} = \lim_{n \to \infty} (1 - 1/2 + 1/3 - \cdots - 1/2n)$ $= \ln 2$ (Example 18, Chapter 2). From the obvious relation $S_{2n+1} = S_{2n} + 1/(2n+1)$ it follows that $\lim_{n \to \infty} S_{2n+1} = \ln 2$ also. Consequently, $\lim_{n \to \infty} S_n = \ln 2$ exists, and by definition the series $\sum_{n=1}^{\infty} (-1)^{n-1}/n$ is convergent.

4.1 Absolute and conditional convergence

We have just seen that the series $\sum_{n=1}^{\infty} (-1)^{n-1}/n$ is convergent, but the series of positive terms, the harmonic series,

$$\sum_{n=1}^{\infty} \frac{1}{n} = 1 + \frac{1}{2} + \frac{1}{3} + \cdots + \frac{1}{n} + \cdots$$

diverges (**3.3-1**, Corollary).

A convergent series $\sum_{n=1}^{\infty} a_n$ for which the series $\sum_{n=1}^{\infty} |a_n|$ is divergent is said to be conditionally convergent.

If $\sum_{n=1}^{\infty} |a_n|$ is convergent, $\sum_{n=1}^{\infty} a_n$ is said to be absolutely convergent. For example, the series $\sum_{n=1}^{\infty} (-1)^{n-1}/2^{n-1}$ is absolutely convergent, since $\sum_{n=1}^{\infty} 1/2^{n-1}$ is convergent (note that both series are geometric series).

4.1-1 Theorem. The absolute convergence of a series implies its convergence.

Proof. Since $\sum_{n=1}^{\infty} |a_n|$ is convergent, by Cauchy's criterion the inequality

$$|a_{n+1}| + |a_{n+2}| + \cdots + |a_{n+k}| < \varepsilon$$

holds for $n > n_0$, $k = 1, 2, 3, \ldots$ **(3.3-1)**. If we note that

$$|a_{n+1} + a_{n+2} + \cdots + a_{n+k}| \leq |a_{n+1}| + |a_{n+2}| + \cdots + |a_{n+k}| < \varepsilon ,$$

it follows that Cauchy's condition for convergence holds for the series $\sum_{n=1}^{\infty} a_n$ also. This completes the proof.

4.1-2 Theorem. If a series is conditionally convergent, then the series of its positive terms and the series of absolute values of its negative terms are both divergent.

Proof. In $S_n = \sum_{i=1}^{n} a_i$ denote the sum of the positive terms by α_{n_1} and the sum of the absolute values of the negative terms by β_{n_2} ($n_1 + n_2 = n$), and let $\sigma_n = \sum_{i=1}^{n} |a_i|$. Then,

$$S_n = \alpha_{n_1} - \beta_{n_2} \quad \text{and} \quad \sigma_n = \alpha_{n_1} + \beta_{n_2} ,$$

and by hypothesis $\lim_{n \to \infty} S_n = S$ exists and $\lim_{n \to \infty} \sigma_n = \infty$.

Since $\alpha_{n_1} = \frac{1}{2}(\sigma_n + S_n)$ and $\beta_{n_2} = \frac{1}{2}(\sigma_n - S_n)$, it follows immediately that

$$\lim_{n \to \infty} \alpha_{n_1} = \infty \quad \text{and} \quad \lim_{n \to \infty} \beta_{n_2} = \infty .$$

This completes the proof.

Note that if the series converges absolutely, then $\lim_{n \to \infty} \sigma_n = \sigma$ exists and it follows that $\lim_{n \to \infty} \alpha_{n_1} = \frac{1}{2}(\sigma + S)$ and $\lim_{n \to \infty} \beta_{n_2} = \frac{1}{2}(\sigma - S)$ exists also, that is, the series of positive terms and the series of negative terms both converge.

Corollary. It follows immediately that a series with variable signs behaves as follows.

(a) If $\lim_{n \to \infty} \alpha_{n_1} = \alpha$ and $\lim_{n \to \infty} \beta_{n_2} = \beta$ exist, $\sum_{n=1}^{\infty} a_n$ converges absolutely.

(b) If $\lim_{n \to \infty} \alpha_{n_1} = \infty$ and $\lim_{n \to \infty} \beta_{n_2} = \infty$, $\sum_{n=1}^{\infty} a_n$ converges conditionally or diverges.

(c) If $\lim_{n \to \infty} \alpha_{n_1} = \alpha$ exists and $\lim_{n \to \infty} \beta_{n_2} = \infty$ or if $\lim_{n \to \infty} \alpha_{n_1} = \infty$ and $\lim_{n \to \infty} \beta_{n_2} = \beta$ exists, $\sum_{n=1}^{\infty} a_n$ diverges.

4.2 Alternating series

If $\{a_n\}$ is a positive sequence,

$$\sum_{n=1}^{\infty} (-1)^{n-1} a_n = a_1 - a_2 + a_3 - a_4 + \cdots + (-1)^{n-1} a_n + \cdots$$

is an alternating series.

4.2-1 Theorem (Leibnitz's[*] criterion). An alternating series S $= \sum_{n=1}^{\infty} (-1)^{n-1} a_n$ is convergent if $\{a_n \downarrow\}$ and $\lim_{n \to \infty} a_n = 0$.

Proof. Since $\{a_n \downarrow\}$, Cauchy's convergence criterion can be written in the form

$$|S_{n+k} - S_n| = a_{n+1} - a_{n+2} + a_{n+3} - a_{n+4} + \cdots + (-1)^{k-1} a_{n+k}$$
$$= a_{n+1} - (a_{n+2} - a_{n+3}) - (a_{n+4} - a_{n+5}) - \cdots - (a_{n+k-1} - a_{n+k}),$$
$$\text{if } k \text{ is odd}$$
$$= a_{n+1} - (a_{n+2} - a_{n+3}) - (a_{n+4} - a_{n+5}) - \cdots - a_{n+k},$$
$$\text{if } k \text{ is even.}$$

Hence, $|S_{n+k} - S_n| < a_{n+1}$. Since $\lim_{n \to \infty} a_n = 0$, it follows that $|S_{n+k} - S_n| < \varepsilon$ for $n > n_0$ and $k = 1, 2, 3, \ldots$. This completes the proof.

Corollary. It follows that

$$|R_n| = |S - S_n| = a_{n+1} - (a_{n+2} - a_{n+3}) - (a_{n+4} - a_{n+5}) - \cdots < a_{n+1},$$

that is, the absolute value of the error of the approximation of S by its partial sum S_n is less than the first term omitted.

If the alternating series is convergent, then $\lim_{n \to \infty} S_{2n+1} = \lim_{n \to \infty} S_{2n} = S$ so that one may approximate the series by partial sums S_{2n}. This is equivalent to the series

$$S = \sum_{n=1}^{\infty} (-1)^{n-1} a_n = \sum_{n=1}^{\infty} (a_{2n-1} - a_{2n})$$

obtained by grouping terms. Thus every alternating series can be reduced to a series of positive terms.

For example,

$$S = \sum_{n=1}^{\infty} \frac{(-1)^{n-1}}{n} = \sum_{n=1}^{\infty} \left[\frac{1}{2n-1} - \frac{1}{2n} \right] = \sum_{n=1}^{\infty} \frac{1}{(2n-1)2n}.$$

If ten terms of the series $S = \sum_{n=1}^{\infty} (-1)^{n-1}/n$ are added, that is, the approximation $S_{10} = 1 - 1/2 + 1/3 - \cdots - 1/10$ is used, the first term omitted is $1/11$, therefore $R_{10} < 1/11$. Note that $R_n = S - S_n$ is positive if n is even and negative if n is odd.

* Gottfried Wilhelm Leibnitz (1646-1716), a German mathematician and philosopher, invented the differential and integral calculus.

On the other hand, one may approximate S by using the series of positive terms $\sum_{n=1}^{\infty} 1/(2n-1)2n$ by the method of upper and lower estimates of the remainder. This leads to considerably better accuracy and requires less effort. (See **3.5-3**, Example 17.)

Example 1. The alternating series

$$\sum_{n=1}^{\infty} \frac{(-1)^{n-1}}{n^2} = 1 - \frac{1}{2^2} + \frac{1}{3^2} - \frac{1}{4^2} + \cdots + \frac{(-1)^{n-1}}{n^2} + \cdots$$

converges, since $\{1/n^2\}$ is monotonically decreasing and $\lim_{n\to\infty} 1/n^2 = 0$. Since the series $\sum_{n=1}^{\infty} 1/n^2$ also converges, the alternating series converges absolutely.

Example 2. The alternating series

$$\sum_{n=1}^{\infty} (-1)^{n-1} \left[\frac{n+2}{3n+1} \right] = \frac{3}{4} - \frac{4}{7} + \frac{5}{10} - \cdots + (-1)^{n-1} \left[\frac{n+2}{3n+1} \right] + \cdots$$

is divergent. Though $\{(n+2)/(3n+1)\}$ is monotonically decreasing, $\lim_{n\to\infty} a_n = \lim_{n\to\infty} (n+2)/(3n+1) = \frac{1}{3} \neq 0$; that is, a necessary condition for convergence of an infinite series is not satisfied.

Example 3. Though the alternating series

$$1 - 1/2 + 1/2^2 - 1/3 + 1/3^2 - 1/4 + 1/4^2 - \cdots - 1/n + 1/n^2 + \cdots \quad (n > 1)$$

satisfies the condition $\lim_{n\to\infty} a_n = 0$, the terms in absolute value do not form a monotonic sequence, and **4.2-1** does not apply. By Corollary (c), **4.1-2**, the series diverges since $\lim_{n\to\infty} a_{n_1} = \lim_{n\to\infty} (1 + 1/2^2 + 1/3^2 + \cdots + 1/n^2)$ converges and $\lim_{n\to\infty} \beta_{n_2} = \lim_{n\to\infty} (1/2 + 1/3 + \cdots + 1/n) = \infty$.

Example 4. The alternating series

$$\sum_{n=1}^{\infty} (-1)^{n-1} \left[\frac{n+2}{n+1} \right] = \frac{3}{2} - \frac{4}{3} + \frac{5}{4} - \frac{6}{5} + \cdots + (-1)^{n-1} \left[\frac{n+2}{n+1} \right] + \cdots$$

is divergent since $\lim_{n\to\infty} |a_n| = \lim_{n\to\infty} (n+2)/(n+1) = 1 \neq 0$.

If we note that

$$S_{2n} = \frac{3}{2} - \frac{4}{3} + \frac{5}{4} - \frac{6}{5} + \cdots + \frac{2n+1}{2n} - \frac{2n+2}{2n+1}$$

$$= \frac{1}{2 \cdot 3} + \frac{1}{4 \cdot 5} + \cdots + \frac{1}{2n(2n+1)} < \frac{1}{2},$$

it follows that $\lim\limits_{n\to\infty} S_{2n} = S_1$ exists. This means that the series

$$\sum_{n=1}^{\infty}\left[\frac{2n+1}{2n} - \frac{2n+2}{2n+1}\right] = \left[\frac{3}{2} - \frac{4}{3}\right] + \left[\frac{5}{4} - \frac{6}{5}\right] + \cdots$$

$$+ \left[\frac{2n+1}{2n} - \frac{2n+2}{2n+1}\right] + \cdots$$

$$= \sum_{n=1}^{\infty} \frac{1}{2n(2n+1)}$$

converges, that is, by inserting parentheses we can make a divergent series converge.

We easily obtain another proof of divergence of the series if we note that

$$\lim_{n\to\infty} S_{2n+1} = \lim_{n\to\infty}\left(S_{2n} + \frac{2n+3}{2n+2}\right) = S_1 + 1 \neq \lim_{n\to\infty} S_{2n} = S_1 ,$$

that is, $\lim\limits_{n\to\infty} S_n$ does not exist. Consequently, by definition, the series diverges.

Note further that if the alternating series converges, then inserting parentheses will not change its sum since all partial sums converge to the same limit.

4.3 Operations with infinite series

4.3-1 Definition.
(a) The sum of the series $\sum_{n=1}^{\infty} a_n$ and $\sum_{n=1}^{\infty} b_n$ is the series $\sum_{n=1}^{\infty}(a_n + b_n)$.

(b) The product of the series $\sum_{n=1}^{\infty} a_n$ by the number c is the series $\sum_{n=1}^{\infty} ca_n$.

(c) The product of the series $\sum_{n=1}^{\infty} a_n$ and $\sum_{n=1}^{\infty} b_n$ is the series $\sum_{n=1}^{\infty} c_n$ where

$$c_n = a_1 b_n + a_2 b_{n-1} + \cdots + a_n b_1 .$$

This definition of a product sometimes is called Cauchy's product of two series. There are many more possible definitions.

Example 5. If $a_n = (-1)^n[n/(n+1)]$ and $b_n = (-1)^{n-1}$, then the sum of two divergent series ($\lim\limits_{n\to\infty} a_n \neq 0$ and $\lim\limits_{n\to\infty} b_n \neq 0$)

$$\sum_{n=1}^{\infty} a_n + \sum_{n=1}^{\infty} b_n = \sum_{n=1}^{\infty}\left[(-1)^n \frac{n}{n+1} + (-1)^{n-1}\right] = \sum_{n=1}^{\infty} \frac{(-1)^{n-1}}{n+1}$$

is a convergent series (**4.2-1**).

Example 6. If $a_n = 1/n$ and the series is multiplied by $\frac{1}{2}$, we have

$$\frac{1}{2} \sum_{n=1}^{\infty} a_n = \frac{1}{2}\left(1 + \frac{1}{2} + \frac{1}{3} + \cdots + \frac{1}{n} + \cdots\right)$$

$$= \frac{1}{2} + \frac{1}{4} + \frac{1}{6} + \cdots + \frac{1}{2n} + \cdots = \sum_{n=1}^{\infty} \frac{1}{2n}.$$

Example 7. Consider $a_n = b_n = (-1)^{n-1}/n^{1/2}$ so that both alternating series are convergent (**4.2-1**). Then

$$c_n = (-1)^{n-1}\left[\frac{1}{1^{1/2}}\frac{1}{n^{1/2}} + \frac{1}{2^{1/2}}\frac{1}{(n-1)^{1/2}} + \cdots + \frac{1}{n^{1/2}}\frac{1}{1^{1/2}}\right].$$

Replacing each root in the denominators by $n^{1/2}$, the largest root, we have

$$|c_n| \geq \frac{n}{n^{1/2}n^{1/2}} = 1.$$

Hence, $\lim_{n\to\infty} c_n \neq 0$, and the product series $\sum_{n=1}^{\infty} c_n = \sum_{n=1}^{\infty}(a_1b_n + a_2b_{n-1} + \cdots + a_nb_1)$ diverges.

4.3-2 Theorem. If $\sum_{n=1}^{\infty}a_n = S$ and $\sum_{n=1}^{\infty}b_n = \sigma$ where S and σ denote sums of the series, then $\sum_{n=1}^{\infty}(a_n + b_n) = S + \sigma$.

Proof. If S_n and σ_n are the partial sums of the first two series, then $(S_n + \sigma_n)$ is the partial sum of $\sum_{n=1}^{\infty}(a_n + b_n)$. Since $\lim_{n\to\infty}(S_n + \sigma_n) = S + \sigma$, the statement follows.

4.3-3 Theorem. If $\sum_{n=1}^{\infty}a_n = S$ and if c is an arbitrary number, then $\sum_{n=1}^{\infty}ca_n = cS$.

Proof. If S_n denotes the partial sum of the first series, then cS_n is the partial sum of $\sum_{n=1}^{\infty}ca_n$. Since $\lim_{n\to\infty}cS_n = c\lim_{n\to\infty}S_n = cS$, the statement follows.

4.4 Groupings and rearrangements

We have seen that the divergent series

$$\sum_{n=1}^{\infty}(-1)^{n-1}\frac{n+2}{n+1} = \frac{3}{2} - \frac{4}{3} + \frac{5}{4} - \frac{6}{5} + \cdots + (-1)^{n-1}\frac{n+2}{n+1} + \cdots$$

can be made to converge by grouping (Example 4, Chapter 4), that is, the series

$$\left[\frac{3}{2} - \frac{4}{3}\right] + \left[\frac{5}{4} - \frac{6}{5}\right] + \cdots + \left[\frac{2n+1}{2n} - \frac{2n+2}{2n+1}\right] + \cdots = \sum_{n=1}^{\infty} \frac{1}{2n(2n+1)}$$

is convergent. Conversely, if the parentheses are omitted, the series $\sum_{n=1}^{\infty} (-1)^{n-1}[(n+2)/(n+1)]$ diverges.

4.4-1 Theorem. If the terms of a convergent series are grouped in parentheses in any manner to form new terms without altering the order of the terms, then the resulting series has the same sum as the original series.

Proof. All partial sums of the new series are contained in the set of partial sums of the old series. Consequently, the partial sums of the new series converge to the same limit as the partial sums of the original series. This completes the proof.

Note that if the series with parentheses converges, the original series might diverge. However, if the series with parentheses diverges, the original series also diverges; for, if it converged, it would still converge after grouping terms.

4.4-2 Theorem. If an infinite series with terms which are sums in parentheses converges to S, then the series with parentheses omitted also converges to S, provided it converges at all.

Proof. If the series without parentheses converges, then by **4.4-1** inserting parentheses does not change its sum. This completes the proof.

If a, b, c, d are numbers, then

$$a + b + c + d = c + b + d + a = d + c + b + a = \cdots,$$

that is, the commutative property of addition holds; in other words, if a finite number of numbers is added, the sum is independent of the order of the terms in the sum.

If in a series $\sum_{n=1}^{\infty} a_n$ we change the order of infinitely many terms, that is, rearrange a series, then, if the new series converges, it does not necessarily have the same sum as the original series.

More precisely: A series $\sum_{n=1}^{\infty} b_n$ is said to be a rearrangement of a series $\sum_{n=1}^{\infty} a_n$ if there is a one-to-one correspondence between the indices n and m such that $b_n = a_m$ for corresponding indices.

Example 8. Consider the conditionally convergent series (see Section 1)

$$\ln 2 = 1 - \frac{1}{2} + \frac{1}{3} - \frac{1}{4} + \frac{1}{5} - \frac{1}{6} + \frac{1}{7} - \cdots + \frac{(-1)^{n-1}}{n} + \cdots.$$

Multiplication by 1/2 yields (**4.3-2**)

$$\frac{1}{2}\ln 2 = \frac{1}{2} - \frac{1}{4} + \frac{1}{6} - \frac{1}{8} + \frac{1}{10} - \frac{1}{12} + \frac{1}{14} - \cdots + \frac{(-1)^{n-1}}{2n} + \cdots .$$

Without affecting the value we may write

$$\frac{1}{2}\ln 2 = 0 + \frac{1}{2} + 0 - \frac{1}{4} + 0 + \frac{1}{6} + 0 - \cdots + 0 + \frac{(-1)^{n-1}}{2n} + 0 + \cdots .$$

On adding the last and original series term by term (**4.3-2**) we get a convergent series

$$\frac{3}{2}\ln 2 = 1 + 0 + \frac{1}{3} - \frac{1}{2} + \frac{1}{5} + 0 + \frac{1}{7} - \frac{1}{4} + \cdots$$
$$+ \frac{1}{4n-3} + 0 + \frac{1}{4n-1} - \frac{1}{2n} + \cdots$$

or

$$\frac{3}{2}\ln 2 = 1 + \frac{1}{3} - \frac{1}{2} + \frac{1}{5} + \frac{1}{7} - \frac{1}{4} + \cdots$$
$$+ \frac{1}{4n-3} + \frac{1}{4n-1} - \frac{1}{2n} + \cdots .$$

The last series is the rearrangement of the original series: take two positive terms from the original series and one negative term, then two more positive terms and another negative term, and so on.

Note that the original and the rearranged series have exactly the same terms and differ only in the order, and yet their sums differ (ln 2 $\neq \frac{3}{2}\ln 2$).

Example 9. The alternating series

$$1 - \frac{1}{2^{1/2}} + \frac{1}{3^{1/2}} - \frac{1}{4^{1/2}} + \cdots + \frac{1}{(2n-1)^{1/2}} - \frac{1}{(2n)^{1/2}} + \cdots$$

converges conditionally, since $\{1/n^{1/2}\}$ is monotonically decreasing to zero, and $\sum_{n=1}^{\infty} 1/n^{1/2}$ diverges (**4.2-1**).

The rearranged series, in which two positive terms are always followed by a negative term,

$$\left(1 + \frac{1}{3^{1/2}} - \frac{1}{2^{1/2}}\right) + \left(\frac{1}{5^{1/2}} + \frac{1}{7^{1/2}} - \frac{1}{4^{1/2}}\right) + \cdots$$
$$+ \left(\frac{1}{(4n-3)^{1/2}} + \frac{1}{(4n-1)^{1/2}} - \frac{1}{(2n)^{1/2}}\right) + \cdots$$

diverges, since

$$a_n = \frac{1}{(4n-3)^{1/2}} + \frac{1}{(4n-1)^{1/2}} - \frac{1}{(2n)^{1/2}} > \frac{2}{(4n)^{1/2}} - \frac{1}{(2n)^{1/2}}$$

$$= \left[1 - \frac{1}{2^{1/2}}\right]\frac{1}{n^{1/2}},$$

and consequently, $\lim\limits_{n\to\infty} na_n \neq 0$.

This example shows that a rearranged series may be divergent.

4.4-3 Theorem. (Riemann's* Theorem). A conditionally convergent series can be made to converge to any arbitrary value, or even to diverge, by a suitable rearrangement of its terms.

Proof. Let A be the sum to which the rearranged series shall converge. Assume that A is positive, to be specific. We can first add just as many (possibly, zero) positive terms so that the sum is greater than A. This is possible since the sum of positive terms of a conditionally convergent series increases beyond all bounds (**4.1-2**). Then add just enough negative terms to insure that the new sum is less than A. This is also possible since the sum of negative terms of a conditionally convergent series also diverges. Then add just enough positive terms to pass A again, then just enough negative terms to repass A again, and so on indefinitely. The difference between the partial sum of the constructed series and A will approach zero. In fact, $|A - \sigma_n|$, where σ_n denotes the partial sum, is always less than the last term added. Since the given series converges, its terms approach zero as n increases. Consequently, by this process, we can approach A as closely as desired.

Example 10. Since the series

$$1 - \frac{1}{2} + \frac{1}{3} - \frac{1}{4} + \frac{1}{5} - \frac{1}{6} + \frac{1}{7} - \cdots + \frac{(-1)^{n-1}}{n} + \cdots$$

is conditionally convergent, the series composed of it positive terms

$$1 + \frac{1}{3} + \frac{1}{5} + \cdots + \frac{1}{2k-1} + \cdots$$

is divergent. We now rearrange the series in the following way:

First we take just enough of the positive terms to pass 2. To be specific, we add $1 + 1/3 + 1/5 + 1/7 + 1/9 + 1/11 > 2$ (note that $1 + 1/3 + 1/5 + 1/7 + 1/9 < 2$). Then add the first negative term, $-1/2$. This yields the series

$$1 + \frac{1}{3} + \frac{1}{5} + \frac{1}{7} + \frac{1}{9} + \frac{1}{11} - \frac{1}{2}.$$

---

* Bernard Riemann (1826–1866), German mathematician, exercised a great influence on the theory of complex variables and on geometry.

Next take just enough more positive terms to pass 4. This will yield a partial sum of the form

$$1 + \frac{1}{3} + \frac{1}{5} + \frac{1}{7} + \frac{1}{9} + \frac{1}{11} - \frac{1}{2} + \frac{1}{13} + \frac{1}{15} + \cdots + \frac{1}{2k+1} > 4 .$$

Now add the next negative term, $-1/4$. This yields the partial sum

$$1 + \frac{1}{3} + \frac{1}{5} + \frac{1}{7} + \frac{1}{9} + \frac{1}{11} - \frac{1}{2} + \frac{1}{13} + \frac{1}{15} + \cdots + \frac{1}{2k+1} - \frac{1}{4} .$$

Proceeding this way we obtain partial sums such that when the term $-1/(2n)$ is added, the partial sum exceeds $2n - (1/n)$, that is, it increases beyond all bounds. This means that the rearranged series diverges.

In Examples 8, 9 and 10, and in **4.4-3** we have seen typical properties of conditionally convergent series. No such thing can happen if the series is absolutely convergent.

4.4-4 Theorem. Any rearrangement of an absolutely convergent series converges to the same sum.

Proof. First, let us prove the theorem on the assumption that the terms of the series are non-negative.

Let $S = \sum_{n=1}^{\infty} a_n$, $a_n \geq 0$, and $\sum_{n=1}^{\infty} b_n$ be a series consisting of the same terms as $\sum_{n=1}^{\infty} a_n$ but taken in another order.

Now

$$\sigma_n = b_1 + b_2 + \cdots + b_n < S ,$$

since every b is some a, and the sum of any finite number of terms of $\sum_{k=1}^{\infty} a_k$ is less than S. It follows that $\{\sigma_n\}$ is bounded and by **3.4-1** has a limit $\sigma \leq S$. But since every a is some b, we can show in exactly the same way that $S \leq \sigma$. Consequently $S = \sigma$.

In the general case of an absolutely convergent series we have $S = \alpha - \beta$, where α and β are the positive subseries. Since α and β are unchanged by a rearrangement of the original series and the partial sums converge to $S = \alpha - \beta$, the statement follows.

Thus, there is a fundamental distinction between absolutely convergent series and conditionally convergent series. In absolutely convergent series rearrangement of the terms does not affect the convergence and the sum of the series, exactly as in the case of finite sums. In conditionally convergent series, on the other hand, the sum of the series can be changed at will by suitable rearrangement of the series, or even the series can be made to diverge. Furthermore, we have seen that the product series of two conditionally convergent series may diverge

(Example 7, Section 3). This cannot happen if the series are absolutely convergent.

4.4-5 Theorem. If one of the series $\sum_{n=1}^{\infty} a_n = S$ and $\sum_{n=1}^{\infty} b_n = \sigma$ converges absolutely, then their Cauchy product $\sum_{n=1}^{\infty} c_n = \delta$ converges and $S\sigma = \delta$.

Proof. Let us denote $S_n = \sum_{i=1}^{n} a_i$, $\sigma_n = \sum_{i=1}^{n} b_i$, $\alpha = \sum_{n=1}^{\infty} |a_n|$, $\beta_n = \sigma_n - \sigma$, $\delta_n = \sum_{i=1}^{n} c_i = \sum_{i=1}^{n} (a_1 b_i + a_2 b_{i-1} + \cdots + a_i b_1)$.

Then it is apparent that

$$\begin{aligned}
\delta_n &= a_1 b_1 + (a_1 b_2 + a_2 b_1) + \cdots + (a_1 b_n + a_2 b_{n-1} + \cdots + a_n b_1) \\
&= a_1 \sigma_n + a_2 \sigma_{n-1} + \cdots + a_n \sigma_1 \\
&= a_1 (\sigma + \beta_n) + a_2 (\sigma + \beta_{n-1}) + \cdots + a_n (\sigma + \beta_1) \\
&= \sigma S_n + a_1 \beta_n + a_2 \beta_{n-1} + \cdots + a_n \beta_1 \\
&= \sigma S_n + \gamma_n ,
\end{aligned}$$

where $\gamma_n = a_n \beta_1 + a_{n-1} \beta_2 + \cdots + a_1 \beta_n$.

Since $\lim_{n\to\infty} \sigma S_n = \sigma S$, the theorem is proved if we show that $\lim_{n\to\infty} \gamma_n = 0$. To do this we follow the technique of proof of **2.6-3**.

Since $\lim_{n\to\infty} \beta_n = \lim_{n\to\infty} (\sigma_n - \sigma) = \sigma - \sigma = 0$, it follows that for any given $\varepsilon > 0$ we can choose an integer n_1 such that $|\beta_n| < \varepsilon/(2\alpha)$ for $n > n_1$. Thus, the inequality

$$|\gamma_n| \leq |a_n \beta_1 + \cdots + a_{n-n_1+1}\beta_{n_1}| + |a_{n-n_1}||\beta_{n_1+1}| + \cdots + |a_1||\beta_n|$$

$$< |a_n \beta_1 + \cdots + a_{n-n_1+1}\beta_{n_1}| + \frac{\varepsilon}{2\alpha}(|a_{n-n_1}| + \cdots + |a_1|)$$

follows. If we note further that n_1 is a fixed integer and $\lim_{n\to\infty} a_n = 0$, it follows that we can choose n_2 so large that

$$|a_n \beta_1 + \cdots + a_{n-n_1+1}\beta_{n_1}| < \frac{\varepsilon}{2}$$

for $n > n_2$. Since $|a_{n-n_1}| + \cdots + |a_1| \leq \sum_{n=1}^{\infty} |a_n| = \alpha$, we obtain

$$|\gamma_n| < \frac{\varepsilon}{2} + \frac{\varepsilon}{2\alpha}\alpha = \varepsilon$$

for $n > n_0$, where n_0 denotes the larger of the integers n_1, n_2.

This completes the proof.

Corollary. If the series $\sum_{n=1}^{\infty} a_n = S$ and $\sum_{n=1}^{\infty} b_n = \sigma$ converge absolutely, then their Cauchy product $\sum_{n=1}^{\infty} (a_1 b_n + a_2 b_{n-1} + \cdots + a_n b_1) = \delta$ converges absolutely and $S\sigma = \delta$.

The conditions of the theorem are satisfied for the series $\sum_{n=1}^{\infty} |a_n|$ and $\sum_{n=1}^{\infty} |b_n|$, consequently, their Cauchy product converges. Hence, the Cauchy product of the original series converges absolutely.

Example 11. The Cauchy product of the geometric series

$$1 + x + x^2 + \cdots + x^{n-1} + \cdots = \frac{1}{1-x},$$

$$1 + y + y^2 + \cdots + y^{n-1} + \cdots = \frac{1}{1-y},$$

$$|x| < 1, \quad |y| < 1$$

is

$$1 + (x+y) + (x^2 + xy + y^2) + \cdots + (x^{n-1} + x^{n-2}y + \cdots + y^{n-1}) + \cdots$$

$$= \frac{1}{(1-x)(1-y)}.$$

Consider special cases. If $y = x$, the product yields

$$1 + 2x + 3x^2 + \cdots + nx^{n-1} + \cdots = \frac{1}{(1-x)^2}.$$

For $y = -y$ we obtain

$$1 + x^2 + x^4 + \cdots + x^{2k} + \cdots = \frac{1}{(1-x^2)},$$

the familiar geometric series for $q = x^2$ (Example 8, Chapter 2).

Example 12. It is easily seen that the series

$$S(x) = 1 + \frac{x}{1!} + \frac{x^2}{2!} + \frac{x^3}{3!} + \cdots + \frac{x^n}{n!} + \cdots$$

converges for all values of x. (Note that by the ratio test $\lim_{n \to \infty} |u_{n+1}/u_n| = \lim_{n \to \infty} |x/(n+1)| = 0 < 1$.) The Cauchy product

$$S(x)S(y) = \left(1 + \frac{x}{1!} + \frac{x^2}{2!} + \cdots + \frac{x^n}{n!} + \cdots\right)\left(1 + \frac{y}{1!} + \frac{y^2}{2!} + \cdots + \frac{y^n}{n!} + \cdots\right)$$

$$= \sum_{n=1}^{\infty} c_n,$$

where

$$c_n = \sum_{i=1}^{n} \frac{x^{i-1} y^{n-i}}{(i-1)!(n-i)!} = \frac{1}{(n-1)!} \sum_{i=1}^{n} \frac{(n-1)!}{(i-1)!(n-i)!} x^{i-1} y^{n-i}$$

$$= \frac{1}{(n-1)!} \sum_{i=1}^{n} \binom{n-1}{i-1} x^{i-1} y^{n-i} = \frac{1}{(n-1)!} (x+y)^{n-1}.$$

can be written in the form

$$S(x)S(y) = \sum_{n=1}^{\infty} \frac{1}{(n-1)!} (x + y)^{n-1} = S(x + y) \quad (0! = 1) \ .$$

We shall see later that the series $S(x) = e^x$, and the functional equation $S(x)S(y) = S(x + y)$ expresses the familiar relation $e^x e^y = e^{x+y}$.

Note that $S(x)S(y)$ can also be expressed in the form

$$S(x)S(y) = \lim_{n \to \infty} \left[\sum_{i=1}^{n} \frac{x^{i-1}}{(i-1)!} \right] \left[\sum_{i=1}^{n} \frac{y^{i-1}}{(i-1)!} \right] \ .$$

But by the systematic process of Cauchy's product one obtains a series which is of the same kind as the original series, and this is an advantage in many investigations.

4.5 Abel's partial summation

Let us consider the series $\sum_{\mu=1}^{\infty} a_\mu b_\mu$, where $\{a_\mu\}$ and $\{b_\mu\}$ are sequences of real numbers. Let $A_\mu = \sum_{i=1}^{\mu} a_i$. Then it is easily seen that the partial sums of the infinite series can be rewritten as follows.

$$\begin{aligned}
S_n = \sum_{\mu=1}^{n} a_\mu b_\mu &= a_1 b_1 + a_2 b_2 + a_3 b_3 + \cdots + a_n b_n \\
&= A_1 b_1 + (A_2 - A_1)b_2 + (A_3 - A_2)b_3 + \cdots + (A_n - A_{n-1})b_n \\
&= A_1(b_1 - b_2) + A_2(b_2 - b_3) + \cdots + A_{n-1}(b_{n-1} - b_n) + A_n b_n \\
&= \sum_{\mu=1}^{n-1} A_\mu(b_\mu - b_{\mu+1}) + A_n b_n \ .
\end{aligned}$$

Hence,

$$S_{n+k} - S_n = \sum_{\mu=n+1}^{n+k} a_\mu b_\mu = \sum_{\mu=n+1}^{n+k-1} A_\mu(b_\mu - b_{\mu+1}) - A_n b_{n+1} + A_{n+k} b_{n+k} \ .$$

These simple identities, known as Abel's partial summation, lead to important tests for convergence of series.

4.5-1 Theorem. The series $\sum_{\mu=1}^{\infty} a_\mu b_\mu$ converges if the series $\sum_{\mu=1}^{\infty} A_\mu(b_\mu - b_{\mu+1})$ converge and $\lim_{n \to \infty} A_n b_n$ exists.

Proof. Under these conditions the partial sums of the infinite series

$$S_n = \sum_{\mu=1}^{n} a_\mu b_\mu = \sum_{\mu=1}^{n} A_\mu(b_\mu - b_{\mu+1}) + A_n b_n$$

converge to a limit S as $n \to \infty$. Consequently the infinite series converges.

Corollaries of this theorem yield special criteria which we list as theorems.

4.5-2 Theorem. (Abel's test). The series $\sum_{\mu=1}^{\infty} a_\mu b_\mu$ is convergent if $\sum_{\mu=1}^{\infty} a_\mu$ converges and the sequence $\{b_n\}$ is monotonic and bounded.

Proof. By hypothesis $\lim_{n \to \infty} A_n = A$ and $\lim_{n \to \infty} b_n = b$ exist. Consequently A_n is bounded, that is, $|A_n| \leq M$ and $\lim_{n \to \infty} A_n b_n = Ab$ exists. To show that $\sum_{\mu=1}^{\infty} A_\mu(b_\mu - b_{\mu+1})$ is convergent we note that the telescoping series $\sum_{\mu=1}^{\infty}(b_\mu - b_{\mu+1}) = b_1 - b$ converges absolutely since all terms $(b_\mu - b_{\mu+1})$ have the same sign in consequence of monotony of $\{b_\mu\}$. Consequently,

$$\left| \sum_{\mu=1}^{\infty} A_\mu(b_\mu - b_{\mu+1}) \right| \leq M \left| \sum_{\mu=1}^{\infty} (b_\mu - b_{\mu+1}) \right| = M(b_1 - b) \,,$$

that is the series converges absolutely. By **4.1-2** the series converges. Thus, by **4.5-1** $\sum_{\mu=1}^{\infty} a_\mu b_\mu$ converges.

4.5-3 Theorem. (Dirichlet's test). The series $\sum_{\mu=1}^{\infty} a_\mu b_\mu$ is convergent if $\sum_{\mu=1}^{\infty} a_\mu$ has bounded partial sums and $\{b_n\downarrow\}$ with $\lim_{n \to \infty} b_n = 0$.

Proof. Since A_μ is bounded, it follows by the same reasoning as in **4.5-2** that $\sum_{\mu=1}^{\infty} A_\mu(b_\mu - b_{\mu+1})$ converges. Furthermore, $\lim_{n \to \infty} A_n b_n = 0$. Thus, the two conditions of **4.5-1** are fulfilled, and the series converges.

4.5-4 Theorem. (du Bois-Reymond's and Dedekind's tests).

(a) The series $\sum_{n=1}^{\infty} a_\mu b_\mu$ is convergent if $\sum_{\mu=1}^{\infty}(b_\mu - b_{\mu+1})$ converges absolutely and $\sum_{\mu=1}^{\infty} a_\mu$ converges.

(b) The series $\sum_{\mu=1}^{\infty} a_\mu b_\mu$ is convergent if $\sum_{\mu=1}^{\infty}(b_\mu - b_{\mu+1})$ converges absolutely, $\lim_{n \to \infty} b_n = 0$, and $\sum_{\mu=1}^{\infty} a_\mu$ has bounded partial sums.

Proof. (a) Since $\sum_{\mu=1}^{\infty} a_\mu$ converges, it follows that $\lim_{\mu \to \infty} A_\mu = A$ exists and A_μ is bounded. Similarly, $\sigma_n = \sum_{\mu=1}^{n}(b_\mu - b_{\mu+1}) = b_1 - b_{n+1}$ converges as $n \to \infty$. Consequently $\lim_{n \to \infty} b_n = b$ exists and so does $\lim_{\mu \to \infty} A_\mu b_\mu = Ab$. Since $\sum_{\mu=1}^{\infty}(b_\mu - b_{\mu+1})$ converges absolutely, it follows that $\sum_{\mu=1}^{\infty} A_\mu(b_\mu - b_{\mu+1})$ converges. Thus again the conditions of **4.5-1** are met, and the series converges.

(b) Under these conditions $\sum_{\mu=1}^{\infty} A_\mu(b_\mu - b_{\mu+1})$ converges and $\lim_{n \to \infty} A_n b_n = 0$ exists. Consequently by **4.5-1** the series converges.

Example 13. The series $\sum_{n=1}^{\infty} a_n \{1 - (1/n)\}^n$ converges if $\sum_{n=1}^{\infty} a_n$ converges.

Since $\{(1 - (1/n)\}^n$ is a monotonic and bounded sequence $[\{1 - (1/n)\}^n < e^{-1}]$ and $\sum_{n=1}^{\infty} a_n$ converges, the conditions of **4.5-2** are met, and the original series converges.

Example 14. If $\{b_n\downarrow\}$ with $\lim_{n\to\infty} b_n = 0$, then the series $\sum_{n=1}^{\infty}(-1)^{n-1}b_n$ converges.

Since $A_\mu = \sum_{n=1}^{\mu}(-1)^{n-1} = 1$ or 0, the series converges by **4.5-3**. This is another proof of Leibnitz's criterion for alternating series (see **4.2-1**).

Example 15. The series $\sum_{n=1}^{\infty}(\sin nx)/n^p$, $p > 0$ converges for every value of the parameter x.

We apply **4.5-3** with $a_\mu = \sin \mu x$, $b_\mu = 1/\mu^p$. Since $\{b_\mu\downarrow\}$ and $\lim_{\mu\to\infty} b_\mu = 0$, it follows that the series converges if $A_\mu = \sum_{n=1}^{\mu} \sin nx$ is bounded.

From

$$2 \sin \frac{x}{2} A_\mu = \sum_{n=1}^{\mu} 2 \sin \frac{x}{2} \sin nx = \sum_{n=1}^{\mu}\left[\cos (2n - 1)\frac{x}{2} - \cos (2n + 1)\frac{x}{2} \right]$$

$$= \cos \frac{x}{2} - \cos (2n + 1)\frac{x}{2}$$

it follows that

$$|A_\mu| = \left|\frac{\cos (x/2) - \cos (2n +1)(x/2)}{2 \sin (x/2)}\right| \leq \frac{1 + 1}{2\,|\sin (x/2)|} = \frac{1}{|\sin (x/2)|}$$

is bounded for all x for which $\sin (x/2) \neq 0$. Consequently, the series converges for all x with a possible exception of $x = 2k\pi$ $(k = 0, \pm 1, \pm 2, \ldots)$. However, for $x = 2k\pi$ the terms of the series vanish, and so the series converges for all x.

4.6 Euler's summation formula

In Chapter 3 we obtained a relation between partial sums $S_n = \sum_{x=1}^{n} f(x)$ and integrals $\int_1^n f(x)\,dx$ (**3.5-3**) which led to a powerful test for convergence and a useful tool for approximation of series. However, the conditions that $f(x)$ is positive and monotonically decreasing severely restrict the scope of applications. The following relation is more general and admits of a far wider range of applications.

4.6-1 Theorem (Euler's summation formula). If $f(x)$ possesses a continuous derivative $f'(x)$ on $[1, n]$, then

$$\sum_{x=1}^{n} f(x) = \int_1^n f(x)\,dx + \int_1^n \left(x - [x] - \frac{1}{2}\right)f'(x)\,dx + \frac{1}{2}[f(1) + f(n)] .$$

Proof. The obvious equality

$$\int_{\mu}^{\mu+1}\left(x - \mu - \frac{1}{2}\right)f'(x)\,dx = \left(x - \mu - \frac{1}{2}\right)f(x)\Big|_{x=\mu}^{x=\mu+1} - \int_{\mu}^{\mu+1}f(x)\,dx$$

obtained by partial integration holds for $\mu = 1, 2, \ldots, n-1$.

In the integrand on the left we can put $\mu = [x]$ for $\mu \le x < \mu + 1$. Since $x - [x] - \frac{1}{2}$ differs from $x - \mu - \frac{1}{2}$ only at one point $x = \mu + 1$ on the interval $[\mu, \mu + 1]$, and this does not change the value of the integral, we get

$$\frac{1}{2}[f(\mu) + f(\mu + 1)] = \int_{\mu}^{\mu+1}f(x)\,dx + \int_{\mu}^{\mu+1}\left(x - [x] - \frac{1}{2}\right)f'(x)\,dx\,.$$

Addition of the relations for $\mu = 1, 2, \ldots, n-1$, and then of the term $\frac{1}{2}[f(1) + f(n)]$ to both sides yields Euler's summation formula.

Since the first necessary condition for convergence of a series $\lim\limits_{n\to\infty} f(n) = 0$ must hold, it follows that $\lim\limits_{n\to\infty} \sum_{x=1}^{n} f(x)$ exists, if both integrals

$$\int_{1}^{\infty}f(x)\,dx \quad \text{and} \quad \int_{1}^{\infty}\left(x - [x] - \frac{1}{2}\right)f'(x)\,dx \text{ exist.}$$

Since $|x - [x] - \frac{1}{2}| \le \frac{1}{2}$ and

$$\int_{1}^{n}\left(x - [x] - \frac{1}{2}\right)f'(x)\,dx \le \int_{1}^{n}\left|x - [x] - \frac{1}{2}\right||f'(x)|\,dx \le \frac{1}{2}\int_{1}^{n}|f'(x)|\,dx\,,$$

it follows that the series $\sum_{x=1}^{\infty} f(x)$ converges if the integrals

$$\int_{1}^{\infty}f(x)\,dx \quad \text{and} \quad \int_{1}^{\infty}|f'(x)|\,dx$$

exist.

Example 16. Show that $\sum_{n=1}^{\infty} (\sin n^{1/2})/n$ converges. Since

$$f(x) = \frac{\sin x^{1/2}}{x}\,, \quad |f'(x)| = \left|\frac{\frac{1}{2}x^{1/2}\cos x^{1/2} - \sin x^{1/2}}{x^2}\right| < \frac{x^{1/2} + 1}{x^2}\,, \quad \int_{1}^{\infty}\frac{x^{1/2}}{x^2}\,dx = 2\,,$$

$$\int_{1}^{\infty}\frac{\sin t}{t}\,dt = 2\cos 1 - 2\int_{1}^{\infty}\frac{\cos t}{t^2}\,dt\,, \quad \int_{1}^{\infty}\frac{x^{1/2} + 1}{x^2}\,dx\,, \quad \left|\int_{1}^{\infty}\frac{\cos t}{t^2}\,dt\right| < \int_{1}^{\infty}\frac{dt}{t^2}$$

exist, it follows that $\int_{1}^{\infty}f(x)\,dx$ and $\int_{1}^{\infty}|f'(x)|\,dx$ exist. Consequently the series converges.

Example 17. Does the series $\sum_{n=2}^{\infty} [\sin(\log n)]/n$ converge? Since

$$|f'(x)| = \left|\frac{\cos(\log x) - \sin(\log x)}{x^2}\right| \le \frac{2}{x^2}\,,$$

consequently $\int_{2}^{\infty}|f'(x)|\,dx \le 2\int_{2}^{\infty}\frac{dx}{x^2}$ exists and

$$\int_2^\infty \frac{\sin(\log x)}{x}\,dx = \int_{\log 2}^\infty \sin t\,dt$$

$(\log x = t)$ does not exist, the series diverges.

Exercises 4.A

Test the alternating series $\sum_{n=1}^\infty (-1)^{n-1} a_n$ for convergence if

1. $a_n = n/(n+1)^2$.
2. $a_n = 1/(a+n)$, $a > 0$.
3. $a_n = \log[(n+2)/(n+1)]$.
4. $a_n = a^{1/n}$, $a > 0$.
5. $a_n = 1/n^{1/2}$.
6. $a_n = (n+2)/(2n+1)$.
7. $a_n = 1/n^p$, $p > 0$.

8. $a_n = 1/n - 1/[n(n+1)]$.
9. $a_n = 1 - a^{1/n}$, $a > 0$.
10. $a_n = [1 - (1/n)]^n$.
11. $a_n = (\log n)/n$.
12. $a_n = 1 - n\log[(n+1)/n]$.
13. $a_n = (\cos^2 n\alpha)/n^2$.

Evaluate the following series correct to four decimal places.

14. $\displaystyle\sum_{n=1}^\infty \frac{(-1)^{n-1}}{n^2}$.

15. $\displaystyle\sum_{n=1}^\infty \frac{(-1)^{n-1}}{(n-1)!}$.

16. $\displaystyle\sum_{n=1}^\infty \frac{(-1)^{n-1}}{n3^n}$.

17. $\displaystyle\sum_{n=1}^\infty \frac{(-1)^{n-1}}{(2n-1)^3}$.

Test for absolute convergence of $\sum_{n=1}^\infty a_n$ if

18. $a_n = \dfrac{(-1)^{n-1}}{n^{1+(1/n)}}$.

19. $a_n = (-1)^{n-1}\dfrac{(n+1)^{1/2} - n^{1/2}}{n}$.

20. $a_n = \cos\tfrac{1}{2}(n\pi)/(n^2 + n + 1)$.

21. $a_n = (-1)^{n-1}\dfrac{3^n + 5n}{4^n + 1}$.

22. $a_n = (-1)^{n-1} n/(n^2 + n + 1)$.

23. $a_n = \dfrac{(-1)^{n-1}}{(n+1)[\log(n+1)]^2}$.

24. $a_n = \sin\left[\dfrac{n+1}{n}\pi\right]$.

25. $a_n = (-1)^{n-1} n^n/(n+1)^{n+1}$.

26. $a_n = \dfrac{\cos(a\log n)}{n^2}$.

27. We have seen that
$$\log 2 = 1 - 1/2 + 1/3 - 1/4 + 1/5 - 1/6 + 1/7 - 1/8 + \cdots + (-1)^{n-1}/n + \cdots$$
(see Example 8). Hence,
$$2\log 2 = 2 - 1 + 2/3 - 1/2 + 2/5 - 1/3 + 2/7 - 1/4 + \cdots + (-1)^{n-1}2/n + \cdots$$
$$= (2 - 1) - 1/2 + (2/3 - 1/3) - 1/4 + (2/5 - 1/5) - 1/6 + \cdots$$
$$= 1 - 1/2 + 1/3 - 1/4 + 1/5 - 1/6 + \cdots + (-1)^{n-1}/n + \cdots$$
$$= \log 2.$$
Thus $2\log 2 = \log 2$ or $2 = 1$. What is wrong with the "proof?"

28. If $\log 2 = \displaystyle\sum_{n=1}^\infty \frac{(-1)^{n-1}}{n}$, show that $\displaystyle\sum_{n=1}^\infty\left[\frac{1}{4n-2} - \frac{1}{4n}\right] = \frac{1}{2}\log 2$. $\left(\text{Hint:}\right.$
Consider $\log 2 = \displaystyle\sum_{n=1}^\infty\left[\frac{1}{2n-1} - \frac{1}{2n}\right].\Big)$

29. If $\displaystyle\sum_{n=1}^\infty\left[\frac{1}{2n-1} - \frac{1}{4n-2} - \frac{1}{4n}\right]$ converges, show that $1 - \dfrac{1}{2} - \dfrac{1}{4}$
$+ \dfrac{1}{3} - \dfrac{1}{6} - \dfrac{1}{8} + \cdots$ also converges, that is, justify the removal

of parentheses.

30. Does the series $1 + \dfrac{1}{2} - \dfrac{1}{3} + \dfrac{1}{4} + \dfrac{1}{5} - \dfrac{1}{6} + \cdots$ converge? $\left(\text{Hint:} \right.$
    Consider $\displaystyle\sum_{n=1}^{\infty} \left[\dfrac{1}{3n - 2} + \dfrac{1}{3n - 1} - \dfrac{1}{3n} \right].\Big)$

31. Prove that $\sum_{n=1}^{\infty} (-1)^{n-1}(2n + 1)/n(n + 1) = 1$.

32. Rearrange the alternating harmonic series to converge to zero.

33. Denote by $S = \sum_{n=1}^{\infty} 1/n^{1/2}$ and by $\sigma = \sum_{n=1}^{\infty} (-1)^{n-1}/n^{1/2}$. It is apparent that $S > 0$, $\sigma > 0$. It is easily seen that
    $$S - \sigma = 2(1/2^{1/2} + 1/4^{1/2} + \cdots + 1/(2n)^{1/2} + \cdots) = S\cdot 2^{1/2},$$
    whence $S = (-\sigma)/(2^{1/2} - 1)$, that is, $S < 0$. What is wrong with the "proof?"

34. $e = \sum_{n=1}^{\infty} 1/(n - 1)! = 1 + 1/1! + 1/2! + 1/3! + \cdots + 1/(n - 1)! + \cdots$.
    Show that on multiplying the series by itself one obtains
    $$e^2 = 1 + 2/1! + 2^2/2! + 2^3/3! + \cdots + 2^{n-1}/(n - 1)! + \cdots.$$

35. Discuss convergence of the series $\sum_{n=1}^{\infty} \cos nx/n^p$, $0 < p \le 1$.

36. Discuss convergence of the series
    $$\sum_{n=4}^{\infty} \frac{\cos (\log \log n)}{\log n}.$$
    (Hint: Apply Euler's formula.)

37. Show that
    $$\sum_{n=0}^{\infty} a_n x^n \sum_{n=0}^{\infty} x^n = \sum_{n=0}^{\infty} S_n x^n,$$
    where $S_n = a_0 + a_1 + a_2 + \cdots + a_n$.

CHAPTER 5

SEQUENCES AND SERIES OF FUNCTIONS: UNIFORM CONVERGENCE

In Chapters 2, 3, and 4 we discussed convergence of sequences and series of real numbers. It was only in particularly simple cases that the terms of sequences and series depended on a parameter or variable (Chapter 2, Examples 5, 6, 8, and 11 b; Chapter 4, Example 15). In this chapter we shall consider sequences and infinite series whose terms depend on a variable x, that is, are functions of this variable. Accordingly we shall denote these terms by $f_n(x)$ and consider sequences $\{f_n\}$ and series $\sum_{n=1}^{\infty} f_n(x)$ defined on an interval for brevity denoted by T.

By definition, a series $\sum_{n=1}^{\infty} f_n(x)$ converges to the sum $S(x)$ if the sequence $\{S_n(x)\}$, $S_n(x) = \sum_{i=1}^{n} f_i(x)$ has a limit $S(x)$. On the other hand, to every convergent sequence $\{S_n(x)\}$ there corresponds an infinite series $\sum_{n=1}^{\infty} [S_n(x) - S_{n-1}(x)]$ where $S_0(x) = 0$, $S_1(x) = f_1(x)$, and $S_n(x) - S_{n-1}(x) = f_n(x)$, $n > 1$. Consequently, every statement which holds for sequences holds also for infinite series. Though there is no real need, occasionally we shall explicitly state theorems for both sequences and series.

5.1 Pointwise convergence

Let each of the functions $f_n(x)$ be defined on the interval T and let the sequence $\{f_n(x)\}$ converge for every x of T. Then the function f defined by the equation

$$f(x) = \lim_{n \to \infty} f_n(x)$$

will be referred to as the limit function of the sequence $\{f_n(x)\}$. We shall say that the sequence $\{f_n(x)\}$ converges pointwise to $f(x)$ on the interval T.

Example 1. Consider $\{f_n(x)\}$, $f_n(x) = x^n$, $T = \{x | 0 \le x \le 1\}$. Since

$\lim\limits_{n\to\infty} x^n = 0$ for $0 \le x < 1$, and $\lim\limits_{n\to\infty} 1^n = 1$, it follows that the sequence converges on T and defines the function

$$f(x) = 0 \quad \text{if } 0 \le x < 1$$
$$= 1 \quad \text{if } x = 1 , \quad_{\diagup}$$

which is the limit function of the sequence $\{f_n(x)\}$.

One obtains the same result if one considers the equivalent series

$$x + (x - 1)x + (x - 1)x^2 + \cdots + (x - 1)x^{n-1} + \cdots .$$

The partial sums $S_n(x)$ of the series are x^n, that is, $S_n(x) = x^n = f_n(x)$ on $0 \le x \le 1$. Thus the series represents $f(x)$ also.

Note that, whereas the functions $f_n(x) = x^n$ converge to a limit function which is discontinuous at $x = 1$, the corresponding curves C_n possess a limit curve C which consists of the portion of the x-axis between $x = 0$ and $x = 1$ and the portion of the line $x = 1$ between $y = 0$ and $y = 1$, that is, C is continuous. The relation in set notation $R = \{(x, y)|0 \le x \le 1,\ y = 0\} \cup \{(x, y)|x = 1,\ 0 \le y \le 1\}$ which represents C is not the graph of the limit function $f(x)$. (See Figure 8.)

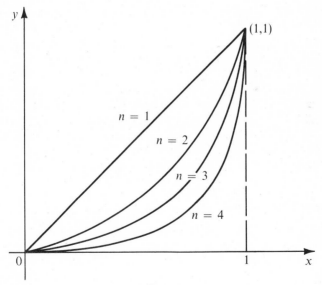

FIG. 8.

Example 2.

$$\{f_n(x)\},\ f_n(x) = x^2 + \frac{x^2}{1 + x^2} + \frac{x^2}{(1 + x^2)^2} + \cdots + \frac{x^2}{(1 + x^2)^{n-1}} .$$

To obtain the limiting function we write the geometric series in the form

$$f_n(x) = x^2 \frac{1 - [1/(1+x^2)^n]}{1 - [1/(1+x^2)]} = 1 + x^2 - \frac{1}{(1+x^2)^{n-1}}, \quad x \neq 0$$

$$= 0, \quad x = 0.$$

Hence,

$$f_n(x) = \lim_{n \to \infty} f_n(x) = 1 + x^2, \quad \text{if } x \neq 0$$

$$= 0, \quad \text{if } x = 0.$$

Thus $f(x)$ is discontinuous at $x = 0$.

If we note that $f_n(x)$ are partial sums of the infinite series $\sum_{n=1}^{\infty} x^2/(1+x^2)^{n-1}$, we may say that the series converges pointwise to $f(x)$ and write

$$f(x) = \sum_{n=1}^{\infty} \frac{x^2}{(1+x^2)^{n-1}}.$$

Here we have the surprising result that an absolutely convergent series of continuous functions represents a discontinuous function.

If we consider the graphs of $f_n(x)$ for $n = 1, 2, 3, \ldots$ we see again that the curves $C_1, C_2, C_3, \ldots$ converge to a continuous limit curve C consisting of the segment of the y-axis $0 \leq y \leq 1$ and of the parabola $y = 1 + x^2$ for $x \neq 0$. (See Figure 9.)

Example 3. Consider $\{f_n(x)\}$, $f_n(x) = xn^\alpha e^{-nx}$, $0 \leq x \leq 1$. If we note that $\lim_{n \to \infty} n^\alpha/e^{nx} = 0$ for every α and $x > 0$ and that $f_n(0)=0$ for all $n = 1, 2, 3, \ldots$ it follows that the limiting function $f(x) = \lim_{n \to \infty} f_n(x) = 0$, $0 \leq x \leq 1$. [To show that $g_n = n^\alpha/e^{nx}$ approaches 0 as $n \to \infty$, consider $\log g_n = n[\alpha((\log n)/n) - x]$ and assume that $\log z$ is continuous for $z > 0$. Since $\lim_{n \to \infty} (\log n)/n = 0$ (Chapter 3, Example 18) and $x > 0$, it follows that $\lim_{n \to \infty} \log g_n = -\infty$, consequently $\lim_{n \to \infty} g_n = 0$.]

It is easily verified that $f_n(x)$ has its maximum at the point $x = 1/n$. If $\alpha < 1$, then

$$\lim_{n \to \infty} f_n\left(\frac{1}{n}\right) = \lim_{n \to \infty} \frac{n^{\alpha-1}}{e} = 0$$

and the limiting curve C is the segment $0 \leq x \leq 1$, that is, C is the graph of $f(x)$.

If $\alpha = 1$, $\lim_{n \to \infty} f_n(1/n) = e^{-1}$, and the limiting curve C consists of the segments $0 \leq x \leq 1$ and $0 \leq y \leq e^{-1}$. If $\alpha > 1$, then the curves C_n converge to the segment of the x-axis $0 \le x \le 1$ plus the entire positive y-axis.

Thus, if $\alpha \ge 1$, the limiting curve C is not the graph of the limiting function $f(x) = 0$ which is continuous on $[0, 1]$. (See Figure 10.)

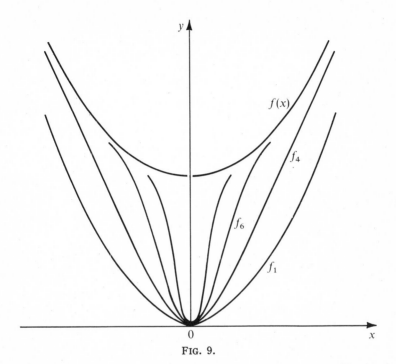

FIG. 9.

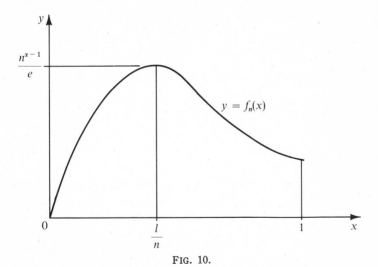

FIG. 10.

These few examples show that important properties of functions under the limit operations are not always preserved. For instance, in Examples 1 and 2 the functions $f_n(x)$ are continuous, but the limiting function $f(x)$ is not, and C_n are graphs of $f_n(x)$, but the limiting curve C is not the graph of $f(x)$. And what about differentiability and integrability? If the functions $f_n(x)$ are differentiable and integrable, to what extent does the limiting function $f(x)$ also possess these properties? For instance, in Example 3 the integral

$$\int_0^1 f_n(x)\,dx = \int_0^1 xn^\alpha e^{-nx}\,dx = n^{\alpha-2} - e^{-n}(n^{\alpha-1} + n^{\alpha-2})$$

exists for all n, but

$$\lim_{n \leftarrow \infty} \int_0^1 f_n(x)\,dx \neq \int_0^1 f(x)\,dx = 0 \quad \text{if } \alpha \geq 2\,.$$

Consequently,

$$\lim_{n \to \infty} \int_0^1 f_n(x)\,dx \neq \int_0^1 \lim_{n \leftarrow \infty} f_n(x)\,dx \quad \text{if } \alpha \geq 2\,.$$

That is, the order of the operations of integration and passing to the limit cannot be interchanged if $\alpha \geq 2$.

The question of whether one can interchange the order of two limit processes often arises in mathematical analysis. Although a sufficient condition for the validity of interchanging certain limits is uniform convergence, it does not provide the complete answer. There are examples where the order of two limits can be interchanged although the sequence is not uniformly convergent.

5.2   Uniform convergence

Let $\{f_n(x)\}$ be a sequence of functions which converge pointwise to a limiting function $f(x)$ on the interval T, that is, $f(x) = \lim_{n \to \infty} f_n(x)$ for every x of T. In other words, for every $\varepsilon > 0$ there exists an integer n_0 such that $n > n_0$ implies

$$|f_n(x) - f(x)| < \varepsilon \quad \text{for a fixed } x.$$

Note that n_0 depends on both x and ε. If there exists an integer n_0 such that it works equally well for every x of the interval, then the convergence is said to be uniform.

5.2-1   Definition. We say that a sequence of functions $\{f(x)\}$ converges uniformly on an interval T to a function $f(x)$ if for every $\varepsilon > 0$

there exists an integer n_0 such that $n > n_0$ implies $|f_n(x) - f(x)| < \varepsilon$ for every x on T.

By definition an infinite series $\sum_{n=1}^{\infty} f_n(x)$ converges uniformly on T to a function $S(x)$ if $\{S_n(x)\}$, $S_n(x) = \sum_{i=1}^{n} f_i(x)$ does so. If we note that $S(x) - S_n(x) = \sum_{i=n+1}^{\infty} f_i(x) = R_n(x)$ is the remainder of the series, we may say that an infinite series converges uniformly on T if for every $\varepsilon > 0$ there exists an integer n_0 such that $n > n_0$ implies $|R_n(x)| < \varepsilon$ for all x on T.

5.2-2 Definition (Cauchy's condition). A sequence $\{f_n(x)\}$ converges uniformly to a function $f(x)$ if for every $\varepsilon > 0$ there exists an integer n_0 such that $n > n_0$ and $k = 1, 2, 3, \ldots$ implies

$$|f_n(x) - f_{n+k}(x)| < \varepsilon \quad \text{for all } x \text{ on } T.$$

Cauchy's condition can be deduced from **5.2-1**, but we omit the proof.

Though the definition of uniform convergence is simple, its underlying nature is not readily grasped. Since it is well known that beginners usually have difficulties here, we shall continue to elaborate on Examples 1, 2, and 3 and discuss the matter in some detail.

Example 4. We consider the sequence $\{f_n(x)\}$, $f_n(x) = x^n$.

(a) $T = \{x | 0 \le x \le 0.9\}$. Since the limiting function $f(x) = \lim_{n \to \infty} x^n$ $= 0$, the requirement for uniform convergence is the inequality $|f_n(x) - f(x)| = x^n < \varepsilon$.

Since $x^n \le (0.9)^n$, the above inequality will be satisfied for all x on T if $(0.9)^n < \varepsilon$. Hence

$$n \log (0.9) < \log \varepsilon$$

and

$$n > \frac{\log \varepsilon}{\log (0.9)}$$

[note that $\log (0.9) < 0$]. If we denote $n_0 = [\log \varepsilon / \log (0.9)]$, it follows that the inequality $x_n < \varepsilon$ holds for all $n > n_0$ and all x on T. Consequently, the sequence converges uniformly.

Note that here the limiting function $f(x) = 0$ is continuous and its graph is the limiting curve C.

(b) $T = \{x | 0 \le x < 1\}$. As in case (a) the limiting function is $f(x) = 0$ and the inequality

$$x^n < \varepsilon$$

to be satisfied is the same. However, the situation is quite different. It is true that for a given $\varepsilon > 0$ and a given x there always can be found an integer n such that the inequality holds. But as x approaches closer and closer to 1, the integer n increases beyond all bounds, and there is no such integer n_0 which would work for all x on the interval $0 \le x < 1$. To be more specific let us take $\varepsilon = 0.01$ and assume that there exists an integer n_0 such that the inequality $x^n < 0.01$ holds for all $n > n_0$ and all x on T. But no matter how large n is, we always can determine a value of $x_0 < 1$ such that, for example, $x_0^n = \frac{1}{2}$, if we take $x_0 = (\frac{1}{2})^{1/n}$ which is on T and does not satisfy the inequality. Furthermore, no value of x on the interval $(\frac{1}{2})^{1/n} \le x < 1$ which is contained in T satisfies the above inequality. This contradicts the assumption.

Consequently, the sequence in case (b) does not converge uniformly. However, $f(x)$ is continuous and its graph is C.

Note that the integer n always depends on both ε and x. In case of the inequality $x^n < \varepsilon$ we have

$$n > \frac{\log \varepsilon}{\log x} .$$

If for a fixed $\varepsilon > 0$ the integers $n(\varepsilon)$ are bounded on T, then there exists an integer n_0 such that $n > n_0$ implies the inequality $x^n < \varepsilon$ for all x on T. In case (a) such an integer was found to be $n_0 = [\log \varepsilon/\log(0.9)]$.

If n is not bounded, there is no integer n_0 and consequently the sequence does not converge uniformly on T. This is the case in (b) where $n > |\log \varepsilon/\log x| \to \infty$ as $x \to 1$.

(c) $T = \{x | 0 \le x \le 1\}$. This essentially is case (b). The difference is that the limiting function

$$f(x) = 0 , \quad \text{if } 0 \le x < 1$$
$$= 1 , \quad \text{if } x = 1$$

is discontinuous and the limiting curve C is not the graph of $f(x)$.

Example 5.

$$\{f_n(x)\}, \ f_n(x) = x^2 + \frac{x^2}{1 + x^2} + \frac{x^2}{(1 + x^2)^2} + \cdots + \frac{x^2}{(1 + x^2)^{n-1}} .$$

(a) $T = \{x | -\infty < x < \infty\}$. Since the series is a geometric series and $f_n(0) = 0$, it follows that

$$f(x) = \lim_{n \to \infty} f_n(x) = \lim_{n \to \infty} x^2 \frac{1 - [1/(1 + x^2)^n]}{1 - [1/(1 + x^2)]} = 1 + x^2 , \quad \text{if } x \neq 0$$
$$= 0 , \quad \text{if } x = 0 .$$

Then the condition for uniform convergence $(x \neq 0)$

$$|f_n(x) - f(x)| = \frac{1}{(1 + x^2)^{n-1}} < \varepsilon$$

is satisfied if $n - 1 > \log(1/\varepsilon)/\log(1 + x^2)$ is bounded. Since $\log(1 + x^2)$ $\to 0$ as $x \to 0$, it follows that $n - 1 > \log(1/\varepsilon)/\log(1 + x^2) \to \infty$ as $x \to 0$, that is, n is not bounded. Consequently, the sequence does not converge uniformly. The limiting curve C (see Figure 9) is not the graph of the discontinuous function $f(x)$.

(b) $T = \{x | x^2 \geq \delta, \delta > 0\}$. Here the point $x = 0$ is excluded. Since $1/(1 + x^2)^{n-1} \leq 1/(1 + \delta)^{n-1}$ on T, it follows that the inequality $|f_n(x) - f(x)|$ $< \varepsilon$ holds on T if $1/(1 + \delta)^{n-1} < \varepsilon$. Simple calculation yields

$$n_0 = 1 + \left[\frac{\log(1/\varepsilon)}{\log(1 + \delta)} \right].$$

This proves that the sequence converges uniformly on T. Note that $f(x)$ is continuous $[f(x) = 1 + x^2, x^2 \geq \delta]$ and the limiting curve C is the graph of it on T.

It follows by definition that the infinite series

$$f(x) = \sum_{n=1}^{\infty} \frac{x^2}{(1 + x^2)^{n-1}}$$

converges uniformly if $x^2 \geq \delta > 0$, that is, zero is not on T and does not converge uniformly if T contains $x = 0$.

Note that instead of the sequence we could have used the infinite series for our discussion. The condition for uniform convergence of $\sum_{n=1}^{\infty} x^2/(1 + x^2)^{n-1}$ is

$$|R_n(x)| = \frac{1}{(1 + x^2)^{n-1}} < \varepsilon.$$

(See **5.2-1**.) Thus the proof for the series follows exactly the same lines as above.

Example 6. $\{f_n(x)\}$, $f_n(x) = xn^\alpha e^{-nx}$, $T = \{x | 0 \leq x \leq 1\}$. Since $f(x)$ $= \lim_{n \to \infty} f_n(x) = 0$ for every x on T, the condition for uniform convergence is

$$|f_n(x) - f(x)| = xn^\alpha e^{-nx} < \varepsilon \quad \text{for all } x \text{ on } T.$$

It is easily seen that $f_n(x)$ possesses a maximum

$$f_n(1/n) = n^{\alpha-1} e^{-1},$$

which is larger than $\frac{1}{2}e^{-1}$ if $\alpha \geq 1$. Consequently, the condition for uniform convergence cannot be satisfied for $\alpha \geq 1$, and the sequence does not converge uniformly on T. Though $f(x)$ is continuous, the limiting curve C is not the graph of it.

However, if $\alpha < 1$, the maximum $e^{-1} n^{\alpha-1}$ approaches zero as n increases. Since $xn^\alpha e^{-nx} \leq e^{-1} n^{\alpha-1}$ on T, it follows that $n_0 = (e\varepsilon)^{1/(\alpha-1)}$.

Consequently, the sequence converges uniformly if $\alpha < 1$.

Example 7. We consider one more very simple example of an alternating geometric series

$$f(x) = \sum_{n=1}^{\infty} \frac{x^2(-1)^{n-1}}{(1+x^2)^{n-1}} , \quad T = \{x|-a \le x \le a, \, a > 0\}$$

which is similar to Example 5 and exhibits quite different behavior. Here the condition for uniform convergence is

$$|R_n(x)| = \sum_{i=n+1}^{\infty} \frac{x^2(-1)^{i-1}}{(1+x^2)^{i-1}} < \frac{x^2}{(1+x^2)^n} < \varepsilon .$$

Assume $\varepsilon < 1$. It is apparent that

$$\frac{x^2}{(1+x^2)^n} \le \varepsilon^2 < \varepsilon \quad \text{for} \quad |x| \le \varepsilon .$$

If $|x| > \varepsilon$, then

$$\frac{x^2}{(1+x^2)^n} < \frac{a^2}{(1+\varepsilon^2)^n} < \varepsilon$$

for

$$n > n_0 = \left[\frac{\log (a^2/\varepsilon)}{\log (1+\varepsilon^2)} \right].$$

Thus it follows that $|R_n(x)| < \varepsilon$ for $n > n_0$ and all x on T. Consequently, the series converges uniformly on T.

Note that

$$\lim_{n\to\infty} S_n(x) = \lim_{n\to\infty} \sum_{i=1}^{\infty} \frac{(-1)^{i-1}x^2}{(1+x^2)^{i-1}} = \frac{x^2(1+x^2)}{(2+x^2)} = f(x)$$

is continuous on T, and the limiting curve C is the graph of $f(x)$.

5.3 Geometric meaning of uniform convergence

That a sequence $\{f_n(x)\}$ converges to a limiting function $f(x)$ on T means that it converges to $f(x)$ pointwise. That is, the limit relationship $f(x) = \lim_{n\to\infty} f_n(x)$ holds at each point x on the interval T. This does not mean, however, that if we assign an arbitrary degree of accuracy, say, $\varepsilon = 0.01$ or $\varepsilon = 10^{-6}$, then from a certain index n_0 onward all the functions $f_n(x)$ will be between $f(x) + \varepsilon$ and $f(x) - \varepsilon$ for all values of x on T. In other words, it does not mean that the graphs $y = f_n(x)$ will lie entirely in the strip indicated in Figure 11 if $n > n_0$.

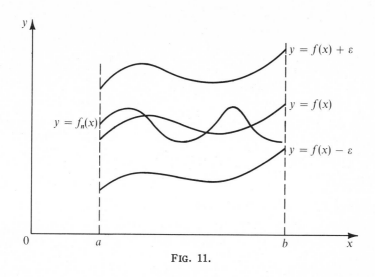

FIG. 11.

If the sequence $\{f_n(x)\}$ converges uniformly, the inequality

$$|f_n(x) - f(x)| < \varepsilon$$

holds for $n > n_0$ and all x on T; consequently, the graphs of $y = f_n(x)$ with indices $n > n_0$ will be contained in the strip (Figure 11).

For illustration of the behavior of nonuniform convergence we refer to Example 6. For $\alpha \geq 1$ the sequence $\{f_n(x)\}$ does not converge uniformly to the limiting function $f(x) = 0$. It is easily seen that the strip determined by $y = \varepsilon$ and $y = -\varepsilon$ on T cannot contain $y = f_n(x)$ if $\varepsilon < e^{-1}$ and $\alpha \geq 1$, since $f_n(1/n) \geq e^{-1}$. If $\alpha > 1$, then $f(1/n) = e^{-1}n^{\alpha-1}$ is not bounded.

5.4 Continuity of the limit function

We have seen that the limiting function $f(x)$ of a sequence $\{f(x)\}$ of continuous functions may be discontinuous (see Examples 4 and 5). We know that the sum of a finite number of continuous functions is continuous. However, the sum of an infinite series of continuous functions may be discontinuous, even if it converges absolutely (Examples 4 and 5). But if a sequence or an infinite series converges uniformly to the function $f(x)$, then $f(x)$ is continuous. We prove the following important theorem.

5.4-1 Theorem. If the sequence $\{f_n(x)\}$ of continuous functions converges uniformly to $f(x)$ on the open interval $T = \{x | a < x < b\}$, then

$f(x)$ is continuous on T.

Proof. We have to show that if $x = x_0$ is on T, then $\lim\limits_{x \to x_0} f(x) = f(x_0)$. It follows that

$$|f(x) - f(x_0)| = |f(x) - f_n(x) + f_n(x) - f_n(x_0) + f_n(x_0) - f(x_0)|$$
$$\leq |f(x) - f_n(x)| + |f_n(x) - f_n(x_0)| + |f_n(x_0) - f(x_0)| .$$

Since $f_n(x)$ converges uniformly to $f(x)$, we can choose n_0 such that for $n > n_0$ the inequality

$$|f(x) - f_n(x)| < \varepsilon/3$$

holds for all x on T. Consequently, $|f_n(x_0) - f(x_0)| < \varepsilon/3$.

Since $f_n(x)$ is continuous at $x = x_0$, it follows that there exists a $\delta > 0$ such that

$$|f_n(x) - f_n(x_0)| < \varepsilon/3$$

for $|x - x_0| < \delta$ and any fixed $n > n_0$.

Hence

$$|f(x) - f(x_0)| < \varepsilon/3 + \varepsilon/3 + \varepsilon/3 = \varepsilon , \quad |x - x_0| < \delta ,$$

and this means precisely that $\lim\limits_{x \to x_0} f(x) = f(x_0)$.

If T is closed and $x_0 = a$ or b, then the limit is right-sided or left-sided, respectively.

Note that the continuity relation $\lim\limits_{x \to x_0} f(x) = f(x_0)$ can be written in the form

$$\lim\limits_{x \to x_0} \lim\limits_{n \to \infty} f_n(x) = \lim\limits_{n \to \infty} \lim\limits_{x \to x_0} f_n(x) ,$$

that is, the order of limits can be interchanged if the functions $f_n(x)$ are continuous at x_0 and if the sequence $\{f_n(x)\}$ converges uniformly to $f(x)$.

On the other hand, we have seen that a sequence of continuous functions may converge nonuniformly to a continuous limiting function. [See Exercises 4(b) and 6 (for $\alpha \geq 1$).] However, if a sequence $\{f_n(x)\}$ of continuous functions converges monotonically to a continuous function $f(x)$ on a closed interval T, then it has been proved that convergence must be uniform (theorem of Dini).

5.5 Integrals and derivatives of sequences

5.5-1 Theorem. If the integrable functions $f_n(x)$ converge uniformly to $f(x)$ on $T = \{x | a \le x \le b\}$, then $\{\int_a^x f_n(t)\,dt\}$ converges uniformly to $\int_a^x f(t)\,dt$.

Proof. Since $\{f_n(x)\}$ converges uniformly to $f(x)$, we can choose n_0 so that for $n > n_0$ the inequality $|f_n(x) - f(x)| < \varepsilon/(b-a)$ holds on T. Then

$$\left| \int_a^x f_n(t)\,dt - \int_a^x f(t)\,dt \right| \le \int_a^x |f_n(t) - f(t)|\,dt < \frac{\varepsilon}{b-a}(x-a) < \varepsilon$$

for all x on T, if $n > n_0$. This completes the proof.

If, in addition, the functions $f_n(x)$ are continuous on T, so is $\int_a^x f(t)\,dt$. Note that the relation

$$\lim_{n \to \infty} \int_a^x f_n(t)\,dt = \int_a^x f(t)\,dt$$

can be written

$$\lim_{n \to \infty} \int_a^x f_n(t)\,dt = \int_a^x \lim_{n \to \infty} f_n(t)\,dt \ ,$$

that is, if the conditions of the theorem are met, the order of a limit process and integration can be interchanged.

In case of an infinite series the theorem states

$$\int_a^x dt \sum_{n=1}^{\infty} f_n(t) = \sum_{n=1}^{\infty} \int_a^x f_n(t)\,dt \ .$$

For illustration we refer to Example 7.

5.5-2 Theorem. If the sequence $\{f_n(x)\}$ converges to $f(x)$ and the sequence $\{f_n'(x)\}$ of continuous derivatives converges uniformly on T, then $\lim_{n \to \infty} f_n'(x) = f'(x)$.

Proof. Since $\{f_n'(x)\}$ converges uniformly on T, $\lim_{n \to \infty} f_n'(x) = \alpha(x)$ represents a continuous function (**5.4-1**). It follows, by **5.5-1**, that

$$\int_a^x \alpha(t)\,dt = \lim_{n \to \infty} \int_a^x f_n'(t)\,dt = \lim_{n \to \infty} [f_n(x) - f_n(a)] \ .$$

Since, by hypothesis, $\lim_{n \to \infty} [f_n(x) - f_n(a)] = f(x) - f(a)$, it follows that

$$f(x) = f(a) + \int_a^x \alpha(t)\,dt \ .$$

Since $\alpha(x)$ is continuous, the right-hand side of the last equality has the derivative $\alpha(x)$; consequently, $f(x)$ is differentiable and $f'(x) = \alpha(x)$, that is,

$$\lim_{n \to \infty} f'_n(x) = f'(x) .$$

In case of an infinite series $f(x) = \sum_{n=1}^{\infty} f_n(x)$, the theorem states that

$$f'(x) = \sum_{n=1}^{\infty} f'_n(x) \quad \text{or} \quad \left[\sum_{n=1}^{\infty} f_n(x) \right]' = \sum_{n=1}^{\infty} f'_n(x) .$$

Example 8. $\{f_n(x)\}$, $f_n(x) = x + x^n/n$, $f'_n(x) = 1 + x^{n-1}$.

(a) $T = \{x \mid 0 \le x \le \delta < 1\}$. $f(x) = \lim_{n \to \infty} f_n(x) = x$, $\lim_{n \to \infty} f'_n(x) = 1$ on T. Since $|f_n(x) - f(x)| = x^n/n < 1/n < \varepsilon$ for $n > n_0 = [1/\varepsilon]$ and all x on T and $|f'_n(x) - 1| = x^{n-1} < \delta^{n-1} < \varepsilon$ for $n - 1 > n'_0 = [\log \varepsilon / \log \delta]$ on T, it follows that $\{f_n(x)\}$ and $\{f'_n(x)\}$ converge uniformly on T. Thus the conditions of **5.5-2** are met, and $\lim_{n \to \infty} f'_n(x) = f'(x)$.

(b) $T = \{x \mid 0 \le x \le 1\}$. Here $f(x) = x$, but $\lim_{n \to \infty} f'_n(x) = 1$ if $0 \le x < 1$, and 2 if $x = 1$, and $f'(x) \ne \lim_{n \to \infty} f'_n(x)$ on T (for $x = 1$). It is easily checked that $\{f'_n(x)\}$ does not converge uniformly on T.

Note that uniform convergence is only a sufficient condition. Both sequences $\{f_n(x)\}$ and $\{f'_n(x)\}$ might not converge uniformly on T and yet $\lim_{n \to \infty} f'_n(x) = f'(x)$ might hold. An example of this sort is Example 6 for $\alpha \ge 1$.

5.5-3 Theorem (Weierstrass' M-test). Let $\{M_n\}$ be a sequence of non-negative numbers such that $0 \le |f_n(x)| \le M_n$, $n = 1, 2, 3, \ldots$ and for every x on T. If $\sum_{n=1}^{\infty} M_n$ converges, then $\sum_{n=1}^{\infty} f_n(x)$ converges uniformly on T.

Proof. Since $\sum_{n=1}^{\infty} M_i$ converges, it follows that $\sum_{i=n+1}^{\infty} M_i < \varepsilon$ for $n > n_0$. Consequently,

$$|R_n(x)| = \left| \sum_{i=n+1}^{\infty} f_i(x) \right| \le \sum_{i=n+1}^{\infty} M_i < \varepsilon$$

if $n > n_0$ for all x on T. This completes the proof.

Example 9. $\sum_{n=1}^{\infty} (\cos nx)/n^2$ converges uniformly for all x, since $|(\cos nx)/n^2| \le 1/n^2$ and $\sum_{n=1}^{\infty} 1/n^2$ converges.

5.6 Theorems on power series

Let $\{a_\mu\}$ be a sequence of real numbers. A series $\sum_{\mu=0}^{\infty} a_\mu x^\mu$ [or a somewhat more general series $\sum_{\mu=0}^{\infty} a_\mu(x - x_0)^\mu$] is called a power series. Series of this kind play an important role in analysis.

5.6-1 Theorem. If a power series $\sum_{\mu=0}^{\infty} a_\mu x^\mu$ converges for $x = x_1$, then it converges absolutely for every $|x_0| < |x_1|$.

Proof. If the series $\sum_{n=0}^{\infty} a_n x_1^n$ converges, then $\lim_{n \to \infty} a_n x_1^n = 0$; consequently, $a_n x_1^n$ is bounded for all n, that is, $|a_n x_1^n| < K$.

Since $|a_n x_0^n| = |a_n x_1^n| |x_0/x_1|^n < K\delta^n$, $\delta = |x_0/x_1| < 1$, it follows that

$$\left| \sum_{n=0}^{\infty} a_n x_0^n \right| \leq \sum_{n=0}^{\infty} |a_n x_0^n| < K \sum_{n=1}^{\infty} \delta_n = \frac{K}{1-\delta} ,$$

which implies that $\sum_{n=0}^{\infty} a_n x_0^n$ is absolutely convergent.

5.6-2 Theorem. If a power series $\sum_{n=0}^{\infty} a_n x^n$ converges on $T = \{x| \, |x| < b\}$, then it converges uniformly on $T' = \{x| \, |x| \leq r < b\}$.

Proof. Since $\sum_{i=0}^{\infty} |a_i| r^i$ converges, by **5.6-1**, we have

$$|R_n(x)| = \left| \sum_{i=n+1}^{\infty} a_i x^i \right| \leq \sum_{i=n+1}^{\infty} |a_i| \, |x|^i \leq \sum_{i=n+1}^{\infty} |a_i| r^i < \varepsilon$$

for $n > n_0$ and all x on T'. This completes the proof.

5.7 Abel's partial summation

Though of great practical importance, **5.6-1** and **5.6-2**, tests for uniform convergence, can be applied only if the series converge absolutely. This narrows the scope of applications. For example, we have seen that the series $\sum_{n=1}^{\infty} (\sin nx)/n^p$, $0 < p \leq 1$ converges for every real x (Chapter 4, Example 15), but it does not converge absolutely. Does it converge uniformly on some interval T?

The answer to this question is a more powerful test for uniform convergence which is easily obtained from Abel's partial summation formula (Section 4.5). If we consider $a_n(x)$ and $b_n(x)$ as functions defined on some interval T and note that "uniformly bounded" means that the terms of a sequence $\{S_n(x)\}$ satisfy the inequality $|S_n(x)| = |\sum_{i=1}^{n} a_i(x)| < K$ for all x on T and all n, where K denotes a positive number, the proofs of the theorems follow the very same lines as in (Chapter 4). First we obtain from Abel's identity a general theorem which follows.

5.7-1 Theorem. The infinite series $\sum_{n=1}^{\infty} a_n(x)b_n(x)$ converges uniformly on T if on T:
(a) the series $\sum_{\mu=1}^{\infty} A_\mu(x)[b_\mu(x) - b_{\mu+1}(x)]$ converges uniformly,
(b) the sequence $\{A_n(x)b_{n+1}(x)\}$ converges uniformly.

Proof. If $\sigma(x) = \sum_{\mu=1}^{\infty} A_\mu(x)[b_\mu(x) - b_{\mu+1}(x)]$ and $\lambda(x) = \lim_{n \to \infty} A_n(x)b_{n+1}(x)$,

91

it follows from Abel's identity

$$S_n(x) = \sum_{i=1}^{n} a_i(x)b_i(x) = \sum_{i=1}^{n} A_i(x)[b_i(x) - b_{i+1}(x)] + A_n(x)b_{n+1}(x)$$

that

$$|S_n(x) - \sigma(x) - \lambda(x)| \le \left| \sum_{i=1}^{n} A_i(x)[b_i(x) - b_{i+1}(x)] - \sigma(x) \right| + |A_n(x)b_{n+1}(x) - \lambda(x)|.$$

Since the series and the sequence converge uniformly on T, we can choose n_0 such that for $n > n_0$ and all x on T the inequality

$$|S_n(x) - \sigma(x) - \lambda(x)| < \varepsilon/2 + \varepsilon/2 = \varepsilon$$

holds. This means that $S_n(x)$ converges uniformly on T. Consequently, by definition the series $\sum_{n=1}^{\infty} a_n(x)b_n(x)$ converges uniformly on T.

Exactly as in Chapter 4, more special tests can be deduced from **5.7-1**. The proofs of the tests follow quite similar lines and are left to the reader as exercises.

5.7-2 Theorem (Abel's test). The series $\sum_{\mu=1}^{\infty} a_\mu(x)b_\mu(x)$ converges uniformly on T if on T:

(a) $\sum_{\mu=1}^{\infty} a_\mu(x)$ converges uniformly,

(b) $\{b_n(x)\}$ is a monotonic sequence for every fixed x,

(c) $\{b_n(x)\}$ is uniformly bounded, that is, $|b_n(x)| < K$ for every n and x.

5.7-3 Theorem (Dirichlet's test). $\sum_{\mu=1}^{\infty} a_\mu(x)b_\mu(x)$ converges uniformly on T if on T:

(a) $\{S_n(x)\}$, $S_n(x) = \sum_{i=1}^{n} a_i(x)$ is uniformly bounded,

(b) $\{b_n(x)\}$ is monotonic for every fixed x and converges uniformly to 0.

5.7-4 Theorem (du Bois-Reymond's and Dedekind's tests). (A) $\sum_{\mu=1}^{\infty} a_\mu(x)b_\mu(x)$ converges uniformly on T if on T:

(a) $\sum_{\mu=1}^{\infty} a_\mu(x)$ and $\sum_{\mu=1}^{\infty} |b_\mu(x) - b_{\mu+1}(x)|$ converge uniformly,

(b) $\{b_n(x)\}$ is uniformly bounded.

(B) $\sum_{\mu=1}^{\infty} a_\mu(x)b_\mu(x)$ converges uniformly on T if on T:

(a) $\sum_{\mu=1}^{\infty} |b_\mu(x) - b_{\mu+1}(x)|$ converges uniformly,

(b) $\{S_n(x)\}$, $S_n(x) = \sum_{i=1}^{n} a_i(x)$ is uniformly bounded,

(c) $\{b_n(x)\}$ converges uniformly to 0.

Example 10. $\sum_{n=1}^{\infty} (\sin nx)/n^p$, $0 < p \le 1$. From the relation

$$S_n(x) = \sum_{i=1}^{n} \sin ix = \left[\cos \frac{x}{2} - \cos (2n+1)\frac{x}{2} \right] \Big/ 2 \sin \frac{x}{2}$$

(see Chapter 4, Example 15) it follows that

$$|S_n(x)| \le \frac{1+1}{2|\sin(x/2)|} \le \frac{1}{\sin(x/2)} \quad \text{on} \quad T = \left\{ x \mid \delta \le x \le 2\pi - \delta, \ 0 < \delta < \frac{\pi}{2} \right\},$$

that is, $|S_n(x)|$ is uniformly bounded on T. Since $b_n = 1/n^p$ is monotonic and converges to 0, the conditions of **5.7-3** are met. Consequently, the series converges uniformly for all x satisfying the condition $|x - 2k\pi| \ge \delta$, $0 < \delta < \pi/2$, $k = 0, 1, 2, 3, \ldots$.

5.7-5 Theorem (Abel). If the power series $f(x) = \sum_{n=1}^{\infty} c_n x^n$ converges for $x = R$, then it converges uniformly on the interval $0 \le x \le R$ and represents a continuous function.

Proof. We write

$$f(x) = \sum_{n=0}^{\infty} c_n x^n = \sum_{n=0}^{\infty} (c_n R^n) \left(\frac{x}{R} \right)^n = \sum_{n=0}^{\infty} a_n(x) b_n(x)$$

where $a_n(x) = c_n R^n$ and $b_n(x) = (x/R)^n$. Since $\{b_n(x)\}$ is a monotonic and uniformly bounded sequence ($b_n(x) \le 1$) for all x on $T = [0, R]$ and $\sum_{n=0}^{\infty} a_n(x)$ converges uniformly (a convergent series of constant terms always satisfies the conditions of uniform convergence), it follows that the conditions of **5.7-2** are met. Consequently, the series converges and represents a continuous function $f(x)$ on T. As a consequence of continuity we have

$$\lim_{x \to R^-} f(x) = f(R) = \sum_{n=0}^{\infty} c_n R^n .$$

Exercises 5.A

Find the limiting functions and the limiting curves of the sequences $\{f_n(x)\}$ and graph $f_n(x)$ for $n = 1, 2, 3$. Is the limiting curve C the graph of $\lim_{n \to \infty} f_n(x) = f(x)$?

1. $f_n(x) = \dfrac{1}{1 + x^{2n}}, \quad -\infty < x < \infty$

2. $f_n(x) = \dfrac{nx}{1 + n^2 x^2}, \quad -1 \le x \le 1$

3. $f_n(x) = \dfrac{n^2 x^2}{1 + n^2 x^2}, \quad -1 \le x \le 1$

4. $f_n(x) = \dfrac{x^{2n}}{1 + x^{2n}}, \quad -2 \le x \le 2$

5. $f_n(x) = \dfrac{2x + n}{x + n}, \quad 0 \le x \le b$

6. $f_n(x) = \dfrac{nx}{nx + 1}, \quad 0 \le x < \infty$

7. $f_n(x) = \left(1 + \dfrac{x}{n} \right)^n, \quad 0 \le x \le b$.

In the following discuss the nature of convergence of the sequence $\{f_n(x)\}$ to the limiting function on the given interval. Determine whether

$$\lim_{n\to\infty} \int_a^b f_n(x)\,dx = \int_a^b f(x)\,dx \quad \text{and} \quad \lim_{n\to\infty} f_n'(x) = f'(x)\,.$$

8. $f_n(x) = nxe^{-nx}$, $[0, 1]$

9. $f_n(x) = \dfrac{nx^2 + 1}{nx + 1}$, $[0, 1]$

10. $f_n(x) = \dfrac{nx}{1 + n^2 x^4}$, $[0, a]$

11. $f_n(x) = nx(1 - x^2)^n$, $[0, 1]$

12. $f_n(x) = (\sin x)^n$, $[0, \pi]$

13. $f_n(x) = xe^{-nx^2}$, $[0, 1]$

14. $f_n(x) = \displaystyle\int_0^x f_{n-1}(t)\,dt$, $[0, a]$, f_0 is continuous.

Discuss the nature of convergence of the following series on the indicated intervals and determine whether differentiation and integration term by term are permissible.

15. $f(x) = \displaystyle\sum_{n=1}^\infty (-1)^{n-1} x^n$, $\left[-\dfrac{1}{2}, \dfrac{1}{2}\right]$

16. $f(x) = \dfrac{1}{2}(1 - x^2)^{1/2} + \dfrac{1}{2^2}(1 - x^4)^{1/2} + \dfrac{1}{2^3}(1 - x^8)^{1/2} + \cdots$
$$+ \dfrac{1}{2^n}(1 + x^{2^n})^{1/2} + \cdots\,, \quad [-1, 1]$$

17. $f(x) = \displaystyle\sum_{n=1}^\infty \dfrac{\sin n^4 x}{n^2}$, $(-\infty, \infty)$

18. $f(x) = \displaystyle\sum_{n=1}^\infty e^{nx}$, $[-2, -1]$

19. $f(x) = \displaystyle\sum_{n=1}^\infty x^{n-1}$, $(-1, 1)$

20. $f(x) = \displaystyle\sum_{n=1}^\infty \dfrac{\cos(2n-1)x}{(2n-1)2n}$, $(-\infty, \infty)$

21. $f(x) = \displaystyle\sum_{n=1}^\infty \dfrac{\cos nx}{n^\alpha}$, $0 < \alpha \le 1$, $(-\infty, \infty)$

22. $f(x) = \displaystyle\sum_{n=1}^\infty \dfrac{\sin n^{1/2} x}{n^{3/2}}$, $(-\infty, \infty)$

23. $f(x) = \displaystyle\sum_{n=1}^\infty \dfrac{1}{n^4}$, $x > 1$

24. $f(x) = \displaystyle\sum_{n=1}^\infty \dfrac{\sin n^2 x}{n^5}$, $(-\infty, \infty)$.

CHAPTER 6

POWER SERIES

In Chapter 5 we considered functions $f(x)$ defined by infinite series

$$f(x) = \sum_{n=0}^{\infty} f_n(x) \, .$$

The purpose of this chapter is to discuss in more detail a special case of these functions defined by so called power series. The general term of a power series is obtained by putting $f_n(x) = a_n(x - x_0)^n$ where x_0 and $\{a_n\}$ are fixed constants. We say that

$$f(x) = \sum_{n=0}^{\infty} a_n(x - x_0)^n$$

is a power series in $x - x_0$. By a simple transformation $x - x_0 = t$, that is, a translation of the origin along the x-axis, the series can be reduced to $\sum_{n=0}^{\infty} a_n t^n$. Therefore, without any loss of generality we may study power series of the more special form

$$f(x) = \sum_{n=0}^{\infty} a_n x^n \, .$$

Power series play a very important role in mathematical analysis, and expansion of functions in power series is of great importance both in theory and practice. First let us consider some examples.

6.1 Examples. $\sum_{n=1}^{\infty} M_n$.

(1) $M_n = n^n x^n$. It is easily seen that the power series $\sum_{n=1}^{\infty} n^n x^n$ converges only for $x = 0$. Since $S_n(0) = 0$ for all n, it follows that $\lim_{n \to \infty} S_n(0) = 0$. Consequently, by definition the series converges. If $|x| > 0$ we can find an integer n_0 such that $|x| > 1/n_0$. Then $|nx| > 1$ for $n > n_0$

$|n^n x^n|$ will increase beyond all bounds as n increases, and $\lim_{n\to\infty} M_n \neq 0$. Consequently the series diverges if $x \neq 0$.

The same result follows at once if the familiar root test $\lim_{n\to\infty} (|M_n|)^{1/n} = \lim_{n\to\infty} |nx| = 0$, if $x = 0$, and ∞, if $x \neq 0$, is applied.

(2) $M_n = x^n/n!$. In this case the ratio test yields

$$\lim_{n\to\infty} \left| \frac{M_{n+1}}{M_n} \right| = \lim_{n\to\infty} \frac{|x|}{n+1} = 0 \ .$$

whatever number x is chosen. Since the limit is less than 1 for every x, it follows that the series $\sum_{n=1}^{\infty} x^n/n!$ converges for all x, that is, the interval of convergence is $-\infty < x < \infty$ or $(-\infty, \infty)$.

(3) $M_n = x^n/n$. Here again the ratio test yields

$$\lim_{n\to\infty} \left| \frac{M_{n+1}}{M_n} \right| = \lim_{n\to\infty} \left| \frac{n}{n+1} x \right| = |x| \ .$$

Consequently, the series $\sum_{n=1}^{\infty} x^n/n$ converges for $|x| < 1$ and diverges for $|x| > 1$. For $|x| = 1$ the test is inconclusive. For $x = \pm 1$ we obtain the familiar series $\sum_{n=1}^{\infty} 1/n$ and $\sum_{n=1}^{\infty} (-1)^n/n$, respectively. Since the first series diverges and the second converges, it follows that the series $\sum_{n=1}^{\infty} x^n/n$ converges on the interval $[-1, 1)$.

(4) If we differentiate the series $\sum_{n=1}^{\infty} x^n/n$ term by term we obtain the familiar geometric series $\sum_{n=1}^{\infty} x^{n-1}$ which converges for $|x| < 1$, that is, on the open interval $(-1, 1)$.

(5) If we integrate the series $\sum_{n=1}^{\infty} x^n/n$ termwise we obtain the series $\sum_{n=1}^{\infty} x^{n+1}/[n(n+1)]$ $(C = 0)$ which converges on the closed interval $[-1, 1]$.

(6) The series $\sum_{n=1}^{\infty} [(-1)^n/n](x/2)^n$ converges on the interval $(-2, 2]$.

These examples suggest that if T denotes the set of points x for which a power series converges, then either (1) T consists of one point $x = 0$, or (2) T consists of all real numbers, or (3) T is an interval of one of the following forms: $(-a, a)$, $[-a, a]$, $(-a, a]$, $[-a, a)$, $a > 0$. The positive number a is called the radius of convergence of the series $\sum_{n=0}^{\infty} a_n x^n$. We have just seen that a series may converge at both endpoints $x = \pm a$, at just one or at neither. If the series converges on the entire x-axis, we say that the radius of convergence of the series $\sum_{n=0}^{\infty} a_n x^n$ is infinite and write $a = \infty$. If the series converges only at $x = 0$, we indicate it by writing $a = 0$.

Since by **5.6-1** a power series $\sum_{n=0}^{\infty} a_n x^n$ converges absolutely for $|x| < |x_1|$ if it converges at $x = x_1$, the radius of convergence is easily obtained if $\lim_{n\to\infty} (|a_n|)^{1/n}$ exists. It follows by the root test that the positive series $\sum_{n=0}^{\infty} |a_n| |x|^n$ converges or diverges according as $\lim_{n\to\infty} (|a_n|^{1/n} |x|$

< 1 or > 1. Thus the interval of convergence $|x| < 1/\lim_{n \to \infty} (|a_n|)^{1/n}$ and the radius of convergence $a = 1/\lim_{n \to \infty} (|a_n|)^{1/n}$ of the series $\sum_{n=0}^{\infty} a_n x^n$ are determined.

If the ratio test for convergence is applied, it follows that the radius of convergence is

$$a = \lim_{n \to \infty} \left| \frac{a_n}{a_{n+1}} \right| ,$$

if the limit exists. Note that if the latter limit exists, so does $\lim_{n \to \infty} (|a_n|)^{1/n}$. However, the converse is not true, that is, if the root limit exists, the ratio limit might not exist.

Exercises 6.A

Determine the radius of convergence of the series $\sum_{n=1}^{\infty} a_n x^n$ and indicate whether the series converges at the endpoints of the interval.

1. $a_n = n$
2. $a_n = 1/(n + 1)$
3. $a_n = 1/\log (n + 1)$
4. $a_n = 1/n^{1/2}$
5. $a_n = 2^n$
6. $a_n = n^2/n!$
7. $a_n = (n^{1/n} - 1)^n$
8. $a_n = \dfrac{(n!)^2}{2n!}$
9. $a_n = 1/n^{1+1/n}$
10. $a_n = (n + 1)^n/n!$
11. $a_n = n/4^n$
12. $a_n = 2^{n^{1/2}}$
13. $a_n = (- 1)^{n-1}$
14. $a_n = (- 1)^{n-1}/n$
15. $a_n = (- 1)^{n-1}(1 + \frac{1}{2} + \cdots + 1/n)$
16. $a_n = 1/n^{1/2} + (- 1)^{n-1}/n$
17. $a_n = 1/\log \log 2n$
18. $a_n = (- 1)^{n-1}\dfrac{1 \cdot 3 \cdot 5 \cdots (2n - 1)}{2 \cdot 4 \cdot 6 \cdots 2n}$
19. $a_n = 1/(n^2 + 1)$
20. $a_n = (n!)^2/[(2n)!n^2]$.

6.2 Integration and differentiation of power series

Let us assume that the radius of convergence of the power series $\sum_{n=0}^{\infty} a_n x^n$ is the positive number a, and that $\lim_{n \to \infty} (|a_n|)^{1/n} = 1/a$ exists. If the series is integrated on the interval $0 \le x < a$, the series $\sum_{n=0}^{\infty} a_n x^{n+1}/(n + 1)$ follows. Similarly, differentiation yields the series $\sum_{n=1}^{\infty} n a_n x^{n-1}$. It is easily seen that both series are again power series which possess the same radius of convergence as the original series.

6.2-1 Theorem. Termwise integration and differentiation of a power series does not change the radius of convergence, that is, the series $\sum_{n=0}^{\infty} a_n[x^{n+1}/(n + 1)]$ and $\sum_{n=1}^{\infty} n a_n x^{n-1}$ have the same radius of convergence as the original series.

Proof. If we note that $\lim\limits_{n\to\infty} n^{1/n} = 1$, it follows at once that:

(a) $\lim\limits_{n\to\infty} (|a_n|/n)^{1/n} = \lim\limits_{n\to\infty} (|a_n|)^{1/n}/\lim\limits_{n\to\infty} n^{1/n} = \lim\limits_{n\to\infty} (a_n|)^{1/n} = 1/a$,

(b) $\lim\limits_{n\to\infty} (n|a_n|)^{1/n} = \lim\limits_{n\to\infty} n^{1/n} \lim\limits_{n\to\infty} (|a_n|)^{1/n} = \lim\limits_{n\to\infty} (|a_n|)^{1/n} = 1/a$,

where a is the radius of convergence of the series $\sum_{n=0}^{\infty} a_n x^n$. This completes the proof.

If a function $f(x)$ is defined by a power series

$$f(x) = \sum_{n=0}^{\infty} a_n x^n , \quad |x| < a ,$$

then the conditions of **5.5-1** are met and the relations

$$\int_0^x f(x)\,dx = \sum_{n=0}^{\infty} a_n \frac{x^{n+1}}{n+1} ,$$

$$f'(x) = \sum_{n=1}^{\infty} n a_n x^{n-1} ,$$

hold since both series converge uniformly on every fixed interval contained in the interval $|x| < a$ where a is the radius of convergence of $\sum_{n=0}^{\infty} a_n x^n$ (**5.6-2**).

Example 7. $f(x) = 1/(1 + x) = \sum_{n=0}^{\infty} (-1)^n x^n = 1 - x + x^2 + \cdots + (-1)^n x^n + \cdots$. Here the power series is the familiar geometric series. The radius of convergence is 1, and the series diverges at both endpoints $x = \pm 1$.

Note that $f(x)$ and its series differ in many ways. For example, $f(1) = \frac{1}{2}$, but for $x = 1$ the series $\sum_{n=0}^{\infty} (-1)^n = 1 - 1 + 1 - 1 + \cdots$ is meaningless. The relation

$$\frac{1}{1+x} = 1 - x + x^2 - \cdots + (-1)^n x^n + \cdots$$

holds only if $|x| < 1$.

Furthermore, by **6.2-1**, **5.5-1**, and **5.5-2** the relations

$$\int_0^x \frac{dt}{1+t} = \ln(1+x) = x - \frac{x^2}{2} + \frac{x^3}{3} - \cdots + (-1)^n \frac{x^{n+1}}{n+1} + \cdots ,$$

$$\left(\frac{1}{1+x}\right)' = -\frac{1}{(1+x)^2} = -1 + 2x - \cdots + (-1)^n n x^{n-1} + \cdots$$

hold also on the open interval $|x| < 1$.

Note that if the series $\sum_{n=0}^{\infty} f_n(x)$ converges pointwise to $f(x)$ on $a \le x \le b$, the relations

$$\int_a^x f(t)\,dt = \sum_{n=1}^{\infty} \int_a^x f_n(t)\,dt , \quad f'(t) = \sum_{n=0}^{\infty} f_n'(t)$$

might not hold, that is, pointwise convergence of the series to $f(x)$ is not sufficient.

Note further that series

$$\ln(1+x) = x - \frac{x^2}{2} + \frac{x^3}{3} - \cdots + \frac{(-1)^n x^{n+1}}{n+1} + \cdots$$

converges at the endpoint $x = 1$, and by Abel's Theorem (**5.7-5**) the relation holds on the interval $-1 < x \leq 1$. Consequently, for $x = 1$ we obtain the familiar formula (Chapter 4, Example 8)

$$\ln 2 = 1 - \frac{1}{2} + \frac{1}{3} - \cdots + \frac{(-1)^n}{n+1} + \cdots .$$

It is not feasible to calculate $\ln 2$, say, correct to six decimals for one would have to add a million terms. A slight modification, however, yields another series which converges rapidly.

If in the above relation we replace x by $-x$ we obtain

$$\ln(1-x) = -x - \frac{x^2}{2} - \frac{x^3}{3} - \cdots - \frac{x^{n+1}}{n+1} - \cdots .$$

By combining the two series the relation

$$\ln(1+x) - \ln(1-x) = \ln\frac{1+x}{1-x} = 2\left(x + \frac{x^3}{3} + \frac{x^5}{5} + \cdots + \frac{x^{2n-1}}{2n-1} + \cdots\right)$$

is obtained. As x varies from -1 to 1, the ratio $(1+x)/(1-x)$ ranges over all positive numbers. Thus the relation can be used to calculate the value of the natural logarithm of any positive number.

Since $(1+x)/(1-x) = 2$ for $x = \frac{1}{3}$ it follows that

$$\ln 2 = 2\left(\frac{1}{3} + \frac{1}{3} \cdot \frac{1}{3^3} + \frac{1}{5} \cdot \frac{1}{3^5} + \cdots + \frac{1}{2n-1} \cdot \frac{1}{3^{2n-1}} + \cdots\right).$$

This series converges rapidly. If $\ln 2$ is approximated by n terms of the series, that is,

$$\ln 2 \approx 2\left(\frac{1}{3} + \frac{1}{3} \cdot \frac{1}{3^3} + \frac{1}{5} \cdot \frac{1}{3^5} + \cdots + \frac{1}{2n-1} \cdot \frac{1}{3^{2n-1}}\right) = 2S_n$$

then the error R_n of this approximation is

$$R_n = 2\left(\frac{1}{2n+1} \cdot \frac{1}{3^{2n+1}} + \frac{1}{2n+3} \cdot \frac{1}{3^{2n+3}} + \cdots\right)$$

$$< \frac{2}{2n+1} \cdot \frac{1}{3^{2n+1}}\left(1 + \frac{1}{3^2} + \frac{1}{3^4} + \cdots\right) = \frac{1}{4} \cdot \frac{1}{2n+1} \cdot \frac{1}{3^{2n-1}} .$$

If $n = 5$, it is easily calculated that $R_5 < 10^{-5}$. Consequently, addition of 5 terms yields an approximation correct to five decimals.

We note further that the remainder R_n of the series (error of the approximation) can be obtained in a closed form. Such closed forms are of theoretical and practical importance.

If the identity

$$\frac{1}{1-x} = 1 + x + x^2 + \cdots + x^{n-1} + \frac{x^n}{1-x}$$

is integrated from 0 to x, $|x| < 1$, the relation

$$-\ln(1-x) = x + \frac{x^2}{2} + \frac{x^3}{3} + \cdots + \frac{x^n}{n} + \int_0^x \frac{t^n}{1-t}\,dt$$

follows. Replacing x by $-x$ yields

$$-\ln(1+x) = -x + \frac{x^2}{2} - \frac{x^3}{3} + \cdots + \frac{(-1)^n x^n}{n} + (-1)^{n+1}\int_0^x \frac{t^n}{1+t}\,dt\,.$$

Combining of the last two relations yields

$$\frac{1}{2}\ln\frac{1+x}{1-x} = x + \frac{x^3}{3} + \cdots + \frac{x^{2n-1}}{2n-1} + \int_0^x \frac{t^{2n}}{1-t^2}\,dt\,.$$

Since $|R_n| = \left|\int_0^x \frac{t^{2n}}{1-t^2}\,dt\right| < \frac{1}{1-x^2}\left|\int_0^x t^{2n}\,dt\right| = \frac{1}{1-x^2}\frac{|x|^{2n+1}}{2n+1}$, it follows that $\lim\limits_{n\to\infty} |R_n| = 0$ for $|x| < 1$. Therefore

$$\ln\frac{1+x}{1-x} = 2\left(x + \frac{x^3}{3} + \frac{x^5}{5} + \cdots + \frac{x^{2n-1}}{2n-1} + \cdots \right).$$

Note that this relation has been obtained directly without using any of the previous theorems. Note further that the closed form of the remainder yields the same estimate of the error of the above approximation for $x = \frac{1}{3}$, that is, $R_n < \dfrac{2}{1-(\frac{1}{3})^2} \cdot \dfrac{(\frac{1}{3})^{2n+1}}{2n+1} < 10^{-5}$, if $n = 5$.

6.3 Some properties of functions represented by power series

We have seen that a function $f(x)$ represented by a power series

$$f(x) = \sum_{\mu=0}^{\infty} a_\mu x^\mu$$

with a radius of convergence $r > 0$ can be integrated and differentiated term by term within its interval of convergence $|x| \le a < r$ (**6.2**). If we apply this result again to the power series

$$f'(x) = \sum_{\mu=1}^{\infty} \mu a_\mu x^{\mu-1} ,$$

which has the same radius of convergence r, we have

$$f''(x) = \sum_{\mu=2}^{\infty} \mu(\mu - 1) a_\mu x^{\mu-2} ,$$

and continuing the process we obtain

$$f^{(n)}(x) = \sum_{\mu=n}^{\infty} a_\mu \mu(\mu - 1) \cdots (\mu - n + 1) x^{\mu-n} ,$$

that is, $f(x)$ possesses continuous derivatives of any order for $|x| \le a < r$.

If we put $x = 0$ in the last formula we at once obtain

$$a_\mu = \frac{1}{\mu!} f^{(\mu)}(0) ,$$

that is, $f(x)$ can be written in the form

$$f(x) = \sum_{\mu=0}^{\infty} \frac{f^{(\mu)}(0)}{\mu!} x^\mu \quad (0! = 1)$$

which is called the Taylor series of the function which it represents.

6.3-1 Theorem (Uniqueness theorem for power series). If $f(x)$ is represented by a power series

$$f(x) = \sum_{\mu=0}^{\infty} a_\mu x^\mu$$

then this representation is unique.

Proof. Assume that there exists another representation $f(x) = \sum_{\mu=0}^{\infty} b_\mu x^\mu$ where, in general, b_μ differs from a_μ. Since the coefficients b_μ are uniquely determined by the function itself, that is $b_\mu = f^{(\mu)}(0)/\mu!$, it follows that $b_\mu = a_\mu = f^{(\mu)}(0)/\mu!$ for $\mu = 0, 1, 2, \dots$.

Note that if $f(x) = \sum_{\mu=0}^{\infty} a_\mu (x - c)^\mu$, $|x - c| < r$, then

$$f(x) = \sum_{\mu=0}^{\infty} \frac{f^{(\mu)}(c)}{\mu!} (x - c)^\mu .$$

6.4 Taylor's formula

Integrating by parts the identity

$$f(x) = f(a) + \int_a^x f'(t)\,dt \ ,$$

taking $u = f'(t)$, $v = -(x-t)$, $du = f''(t)\,dt$, $dv = dt$, we have

$$f(x) = f(a) - f'(t)(x-t)\Big|_a^x + \int_a^x f''(t)(x-t)\,dt$$

$$= f(a) + f'(a)(x-a) + \int_a^x f''(t)(x-t)\,dt \ .$$

Integrating by parts again, taking $u = f''(t)$, $v = -(x-t)^2/2!$, $du = f'''(t)\,dt$, $dv = (x-t)\,dt$, we obtain

$$f(x) = f(a) + f'(a)(x-a) + f''(a)\frac{(x-a)^2}{2!} + \frac{1}{2!}\int_a^x f'''(t)(x-t)^2\,dt \ .$$

If this procedure is repeated it follows by mathematical induction that

$$f(x) = f(a) + f'(a)(x-a) + \cdots + \frac{f^{(n)}(a)}{n!}(x-a)^n + \frac{1}{n!}\int_a^x (x-t)^n f^{(n+1)}(t)\,dt \ .$$

This is called Taylor's formula with remainder

$$R_n = \frac{1}{n!}\int_a^x (x-t)^n f^{(n+1)}(t)\,dt \ ,$$

valid under the assumption that $f(x)$ and its first $n+1$ derivatives are continuous in a closed interval containing $x = a$.

If the remainder R_n approaches 0 as n increases, a polynomial of degree n in $(x-a)$ approaches $f(x)$ on an interval. This is the case, for example, if $|f^{(n+1)}(t)| \leq M$ on $a \leq t \leq x$, since

$$|R_n| \leq \frac{M}{n!}\int_a^x (x-t)^n\,dt = \frac{M(x-a)^{n+1}}{(n+1)!} \ ,$$

and, consequently, $\lim\limits_{n\to\infty} R_n = 0$.

The Lagrangian form, another form of the remainder, can be easily obtained if we note that

$$\frac{m}{n!}\int_a^x (x-t)^n\,dt \leq \frac{1}{n!}\int_a^x (x-t)^n f^{(n+1)}(t)\,dt \leq \frac{M}{n!}\int_a^x (x-t)^n\,dt$$

where m and M are the minimum and maximum of $f^{(n+1)}(t)$ on $a \leq t \leq x$, respectively. Upon carrying out the integration we find

$$\frac{m(x-a)^{n+1}}{(n+1)!} \leq R_n(x) \leq \frac{M(x-a)^{n+1}}{(n+1)!} \ .$$

Since the continuous function $f^{(n+1)}(t)$ assumes all values between its maximum M and minimum m there exists a number $t = \rho$ such that

$$R_n(x) = \frac{(x - a)^{n+1}}{(n + 1)!} f^{(n+1)}(\rho) \quad a \le \rho \le x \,.$$

The special case $a = 0$ gives Maclaurin's formula

$$f(x) = f(0) + \frac{f'(0)}{1!}x + \frac{f''(0)}{2!}x^2 + \cdots + \frac{f^{(n)}(0)}{n!}x^n + \frac{f^{(n+1)}(\rho)}{(n + 1)!}x^{n+1} \,.$$

If we put $x = a + h$, $\rho = a + \theta h$, $0 < \theta < 1$, Taylor's formula takes the form

$$f(a + h) = f(a) + \frac{f'(a)}{1!}h + \frac{f''(a)}{2!}h^2 + \cdots + \frac{f^{(n)}(a + \theta h)}{n!}h^{n+1} \,, \quad (a < \rho < x) \,.$$

If $f^{(n)}(t)$ exists for every n on $a \le t \le x$ and $\lim_{n\to\infty} R_n(t) = 0$, we obtain an expansion of $f(t)$ in a convergent infinite power series

$$f(t) = f(a) + \frac{f'(a)}{1!}(t - a) + \frac{f''(a)}{2!}(t - a)^2 + \cdots + \frac{f^{(n)}(a)}{n!}(t - a)^n + \cdots \,.$$

The last series is called the Taylor's series of the function $f(t)$ about the point $t = a$.

Note that $\lim_{n\to\infty} R_n(t) = 0$ is essential for the series to converge to the sum $f(t)$. The mere convergence of the series does not imply that it converges to $f(t)$.

6.4-1 Theorem. If $f(x)$ admits the Maclaurin series

$$f(x) = \sum_{n=0}^{\infty} a_n x^n$$

on the interval $0 \le x < a$, then the infinite series also converges to $f(x)$ on the wider interval $-a < x < a$.

Proof. If we write $f(x)$ in the form

$$f(x) = g(x) + h(x) \,,$$

where $g(x) = \frac{1}{2}[f(x) + f(-x)]$ is even and $h(x) = \frac{1}{2}[f(x) - f(-x)]$ is odd, then on $0 \le x < a$ we have

$$g(x) = a_0 + a_2 x^2 + a_4 x^4 + \cdots$$
$$h(x) = a_1 x + a_3 x^3 + a_5 x^5 + \cdots$$

for the series $\sum_{n=0}^{\infty} a_n x^n$ converges absolutely and apparently the functions

$g(x)$ and $h(x)$ defined by these series are the even and odd parts of $f(x)$.

Now the series $\sum_{\mu=0}^{\infty} a_{2\mu} x^{2\mu}$ and $\sum_{\mu=0}^{\infty} a_{2\mu+1} x^{2\mu+1}$ converge to $g(x)$ and $h(x)$, respectively, on the wider interval $-a < x < a$, consequently, their sum $g(x) + h(x) = f(x) = \sum_{n=0}^{\infty} a_n x^n$ also converges to $f(x)$ on the wider interval $-a < x < a$.

Corollary. If

$$f(x) = \sum_{\mu=0}^{\infty} a_\mu x^\mu + R_n(x)$$

and $\lim_{n \to \infty} R_n(x) = 0$ for $0 \le x < a$, then $\lim_{n \to \infty} R_n(x) = 0$ on the wider interval $-a < x < a$.

Proof. Since by **6.4-1** the limit of the partial sums $\sum_{\mu=0}^{n} a_\mu x^\mu$ converges to $f(x)$ on $-a < x < a$ as $a \to \infty$, it follows that

$$\lim_{n \to \infty} R_n(x) = \lim_{n \to \infty} \left[f(x) - \sum_{\mu=0}^{\infty} a_\mu x^\mu \right] = f(x) - f(x) = 0$$

on $-a < x < a$.

Example 8. If $f(x) = e^x$ we have

$$f^{(n)}(x) = e^x, \quad f^{(n)}(0) = 1, \quad R_n(x) = \frac{e^\rho}{(n+1)!} x^{n+1}, \quad 0 \le \rho \le x.$$

Hence, Maclaurin's formula yields

$$e^x = 1 + x + \frac{x^2}{2!} + \cdots + \frac{x^n}{n!} + \frac{e^\rho}{(n+1)!} x^{n+1}.$$

Since e^ρ is bounded $(1 \le e^\rho \le e^x)$ for all positive x, it follows that

$$\lim_{n \to \infty} R_n(x) = \lim_{n \to \infty} \frac{e^\rho x^{n+1}}{(n+1)!} = 0.$$

Hence,

$$e^x = 1 + x + \frac{x^2}{2!} + \frac{x^3}{3!} + \cdots + \frac{x^n}{n!} + \cdots, \quad 0 \le x < \infty.$$

Since $\lim_{n \to \infty} R_n(x) = 0$ for $x < 0$ (or by **6.4-1**), the series is valid on the interval $-\infty < x < \infty$.

The even and odd parts of e^x are called the hyperbolic cosine (cosh) and hyperbolic sine (sinh)

$$\cosh x = \frac{e^x + e^{-x}}{2} = 1 + \frac{x^2}{2!} + \frac{x^4}{4!} + \cdots + \frac{x^{2n}}{(2n)!} + \cdots,$$

$$\sinh x = \frac{e^x - e^{-x}}{2} = x + \frac{x^3}{3!} + \frac{x^5}{5!} + \cdots + \frac{x^{2n+1}}{(2n+1)!} + \cdots ,$$

respectively.

For $x = 1$ we have

$$e = 1 + \frac{1}{1!} + \frac{1}{2!} + \frac{1}{3!} + \cdots + \frac{1}{n!} + \frac{e^\rho}{(n+1)!} , \quad 0 < \rho < 1 .$$

Since $1 \le e^\rho < 3$, we have

$$R_n(1) < \frac{3}{(n+1)!} .$$

If we put $n = 9$, then

$$R_9(1) < \frac{3}{10!} = \frac{3}{3\,628\,800} < 0.000\,001$$

and e is calculated correctly to the sixth decimal place by

$$1 + 1 + \frac{1}{2!} + \cdots + \frac{1}{9!} = 2.718281 \ldots$$

(compare with **2.5**).

It is easily seen that e is an irrational number. If the series for e is multiplied by $n!$ we have

$$n!\,e = \text{an integer} + \frac{e^\rho}{(n+1)} , \quad (0 < \rho < 1) .$$

If e were a rational number, that is, $e = p/q$, where p and q are positive integers, then $n!\,e$ would be an integer when $n > q$, whereas the right-hand side is a fractional number when $n \ge 2$.

Example 9. $f(x) = \ln(1 + x)$ is defined for $x > -1$. Since

$$f^{(n)}(x) = (-1)^{n-1}\frac{(n-1)!}{(1+x)^n} , \quad f^{(n)}(0) = (-1)^{n-1}(n-1)! ,$$

$$R_n(x) = (-1)^n\left[\frac{x}{1+\rho}\right]^{n+1} , \quad -1 < \rho \le x ,$$

Maclaurin's formula yields

$$\ln(1+x) = x - \frac{x^2}{2} + \frac{x^3}{3} - \frac{x^4}{4} + \cdots + \frac{(-1)^{n-1}x^n}{n} + \frac{(-1)^n}{n+1}\left[\frac{x}{1+\rho}\right]^{n+1} .$$

When $0 \le x < 1$ the inequality

$$|R_n(x)| = \frac{1}{n+1}\left|\frac{x}{1+\rho}\right|^{n+1} < \frac{1}{n+1}$$

holds. Hence, $\lim_{n\to\infty} R_n(x) = 0$. By the Corollary of **6.4-1** it follows that $\lim_{n\to\infty} R_n(x) = 0$ on the wider interval $-1 < x < 1$. Consequently,

$$\ln(1+x) = x - \frac{x^2}{2} + \frac{x^3}{3} - \frac{x^4}{4} + \cdots + \frac{(-1)^{n-1}}{n}x^n + \cdots$$

holds for $-1 < x < 1$. Since $\lim_{n\to\infty} R_n(1) = 0$ (or by **5.7-5**), the relation holds also for $x = 1$, that is,

$$\ln 2 = 1 - \frac{1}{2} + \frac{1}{3} - \frac{1}{4} + \cdots + \frac{(-1)^{n-1}}{n} + \cdots$$

(see Chapter 2, Example 18 and Chapter 6, Example 7).

Example 10 (Sine and cosine series). (a) $f(x) = \sin x$, $f'(x) = \cos x = \sin[x + (\pi/2)]$, $f^{(n)}(x) = \sin[x + n(\pi/2)]$, $f^{(n)}(0) = \sin n(\pi/2)$. Thus, $f(0) = 0$, $f'(0) = 1$, $f''(0) = 0$, $f'''(0) = -1, \dots$. It follows that Maclaurin's expansion of $\sin x$ contains only odd powers

$$\sin x = x - \frac{x^3}{3!} + \cdots + (-1)^n \frac{x^{2n+1}}{(2n+1)!} + R_{2n+1}(x).$$

Since $|f^{(n)}(x)| \le 1$, it follows that

$$|R_{2n+1}(x)| \le \frac{|x|^{2n+3}}{(2n+3)!},$$

whence $\lim_{x\to\infty} R_{2n+1}(x) = 0$ for $-\infty < x < \infty$. Thus

$$\sin x = x - \frac{x^3}{3!} + \frac{x^5}{5!} - \cdots + (-1)^k \frac{x^{2k+1}}{(2k+1)!} + \cdots$$

holds for all real x.

(b) If $f(x) = \cos x$ then $f'(x) = -\sin x = \cos[x + (\pi/2)]$, $f^{(n)}(x) = \cos[x + n(\pi/2)]$, $f^{(n)}(0) = \cos(n\pi)/2$ and $f(0) = 1$, $f'(0) = 0$, $f''(0) = -1$, $f'''(0) = 0, \dots$, indefinitely repeated. It follows that

$$\cos x = 1 - \frac{x^2}{2!} + \cdots + (-1)^n \frac{x^{2n}}{(2n)!} + R_{2n}.$$

As in case (a), it follows that $\lim_{n\to\infty} R_{2n} = 0$. Consequently,

$$\cos x = 1 - \frac{x^2}{2!} + \frac{x^4}{4!} - \cdots + (-1)^n \frac{x^{2n}}{(2n)!} + \cdots$$

is valid for $-\infty < x < \infty$.

Example 11 (Binomial series). $f(x) = (1 + x)^k$ is defined for all x except $x = -1$ when k is negative.

Since $f^{(n)}(x) = k(k-1) \cdots (k-n+1)(1+x)^{k-n}$, $f^{(n)}(0) = k(k-1) \cdots (k-n+1)$, the coefficient of x^n in Maclaurin's expansion is

$$\frac{f^{(n)}(0)}{n!} = \frac{k(k-1) \cdots (k-n+1)}{n!} = \binom{k}{n},$$

that is, it is the binomial coefficient. If k is a positive integer then $f^{(n)}(x) = 0$ for $n > k$, and the Maclaurin series ends with the term x^k, that is, we obtain the familiar binomial theorem.

To show that $R_n(x)$ approaches zero as $n \to \infty$ for $0 \le x < 1$ we note that the infinite series

$$\sum_{n=0}^{\infty} R_n(x) \quad \text{with} \quad R_n(x) = \binom{k}{n+1}\left[\frac{x}{1+\rho}\right]^{n+1}(1+\rho)^k$$

converges by the ratio test $[\lim_{n\to\infty} |R_{n+1}/R_n| = x/(1+\rho) < 1]$, consequently, $\lim_{n\to\infty} R_n(x) = 0$ (Corollary of **3.3-1**).

By the Corollary of **6.4-1**, $\lim_{n\to\infty} R_n(x) = 0$ on the wider interval $-1 < x < 1$, that is, the relation

$$(1+x)^k = 1 + \binom{k}{1}x + \binom{k}{2}x^2 + \cdots + \binom{k}{n}x^n + \cdots$$

holds on the interval $-1 < x < 1$. Thus we have proved that, when $|x| < 1$, the binomial series converges to $(1+x)^k$ for all k. Note that there is a logical difference between proving merely that the series converges and proving that its sum is equal to $(1+x)^k$.

The binomial series is one of the most important series in analysis. For $k = -1$ we obtain the geometric series

$$\frac{1}{1+x} = (1+x)^{-1} = 1 - x + x^2 - x^3 + \cdots + (-1)^{n-1}x^n + \cdots = \sum_{n=0}^{\infty} (-1)^n x^n \,.$$

Another example is for $k = 1/2$:

$$(1+x)^{1/2} = 1 + \frac{1}{2}x - \frac{1}{2 \cdot 4}x^2 + \frac{1 \cdot 3}{2 \cdot 4 \cdot 6}x^3 - \frac{1 \cdot 3 \cdot 5}{2 \cdot 4 \cdot 6 \cdot 8}x^4 + \cdots ,$$

the first two or three terms of which give useful approximations to a square root.

6.5 Some techniques for obtaining power series

By means of the Taylor formula we obtained power series for some functions and proved that the series converge to these functions. However, the preceding discussions were chiefly of theoretical interest. If the nth derivative $f^{(n)}(x)$ is not easily calculated the actual calculations of the coefficients of the power series are far too involved. There are some simpler practical procedures for that purpose. Since the representation of a function by a power series is unique (**6.3-1**), any method which yields a power series of the given function is applicable. Some of these procedures we shall illustrate by the following examples.

Example 12 (Expansions by using the geometric series).

$$\frac{1}{1-z} = 1 + z + z^2 + \cdots + z^n + \cdots = \sum_{n=0}^{\infty} z^n .$$

(a) $f(x) = 1/(1 + x^2)$. The substitution $z = -x^2$ yields at once the power series

$$\frac{1}{1+x^2} = \sum_{n=0}^{\infty} (-x^2)^n = \sum_{n=0}^{\infty} (-1)^n x^{2n} , \quad x^2 < 1 .$$

(b) Obtain the expansion of $f(x) = 1/(x^2 - 5x + 6)$ (i) in powers of x, and (ii) in powers of $x - 1$.

(i) Using partial fractions we put $f(x)$ in the form

$$f(x) = \frac{1}{(x-2)(x-3)} = \frac{1}{x-3} - \frac{1}{x-2} = -\frac{1}{3} \cdot \frac{1}{1-(x/3)} + \frac{1}{2} \cdot \frac{1}{1-(x/2)}$$

$$= -\frac{1}{3} \sum_{\mu=0}^{\infty} \left(\frac{x}{3}\right)^{\mu} + \frac{1}{2} \sum_{\mu=0}^{\infty} \left(\frac{x}{2}\right)^{\mu} = \sum_{\mu=0}^{\infty} \left(\frac{1}{2^{\mu+1}} - \frac{1}{3^{\mu+1}}\right) x^{\mu} , \quad |x| < 2 .$$

(ii) Put $S = x - 1$, then

$$\frac{1}{(x-2)(x-3)} = \frac{1}{(S-1)(S-2)} = \frac{1}{S-2} - \frac{1}{S-1} = -\frac{1}{2} \cdot \frac{1}{1-(S/2)} + \frac{1}{1-S}$$

$$= -\frac{1}{2} \sum_{\mu=0}^{\infty} \left(\frac{S}{2}\right)^{\mu} + \sum_{\mu=0}^{\infty} S^{\mu} = \sum_{\mu=0}^{\infty} \left(1 - \frac{1}{2^{\mu+1}}\right) S^{\mu}$$

$$= \sum_{\mu=0}^{\infty} \left(1 - \frac{1}{2^{\mu+1}}\right) (x-1)^{\mu} , \quad |x-1| < 1 .$$

Example 13 (Expansions by using the geometric series and integration).

$$f(x) = \arctan x .$$

Since by Example 12(a) $f'(x) = 1/(1 + x^2) = \sum_{\mu=0}^{\infty} (-1)^{\mu} x^{2\mu}$ and integration term by term is permissible (**6.2-1**) for $0 \le x < 1$, we have

108

$$\arctan x = \int_0^x \frac{dt}{1 + t^2} = \sum_{\mu=0}^\infty (-1)^\mu \int_0^x t^{2\mu}\, dt = \sum_{\mu=0}^\infty (-1)^\mu \frac{x^{2\mu+1}}{2\mu + 1}\,,$$

valid for $-1 \leq x \leq 1$.

Example 14 (Expansions by using the binomial series and integration).

$$f(x) = \arcsin x\,, \quad |x| < 1\,.$$

Here

$$f'(x) = \frac{1}{(1 - x^2)^{1/2}} = (1 - x^2)^{-1/2} = 1 + \frac{1}{2}\, x^2 + \frac{1 \cdot 3}{2 \cdot 4}\, x^4 + \cdots$$
$$+ \frac{1 \cdot 3 \cdots (2n - 1)}{2 \cdot 4 \cdots 2n} x^{2n} + \cdots\,.$$

Integration yields

$$\arcsin x = \int_0^x \frac{dt}{(1 - t^2)^{1/2}} = x + \frac{1}{2} \cdot \frac{x^3}{3} + \frac{1 \cdot 3}{2 \cdot 4} \cdot \frac{x^5}{5} + \cdots$$
$$+ \frac{1 \cdot 3 \cdots (2n - 1)}{2 \cdot 4 \cdots 2n} \cdot \frac{x^{2n+1}}{2n + 1} + \cdots\,.$$

The power series represents the principal value of the inverse sine. It is easily checked by Raabe's test that the series converges for $x = 1$, and as there is a mere change of sign in passing from $+ x$ to $- x$, the series converges also for $x = -1$. By **5.7-5** the relation holds on the interval $-1 \leq x \leq 1$.

Example 15. $f(x) = [\log (1 + x)]/(1 + x)$. The power series of the function is easily obtained if we multiply the logarithmic series

$$\log (1 + x) = x - \frac{x^2}{2} + \frac{x^3}{3} - \frac{x^4}{4} + \cdots + (-1)^{n-1}\frac{x^n}{n} + \cdots$$

by the geometric series

$$\frac{1}{1 + x} = 1 - x + x^2 - x^3 + \cdots + (-1)^n x^n + \cdots\,.$$

The multiplication formula

$$\frac{\log (1 + x)}{1 + x} = \sum_{n=0}^\infty c_n x^n$$

where $c_n = a_0 b_n + a_1 b_{n-1} + \cdots + a_n b_0$, $a_0 = 0$, $a_n = (-1)^{n-1}/n$, $b_n = (-1)^n$ yields the remarkable power series

$$\frac{\log(1+x)}{1+x} = x - \left(1 + \frac{1}{2}\right)x^2 + \left(1 + \frac{1}{2} + \frac{1}{3}\right)x^3 + \cdots$$
$$+ (-1)^{n-1}\left(1 + \frac{1}{2} + \cdots + \frac{1}{n}\right)x^n + \cdots$$

valid for $|x| < 1$.

Example 16. $f(x) = \tan x$. The Maclaurin series can be obtained by use of a differential equation. We have $f'(x) = \sec^2 x = 1 + f^2(x)$, $f'(0) = 1$, $f(0) = 0$. By successive differentiation we obtain

$$f'' = 2ff' \qquad\qquad\qquad\qquad\qquad f''(0) = 0$$
$$f''' = 2f'^2 + 2ff'' \qquad\qquad\qquad\quad f'''(0) = 2$$
$$f^{(4)} = 6f'f'' + 2ff''' \qquad\qquad\qquad f^{(4)}(0) = 0$$
$$f^{(5)} = 6f''^2 + 8f'f''' + 2ff^{(4)} \qquad\quad f^{(5)}(0) = 16$$
$$f^{(6)} = 20f''f''' + 10f'f^{(4)} + 2ff^{(5)} \qquad f^{(6)}(0) = 0$$
$$f^{(7)} = 20f'''^2 + 30f''f^{(4)} + 12f'f^{(5)} + 2ff^{(6)} \qquad f^{(7)}(0) = 272 \;.$$

Hence Maclaurin's formula yields the first four terms of the series

$$\tan x = x + \frac{1}{3}x^3 + \frac{2}{15}x^5 + \frac{17}{315}x^7 + \cdots, \quad |x| < \frac{\pi}{2}\;.$$

Example 17. $f(x) = x/(e^x - 1)$. The Maclaurin series can be easily obtained by undetermined coefficients. If we write

$$\frac{x}{e^x - 1} = 1 + \beta_1 x + \beta_2\frac{x^2}{2!} + \beta_3\frac{x^3}{3!} + \cdots$$

and compare the coefficients of each power of x in

$$x = \left(1 + \beta_1 x + \frac{\beta_2}{2!}x^2 + \frac{\beta_3}{3!}x^3 + \cdots\right)\left(x + \frac{x^2}{2!} + \frac{x^3}{3!} + \frac{x^4}{4!} + \cdots\right),$$

we obtain

$$\beta_1 = -\frac{1}{2}, \quad \beta_2 = \frac{1}{6}, \quad \beta_3 = 0, \quad \beta_4 = -\frac{1}{30}, \quad \beta_5 = 0, \quad \beta_6 = \frac{1}{42}, \quad \cdots.$$

These constants are called Bernoulli's numbers and are of importance in applications. (See K. Knopp, *Theory and Application of Infinite Series,* second English edition, Hafner Publishing Co., New York.)

Example 18 (Expansions by using familiar series).
(a) $f(x) = (e^{x^2} - e^{-x^2})/x^2$, $f(0) = 2$.
Substituting $z = x^2$ and $z = -x^2$, respectively, into

$$e^z = 1 + z + \frac{z^2}{2!} + \frac{z^3}{3!} + \cdots + \frac{z^n}{n!} + \cdots$$

and performing the operations as indicated we obtain

$$f(x) = 2\left(1 + \frac{x^4}{6!} + \frac{x^8}{10!} + \cdots + \frac{x^{4k}}{(4k+2)!} + \cdots\right).$$

(b) $f(x) = \sin^3 x$.

Using the familiar relation $\sin^3 x = \frac{1}{4}(3 \sin x - \sin 3x)$ and using the series

$$\sin z = z - \frac{z^3}{3!} + \frac{z^5}{5!} - \cdots + \frac{(-1)^n z^{2n+1}}{(2n+1)!} + \cdots$$

we obtain

$$\sin^3 x = \frac{1}{4}\left[3\left(x - \frac{x^3}{3!} + \cdots + \frac{(-1)^n x^{2n+1}}{(2n+1)!} + \cdots\right) - \left(3x - \frac{(3x)^3}{3!} + \cdots\right.\right.$$
$$\left.\left. + \frac{(-1)^n (3x)^{2n+1}}{(2n+1)!} + \cdots\right)\right]$$
$$= \frac{1}{4} \sum_{n=1}^{\infty} (-1)^{n+1} \frac{3 - 3^{2n+1}}{(2n+1)!} x^{2n+1}.$$

The power series converges for $-\infty < x < \infty$.

Exercises 6.B

1. $f(x) = x^6$. Obtain Taylor's expansions:
   (a) about the point $x = 3$, that is, in powers of $x - 3$;
   (b) about the point $x = -3$;
   (c) What is the Maclaurin's series in this case?
   (d) In cases (a) and (b) above write the remainders for $n = 3$ and $n = 7$.
2. Find the functions that form the even and odd parts of $f(x) = 1/(1-x)$ and their Maclaurin expasions.
3. Expand $f(x) = e^x$ in Taylor's series about the point $x = a$ and write the remainder $R_n(x)$.
4. Obtain 3 terms of Maclaurin's series if
   (a) $f(x) = x \cot x$ (c) $f(x) = \log \cos x$
   (b) $f(x) = \sec x$ (d) $f(x) = e^{\sin x}$.
5. Approximate $f(x)$ by the Maclaurin series and determine the number of terms to be added if the error of the approximation is to be less than 10^{-6}.
   (a) $f(x) = \sin x$, $|x| \le 1$ (b) $f(x) = \log(1 + x)$, $0 \le x \le \frac{1}{2}$.
6. Compute the integrals correct to three decimal places by use of infinite series.

(a) $\int_0^1 (4 - x^3)^{1/2}\, dx$ (b) $\int_0^1 e^{-x^2}\, dx$ (c) $\int_0^{\pi/4} \dfrac{\sin x}{x}\, dx$.

In Exercises 7–14 find Taylor's series of $f(x)$ about the point a and determine the precise interval of convergence if $f(x)$ is:

7. $(e^x)^{1/2}$, $a = 0$
8. $\cos x^2$, $a = 0$
9. $1/(1 - x^4)^{1/2}$, $a = 0$
10. $(4x - 1)/(x^2 + 3x + 2)$, $a = 1$

11. $x/[(x^2 - 1)(x + 2)]$, $a = 0$
12. $1/(c - bx)$, $a = 1$, $b \neq 0$, $c - b \neq 0$
13. $\sin^2 x$, $a = 0$
14. $\cos^3 x$, $a = 0$.

15. Show that $\dfrac{1}{2}\arctan x \log (1 + x^2) = \sum_{k=1}^{\infty} (-1)^{k-1} h_{2k} \dfrac{x^{2k+1}}{(2k + 1)}$ where
    $h_n = 1 + 1/2 + \cdots + 1/n$.

16. It has been proved that the binomial series
$$(1 + x)^k = 1 + \binom{k}{1}x + \binom{k}{2}x^2 + \cdots + \binom{k}{n}x^n + \cdots$$
    holds on the interval $-1 < x < 1$ for all k. Prove that the relation holds for $x = 1$ if $k > -1$ and for $x = -1$ if $k > 0$. If $x = 1$ and $k \leq -1$ or if $x = -1$ and $k < 0$, the series diverges. (Hint: Use Raabe's test and **5.7-5**.)

17. It is easily seen by the ratio test that the series
$$\log (1 + x) = x - \frac{x^2}{2} + \frac{x^3}{3} - \frac{x^4}{4} + \cdots + (-1)^{n-1}\frac{x^n}{n} + \cdots$$
    converges absolutely when $|x| < 1$. By **4.4-4** we may rearrange its terms without changing the value of its sum. For example,
$$\log (1 + x) = x + \frac{x^3}{3} - \frac{x^2}{2} + \frac{x^5}{5} + \frac{x^7}{7} - \frac{x^4}{4} + \cdots, \quad |x| < 1.$$
    Moreover, this series converges when $x = 1$. Consequently, by **5.7-5** it should converge to $\log 2$, but
$$\frac{3}{2}\log 2 = 1 + \frac{1}{3} - \frac{1}{2} + \frac{1}{5} + \frac{1}{7} - \frac{1}{4} + \cdots$$
    as we have seen (Chapter 4, Example 8), that is, the series converges to $\frac{3}{2}\log 2$. What is wrong here?

18. Obtain formally Euler's formula
$$e^{i\theta} = \cos \theta + i \sin \theta$$
    and deduce $i^i = e^{-\pi/2}$.
    Hint: Put $x = i\theta$ in the series
$$e^x = 1 + \frac{x}{1} + \frac{x^2}{2!} + \frac{x^3}{3!} + \cdots + \frac{x^n}{n!} + \cdots$$
    then using $i^2 = -1$, $i^3 = -i$, $i^4 = 1$, $i^5 = i$, ..., separate the real and the imaginary terms of the series. Compare the series with Example 10. The special case follows from Euler's formula for $\theta = \pi/2$.

19. $f(x) = e^{-1/x^2}$ if $x \neq 0$, $f(0) = 0$.
    (a) Show that $f^{(n)}(0) = 0$ for all $n \geq 1$.
    (b) Show that the Maclaurin series converges everywhere and does not represent $f(x)$ except at $x = 0$.

CHAPTER 7

TRIGONOMETRIC SERIES

In the preceding chapter we considered functions defined by power series. In this chapter we shall discuss functions defined by trigonometric series

$$f(x) = b_0 + \sum_{n=1}^{\infty} (b_n \cos nx + c_n \sin nx)$$

where b_0, $\{b_n\}$, $\{c_n\}$, $n = 1, 2, 3, \ldots$ are given sequences of constants.

For $b_0 = 0$, $c_n = 0$, $b_n = 1/n^2$, $n = 1, 2, 3, \ldots$, we obtain the familiar series

$$\sum_{n=1}^{\infty} \frac{\cos nx}{n^2},$$

which converges uniformly for all real x. For $b_0 = 0$, $b_n = 0$, and $c_n = 1/n^\alpha$, $n = 1, 2, 3, \ldots$, we obtained another special trigonometric series

$$\sum_{n=1}^{\infty} \frac{\sin nx}{n^\alpha},$$

which converges uniformly for all x if $\alpha > 1$ and uniformly on the interval $\delta \leq x \leq 2\pi - \delta$, $0 < \delta < \pi/2$, if $0 < \alpha \leq 1$ (see Chapter 5, Examples 9 and 10). It follows by **5.4-1** that both series define continuous functions on the indicated intervals.

Since each term of the series has a period 2π in x, the same must be true of the sum function $f(x)$, that is, $f(x + 2\pi) = f(x)$. Therefore, it is sufficient to consider these functions on any interval of length 2π. Series of this kind were first obtained in theoretical physics, chiefly in acoustics, optics, electrodynamics, and the theory of heat. Fourier started the first more thorough study of certain trigonometric series in 1822. This led to a thorough revision of the concept of function, and hence of the whole foundation of analysis. In some respects trigonometric

113

series constitute a far more powerful instrument in analysis than the power series.

7.1 The Fourier series

We know from Taylor's theorem that when a function $g(x)$ is defined as the sum of a power series $\sum_{n=0}^{\infty} c_n x^n$, then there is a simple formula which relates the numbers c_n to the functions $g(x)$, namely $c_n = g^{(n)}(0)/n!$, $n = 0, 1, 2, \ldots$. Is there a formula which relates the coefficients a_n and b_n in

$$f(x) = \frac{a_0}{2} + \sum_{n=1}^{\infty} (a_n \cos nx + b_n \sin nx)$$

to $f(x)$?

If we assume that such expansion of $f(x)$ is possible and that the series converges uniformly on an interval of length 2π, say, $-\pi \le x \le \pi$, then there exists a simple relation between the function $f(x)$ and the coefficients $a_0, a_n, b_n, n = 1, 2, 3, \ldots$. (The first coefficient in the series is written $a_0/2$ for convenience.)

First note the orthogonality relations:

$$\int_{-\pi}^{\pi} \sin nx \sin mx \, dx = 0 , \quad \text{if } m \ne n ,$$

$$= \pi , \quad \text{if } m = n ;$$

(1) $$\int_{-\pi}^{\pi} \sin nx \cos mx \, dx = 0 ;$$

$$\int_{-\pi}^{\pi} \cos mx \cos nx \, dx = 0 , \quad \text{if } m \ne n ,$$

$$= \pi , \quad \text{if } m = n ;$$

which can be easily verified by using familiar trigonometric identities. For example,

$$\int_{-\pi}^{\pi} \sin nx \sin mx \, dx = \frac{1}{2}\left[\int_{-\pi}^{\pi} \cos(n-m)x \, dx - \int_{-\pi}^{\pi} \cos(n+m)x \, dx \right]$$

$$= \frac{1}{2}\left[\frac{\sin(n-m)x}{n-m} - \frac{\sin(n+m)x}{n+m} \right]_{-\pi}^{\pi}$$

$$= 0 , \quad \text{if } m \ne n ,$$

$$\int_{-\pi}^{\pi} \sin^2 nx \, dx = \frac{1}{2} \int_{-\pi}^{\pi} (1 - \cos 2nx) \, dx = \frac{1}{2}\left[x - \frac{\sin 2nx}{2n} \right]_{-\pi}^{\pi}$$

$$= \pi , \quad \text{if } m = n .$$

If we multiply the relation by $\cos nx$ (this does not affect uniform

114

convergence) and integrate term by term by using the above orthogonality relations, it follows at once that

(2a)
$$a_n = \frac{1}{\pi} \int_{-\pi}^{\pi} f(x) \cos nx \, dx$$

for the coefficients a_n, $n = 0, 1, 2, 3, \ldots$.

Similarly, by multiplying the series by $\sin nx$ and integrating, we obtain

(2b)
$$b_n = \frac{1}{\pi} \int_{-\pi}^{\pi} f(x) \sin nx \, dx \, .$$

Thus we obtained simple relations and, if an integrable function $f(x)$ on $-\pi < x < \pi$ is given, we may compute the a_n and b_n and form the trigonometric series

$$\frac{1}{2} a_0 + (a_1 \cos x + b_1 \sin x) + \cdots + (a_n \cos nx + b_n \sin nx) + \cdots .$$

The series is then called the Fourier series corresponding to $f(x)$ and the coefficients a_0, a_n, b_n, $n = 1, 2, 3, \ldots$ obtained by the integral formulas are called Fourier coefficients of $f(x)$.

We write

$$f(x) \sim \frac{a_0}{2} + \sum_{n=1}^{\infty} (a_n \cos nx + b_n \sin nx)$$

and the symbol "$\sim$" neither implies equality nor convergence of the series.

There is a distinction between trigonometric and Fourier series. We shall show later that, for example, the trigonometric series

$$\sum_{n=1}^{\infty} \frac{\sin nx}{n^{1/2}}$$

is not a Fourier series. Thus Fourier series form a subset of the trigonometric series.

Note that because of periodicity of $f(x)$ and $\cos nx$, $\sin nx$, the interval of integration may be replaced by any other interval of length 2π, for instance, the interval $0 \le x \le 2\pi$ or $-\pi \pm c \le x \le \pi \pm c$ where c is any real number, that is,

$$\int_{-\pi}^{\pi} f(x) \cos nx \, dx = \int_{0}^{2\pi} f(x) \cos nx \, dx = \int_{-\pi \pm c}^{\pi \pm c} f(x) \cos nx \, dx \, .$$

Example 1. Find the Fourier series corresponding to the periodic function $f(x)$ defined as follows:

115

$$f(x) = -k, \quad \text{when } -\pi < x < 0$$
$$= k, \qquad \text{when } 0 < x < \pi \qquad \text{and } f(x + 2\pi) = f(x).$$

The graph of the function consists of separated stretches, not closed at either end, and undefined at $x = k\pi$, $k = 0$, ± 1, ± 2 (Fig. 12).

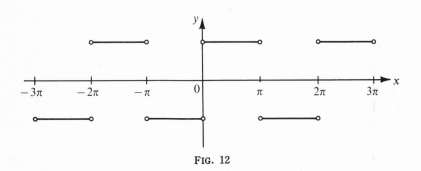

FIG. 12

Simple integration yields

$$a_0 = \frac{1}{\pi} \int_{-\pi}^{\pi} f(x)\,dx = \frac{1}{\pi} \int_{-\pi}^{0} -k\,dx + \frac{1}{\pi} \int_{0}^{\pi} k\,dx = \frac{k}{\pi}(-\pi + \pi) = 0,$$

$$a_n = \frac{1}{\pi} \int_{-\pi}^{\pi} f(x) \cos nx\,dx = \frac{1}{\pi}\left[\int_{-\pi}^{0} (-k) \cos nx\,dx + \int_{0}^{\pi} k \cos nx\,dx \right]$$

$$= \frac{1}{\pi}\left[\frac{-k \sin nx}{n}\bigg|_{-\pi}^{0} + \frac{k \sin nx}{n}\bigg|_{0}^{\pi} \right] = 0,$$

$$b_n = \frac{1}{\pi} \int_{-\pi}^{\pi} f(x) \sin nx\,dx = \frac{1}{\pi}\left[\int_{-\pi}^{0} (-k) \sin nx\,dx + \int_{0}^{\pi} k \sin nx\,dx \right]$$

$$= \frac{1}{\pi}\left[\frac{k \cos nx}{n}\bigg|_{-\pi}^{0} - \frac{k \cos nx}{n}\bigg|_{0}^{\pi} \right]$$

$$= \frac{2k}{n\pi}(1 - \cos n\pi).$$

Since $\cos 2k\pi = 1$ and $\cos(2k + 1)\pi = -1$, $k = 0, 1, 2, \ldots$, it follows that

$$b_1 = \frac{4k}{\pi}, \quad b_2 = 0, \quad b_3 = \frac{4k}{3\pi}, \quad b_4 = 0, \quad b_5 = \frac{4k}{5\pi}, \ldots, \quad b_{2k} = 0,$$

$$b_{2k+1} = \frac{4k}{(2k+1)\pi}, \ldots.$$

Thus the corresponding Fourier series is

116

$$f(x) \sim \frac{4\,k}{\pi}\Big(\sin x + \frac{1}{3}\sin 3\,x + \frac{1}{5}\sin 5\,x + \cdots$$

$$+ \frac{1}{2\,k+1}\sin (2\,k+1)x + \cdots\Big).$$

The series converges for all values of x and it converges uniformly for all x if the neighborhoods of $x = k\pi$, $k = 0, 1, 2, \ldots$ are excluded. [This can be proved exactly as in Chapter 5, Example 10, if the identity $\sin x + \sin 3\,x + \cdots + \sin (2n-1)x = \sin^2 nx / \sin x$ is used.]

Note that the series has the sum 0 when $x = k\pi$, $k = 0, \pm 1, \pm 2, \ldots$ whereas the function $f(x)$ is not defined at these points. If we had defined $f(k\pi) = b$, where b is any constant, the integrals and consequently the Fourier series would not have been changed. Thus it follows that different functions may generate the same Fourier series.

For calculation of the coefficients a_n, b_n it is handy to use the relations

$$\int_{-a}^{a}\lambda(x)\,dx = 2\int_{0}^{a}\lambda(x)\,dx\,, \quad \text{when } \lambda(x) \text{ is even } [\lambda(-x) = \lambda(x)]\,,$$

$$= 0\,, \qquad \text{when } \lambda(x) \text{ is odd } [\lambda(-x) = -\lambda(x)]\,.$$

The relation can be easily obtained by first writing

$$\int_{-a}^{a}\lambda(x)\,dx = \int_{-a}^{0}\lambda(x)\,dx + \int_{0}^{a}\lambda(x)\,dx\,.$$

If in the first integral on the right the substitution $x = -t$ is made, it follows that

$$\int_{-a}^{a}\lambda(x)\,dx = \int_{0}^{a}[\lambda(-x) + \lambda(x)]\,dx\,.$$

Hence, from $\lambda(-x) = \lambda(x)$ or $\lambda(-x) = -\lambda(x)$, the formula follows. This is also apparent from the graph of an even or an odd function.

Since, in Example 1, $f(x)$ is an odd function and $\cos nx$ is an even function, the product $f(x)\cos nx$ is an odd function, the coefficients $a_n \doteq 0$, $n = 0, 1, 2, \ldots$. Thus there was no need of calculating a_n.

Example 2. Obtain the Fourier series if $f(x) = x^2$, $-\pi < x < \pi$, $f(x + 2\,\pi) = f(x)$ (Fig. 13).

Since $f(x)$ is an even function $f(x)\sin nx$ is odd. Consequently, $b_n = 0$, $n = 1, 2, 3, \ldots$.

$$a_0 = \frac{2}{\pi}\int_{0}^{\pi}x^2\,dx = \frac{2\,\pi^2}{3}\,.$$

Since $f(x)\cos nx$ is an even function, integration by parts yields

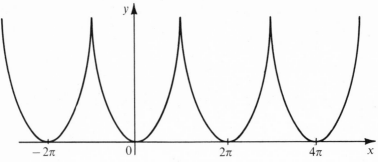

FIG. 13

$$a_n = \frac{2}{\pi} \int_0^\pi x^2 \cos nx \, dx = \frac{2}{\pi} \left[\left[\frac{x^2 \sin nx}{n} \right]_0^\pi - \frac{2}{n} \int_0^\pi x \sin nx \, dx \right]$$

$$= -\frac{4}{n\pi} \int_0^\pi x \sin nx \, dx .$$

A second integration by parts gives

$$a_n = -\frac{4}{n\pi} \left[\left[-x \frac{\cos nx}{n} \right]_0^\pi + \frac{1}{n} \int_0^\pi \cos nx \, dx \right] = \frac{4}{n^2} \cos n\pi = \frac{(-1)^n 4}{n^2} .$$

It follows that

$$f(x) \sim \frac{a_0}{2} + \sum_{n=1}^\infty (a_n \cos nx + b_n \sin nx) = \frac{\pi^2}{3} + 4 \sum_{n=1}^\infty \frac{(-1)^n \cos nx}{n^2} .$$

Note that the function is continuous and the series converges uniformly for all x.

Example 3. Find the Fourier series of $f(x)$ defined as follows:

$$f(x) = -\pi , \quad \text{if } -\pi < x < 0 ,$$
$$= x , \quad \text{if } 0 < x < \pi , \quad f(x + 2\pi) = f(x) \quad \text{(Fig. 14)}.$$

Since the function is neither even nor odd, both a_n and b_n are to be calculated.

$$a_0 = \frac{1}{\pi} \int_{-\pi}^\pi f(x) \, dx = \frac{1}{\pi} \left[\int_{-\pi}^0 (-\pi) \, dx + \int_0^\pi x \, dx \right] = -\frac{\pi}{2} .$$

$$a_n = \frac{1}{\pi} \int_{-\pi}^\pi f(x) \cos nx \, dx = \frac{1}{\pi} \left[\int_{-\pi}^0 (-\pi) \cos nx \, dx + \int_0^\pi x \cos nx \, dx \right]$$

$$= \frac{\cos n\pi - 1}{\pi n^2} ,$$

118

$$b_n = \frac{1}{\pi} \int_{-\pi}^{\pi} f(x) \sin nx\, dx = \frac{1}{\pi} \left[\int_{-\pi}^{0} (-\pi) \sin nx\, dx + \int_{0}^{\pi} x \sin nx\, dx \right]$$

$$= \frac{1 - 2\cos n\pi}{n} \ .$$

If we put $\cos n\pi = (-1)^n$, it follows that

$$f(x) \sim -\frac{\pi}{4} - \frac{2}{\pi} \sum_{k=1}^{\infty} \frac{\cos(2k-1)x}{(2k-1)^2} + \sum_{k=1}^{\infty} \frac{1 - 2(-1)^k}{k} \sin kx \ .$$

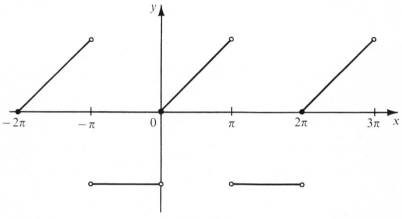

FIG. 14

Note that $f(x)$ is neither odd nor even. Its Fourier series contains both sine and cosine terms. If $f(x)$ is an odd function (Example 1), the corresponding Fourier series contains only sine terms. If $f(x)$ is even (Example 2), its Fourier series contains only cosine terms. [In Example 2 the Fourier series converges uniformly for all x. If the Fourier series of Examples 1 and 3 converged uniformly for all x, this would contradict a theorem of Chapter 5. Name it.]

Exercises 7.A

When $f(x) = f(-x)$, the function is said to be even; its graph is then symmetric with respect to the y axis. When $f(x) = -f(-x)$, the function is said to be odd; its graph is then symmetric with respect to the origin.

In problems 1–7 find which of the functions are even, odd, or neither even nor odd.

1. (a) e^x (b) $|x|$ (c) e^{x^2}

    (d) $(\cos x)/x$ (f) $\ln(1+x)/(1-x)$ (h) $\sin^2 x.$

    (e) $(\sin x)/x$ (g) $\sin x^2$

2. (a) $\sin x \cos x$ (d) $1 - x + x^2$

    (b) $\sin x + \cos x$ (e) $e^{\sin x}.$

    (c) $x^2 \cos nx$

3. $f(x) = x,$ if $-\pi < x < 0$ 6. $f(x) = x + \pi,$ if $-\pi < x < 0$
              $= -x,$ if $0 < x < \pi$ $= -x + \pi,$ if $0 < x < \pi$

4. $f(x) = 0,$ if $-\pi < x < 0$ 7. $f(x) = x,\ 0 < x < 2\pi,$
              $= 3x,$ if $0 < x < \pi$ $f(x + 2\pi) = f(x).$

5. $f(x) = x,\ -\pi < x < \pi$

    In problems 8-12 find Fourier series corresponding to $f(x)$ defined on the interval $-\pi < x < \pi$ and having a period 2π, that is, $f(x + 2\pi) = f(x)$.

8. $f(x) = |x|$ 10. $f(x) = x \cos x$ 12. $f(x) = |\sin x|.$

9. $f(x) = x$ 11. $f(x) = \tfrac{1}{2}\pi - x$

13. In Example 1 we obtained an infinite Fourier series corresponding to $f(x)$. If $k = \pi/4$, the partial sums of the series are

$$S_1 = \sin x, \quad S_2 = \sin x + \frac{1}{3}\sin 3x, \quad S_3 = \sin x + \frac{1}{3}\sin 3x + \frac{1}{5}\sin 5x.$$

    Graph these partial sums and compare with the graph of $f(x)$. Do these partial sums approximate $f(x)$?

14. Graph the partial sums of Example 2: $S_1 = \pi^2/3 - 4\cos x$, $S_2 = \pi^2/3 - 4[\cos x - (\cos 2x)/4]$, $S_3 = \pi^2/3 - 4[\cos x - (\cos 2x)/4 + (\cos 3x)/9]$, and compare with the graph of $f(x)$. Do these partial sums approximate $f(x)$?

7.2 Approximation of a function $f(x)$ by trigonometric polynomials

    Let $c_0,\ c_1,\ c_2,\ \ldots,\ c_n,\ d_1,\ d_2,\ \ldots,\ d_n$ be $2n+1$ arbitrary constants, and

$$\sigma_n(x) = \sum_{\mu=0}^{n} (c_\mu \cos \mu x + d_\mu \sin \mu x)$$

a trigonometric polynomial. It is required to determine these constants such that the polynomial $\sigma_n(x)$ makes the best approximation to $f(x)$ in the sense of the method of least squares, that is, the values that give the integral

$$K = \int_{-\pi}^{\pi} [f(x) - \sigma_n(x)]^2\, dx \geq 0$$

its minimum value.

    If we observe that

$$[f(x) - \sigma_n(x)]^2 = f^2(x) - 2f(x)\sigma_n(x) + \sigma_n^2(x)$$

$$= f^2(x) - 2f(x) \sum_{\mu=0}^{n} (c_\mu \cos \mu x + d_\mu \sin \mu x) + \sum_{\mu=0}^{n} (c_\mu^2 \cos^2 \mu x$$

$$+ d_\mu^2 \sin^2 \mu x) + \sum_{\substack{i,\,j=0 \\ i \neq j}}^{n} (c_i c_j \cos ix \cos jx + d_i d_j \sin ix \sin jx)$$

$$+ 2 \sum_{i,\,j=0}^{n} c_i d_j \cos ix \sin jx \,,$$

integration from $-\pi$ to π and use of orthogonality relations and Fourier coefficients of $f(x)$ [Chapter 7, Relations (1) and (2)] yield

$$K = \int_{-\pi}^{\pi} f^2(x)\, dx - 4 \pi a_0 c_0 - 2\pi \sum_{\mu=1}^{n} (a_\mu c_\mu + b_\mu d_\mu) + 2\pi c_0^2 + \pi \sum_{\mu=1}^{n} (c_\mu^2 + d_\mu^2) \,,$$

which can be written in the form

$$K = \int_{-\pi}^{\pi} f^2(x)\, dx + 2\pi (c_0 - a_0)^2 + \pi \sum_{\mu=1}^{n} [(c_\mu - a_\mu)^2 + (d_\mu - b_\mu)^2] - 2\pi a_0^2$$

$$- \pi \sum_{\mu=1}^{n} (a_\mu^2 + b_\mu^2) \,,$$

where a_0, a_μ, b_μ, are Fourier coefficients of $f(x)$.

It is apparent that K assumes its least value when $c_0 = a_0$, $c_\mu = a_\mu$, $d_\mu = b_\mu$, that is, if the constants in $\sigma_n(x)$ are chosen to be Fourier coefficients of $f(x)$.

Thus, if

$$S_n(x) = a_0 + \sum_{\mu=1}^{n} (a_\mu \cos \mu x + b_\mu \sin \mu x)$$

is the partial sum of the Fourier series corresponding to $f(x)$, then

$$K_{\min} = \int_{-\pi}^{\pi} [f(x) - S_n(x)]^2\, dx = \int_{-\pi}^{\pi} f^2(x)\, dx - 2\pi a_0^2 - \pi \sum_{\mu=1}^{n} (a_\mu^2 + b_\mu^2) \geq 0$$

and hence

$$\int_{-\pi}^{\pi} [f(x) - \sigma_n(x)]^2\, dx \geq \int_{-\pi}^{\pi} [f(x) - S_n(x)]^2\, dx \geq 0 \,.$$

This result which is of great importance we state as a theorem.

7.2-1 Theorem. For any given n, the trigonometric polynomial $\sigma_n(x) = \sum_{\mu=0}^{n} (c_\mu \cos \mu x + d_\mu \sin \mu x)$ is the best approximation to $f(x)$ in the sense of least squares when the constants c_0, c_μ, d_μ ($\mu = 1, 2, \ldots, n$) are Fourier coefficients of $f(x)$.

Corollary 1. Since $K_{\min} \geq 0$ for any n, no matter how large, it follows that

$$2\,a_0^2 + \sum_{\mu=1}^{\infty} (a_\mu^2 + b_\mu^2) \le \frac{1}{\pi} \int_{-\pi}^{\pi} f^2(x)\, dx \ .$$

This so called Bessel's inequality implies convergence of the infinite series

$$\sum_{\mu=1}^{\infty} (a_\mu^2 + b_\mu^2)$$

if $\int_{-\pi}^{\pi} f^2(x)\, dx$ is bounded. Consequently, $\lim_{\mu\to\infty} (a_\mu^2 + b_\mu^2) = 0$ which implies $\lim_{\mu\to\infty} a_\mu = 0$, $\lim_{\mu\to\infty} b_\mu = 0$. That is, if $f(x)$ is Riemann integrable, then the Fourier coefficients of $f(x)$ approach zero as $\mu\to\infty$.

Corollary 2. If a function $\lambda(x)$ is integrable on the interval $a \le x \le b$, then

$$\lim_{n\to\infty} \int_a^b \lambda(x) \cos nx\, dx = 0 \ ,$$

$$\lim_{n\to\infty} \int_a^b \lambda(x) \sin nx\, dx = 0 \ .$$

Proof. First assume that a and b both belong to one and the same interval of the form $2\,k\pi \le x \le (2\,k+1)\pi$.

We define $f(x)$ as follows:

$$f(x) = \lambda(x) \ , \quad \text{if } a \le x \le b \ ,$$
$$= 0 \ , \qquad \text{otherwise} \ ,$$
$$f(x + 2\,\pi) = f(x) \ .$$

Then,

$$\int_a^b \lambda(x) \cos nx\, dx = \int_{-\pi}^{\pi} f(x) \cos nx\, dx = \pi a_n \ ,$$

$$\int_a^b \lambda(x) \sin nx\, dx = \int_{-\pi}^{\pi} f(x) \sin nx\, dx = \pi b_n \ ,$$

where a_n and b_n denote Fourier constants of $f(x)$. Since by Corollary 1 $a_n \to 0$ and $b_n \to 0$ as $n\to\infty$, the statement follows.

If the above assumption is not satisfied, that is, a and b are not contained in the interval $2\,k\pi \le x \le (2\,k+1)\pi$ (k an integer), then we can split up the interval $a \le x \le b$ into a finite number of intervals, each of which satisfies the condition. Then the above integrals can be expressed as a sum of a finite number of Fourier coefficients, each of which tends to 0 as $n\to\infty$. Consequently, the integrals also approach zero as $n\to\infty$.

Corollary 3. The trigonometric series

$$\sum_{n=1}^{\infty} \frac{\sin nx}{n^p}, \quad 0 < p \le \frac{1}{2},$$

which converges for all x, is not a Fourier series. For if it were a Fourier series, then by Corollary 1 the series

$$\sum_{n=1}^{\infty} b_n^2 = \sum_{n=1}^{\infty} \frac{1}{n^{2p}},$$

where $b_n = 1/n^p$, would converge. But this series diverges.

7.3 Piecewise continuous and piecewise smooth functions on an interval

A function $f(x)$ is said to be piecewise continuous if it is continuous on the given interval except for a finite number of jump discontinuities, and such that for each point of discontinuity $f(x)$ approaches a limit as x approaches the point from one side.

A function is said to be piecewise smooth on an interval if it is piecewise continuous and if in addition its first derivative $f'(x)$ is piecewise continuous. The general character of a piecewise smooth function is suggested by Figure 15.

If $f(x)$ approaches a limit as $x \to c$ from the right, that is $\lim_{h\to 0} f(c + h)$, $h > 0$ exists, we denote this limit by $f(c +)$; likewise, if $f(x)$ approaches a limit as $x \to c$ from the left, that is, $\lim_{h\to 0} f(c - h)$, $h > 0$ exists, the limit is denoted by $f(c -)$.

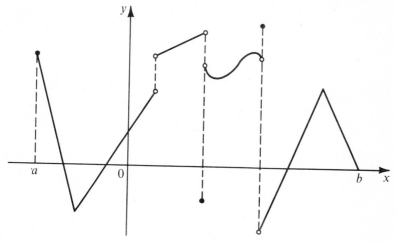

FIG. 15

If $f(c+) = f(c-) = A$, then by definition the function $f(x)$ possesses a limit at c, that is, $\lim_{x \to c} f(x) = A$ exists.

If the right- and left-hand limits exist but differ, say, $f(c+) = B$ and $f(c-) = A$, $A \neq B$, then at the point $x = c$ there is a jump

$$f(c+) - f(c-) = B - A$$

and $f(x)$ has no limit at the point c.

Moreover, when $h > 0$ we define

$$f'(c+) = \lim_{h \to 0} \frac{f(c+h) - f(c+)}{h}, \quad f'(c-) = \lim_{h \to 0} \frac{f(c-h) - f(c-)}{-h},$$

to be the limiting slopes of the graph of $f(x)$ to the right and to the left of $x = c$, respectively, if they exist. These limits, if they exist, should not be confused with the right- and left-hand derivatives at $x = c$ which coincide if $f(c+) = f(c)$ or $f(c-) = f(c)$.

For example, $f(x)$ defined on $-\pi \leq x \leq \pi$ by

$$\begin{aligned} f(x) &= -1, & \text{when } -\pi < x < 0, \\ &= 0, & \text{when } x = 0, \quad x = \pm \pi, \\ &= 1, & \text{when } 0 < x < \pi, \end{aligned}$$

is piecewise continuous and piecewise smooth. The points of discontinuity are $x = 0$, $x = \pm \pi$. $f(0-) = -1$, $f(0+) = 1$, $f(-\pi+) = -1$, and $f(\pi-) = 1$. Limiting slopes to the right and to the left of $x = 0$ are 0, but the right- and left-hand derivatives at $x = 0$ do not exist for

$$\lim_{h \to 0} \frac{1-0}{h} = \infty, \quad \lim_{h \to 0} \frac{-1-0}{-h} = \infty, \quad h > 0.$$

The preceding concepts are essential for understanding the basic theorem of Fourier series.

Exercises 7.B

1. The function $f(x)$ is defined by
$$\begin{aligned} f(x) &= -1, & \text{if } -\pi < x < 0, \\ &= 1, & \text{if } 0 < x < \pi, \quad f(x + 2\pi) = f(x). \end{aligned}$$
Determine the coefficients α_μ and β_μ such that the trigonometric polynomial
$$S_n(x) = \sum_{\mu=0}^{n} (\alpha_\mu \cos \mu x + \beta_\mu \sin \mu x)$$
gives the best approximation to $f(x)$ in the sense of the square error.
2. Compute the minimum square error $\int_{-\pi}^{\pi} [f(x) - S_n(x)]^2 \, dx$ in Exercise 1 for $n = 1, 3, 5$.

3. Let $f(x) = 1$ and the trigonometric polynomial be $S(x) = \alpha_1 \sin x + \alpha_2 \sin 2x + \alpha_3 \sin 3x$. How should the coefficients α_i, $i = 1, 2, 3$ be determined so that

$$\int_0^\pi [1 - S(x)]^2 \, dx$$

is a minimum?

4. Give a direct proof of

$$\lim_{n \to \infty} \int_0^{2\pi} f(x) \sin nx \, dx = 0, \quad \lim_{n \to \infty} \int_0^{2\pi} f(x) \cos nx \, dx = 0$$

if $f(x + 2\pi) = f(x)$ and $f'(x)$ is continuous on $0 \le x \le 2\pi$. [Hint: Integrate the Fourier coefficients by parts and note that $|f'(x)|$ is bounded, that is, $|f'(x)| \le M$.]

5. If $F(x)$ is integrable on the interval $|x| \le \pi$, prove that

$$\lim_{n \to \infty} \int_{-\pi}^\pi F(x) \sin\left(n + \frac{1}{2}\right) x \, dx = 0 .$$

6. Determine which of the following functions defined on $-\pi \le x \le \pi$ are (i) piecewise continuous, (ii) piecewise smooth. Find $f(c+)$, $f(c-)$, $f'(c+)$, $f'(c-)$, where c is a point of discontinuity.
   (a) $f(x) = x^2$, when $-\pi \le x < 1$
   $\quad\quad = 0$, when $x = 1$
   $\quad\quad = x/2$, when $1 < x \le \pi$
   (b) $f(x) = 1/x$, when $-\pi \le x < 0$
   $\quad\quad = 0$, when $x = 0$
   $\quad\quad = 1/x$, when $0 < x \le \pi$
   (c) $f(x) = |x|$, when $|x| \le \pi$
   (d) $f(x) = (\pi^2 - x^2)^{1/2}$, when $|x| \le \pi$
   (e) $f(x) = \sin(1/x)$, when $|x| \le \pi$
   (f) $f(x) = x^2 \sin(1/x)$, $f(0) = 0$, when $|x| \le \pi$
   (g) $f(x) = (x^2)^{1/3}$, when $|x| \le \pi$
   (h) $f(x) = x - 1$, if $x > 0$,
   $\quad\quad = x + 1$, if $x < 0$, on $|x| \le \pi$.

7.4 The convergence of the Fourier series of a piecewise smooth function

In **7.1** we have seen that when a Riemann integrable function $f(x)$ is given we may obtain by integration the Fourier series corresponding to $f(x)$. At once two questions arise:

1. Is the Fourier series convergent for some or all values of x on the interval $-\pi \le x \le \pi$?

2. If the Fourier series converges, does it represent the function, that is, does it converge to $f(x)$?

To date, no complete answer is known to either of these questions.

In other words, necessary and sufficient conditions are unknown.

The Fourier series of Example 1 converges for all x and yet does not represent the function $f(x)$, for they differ at all points $x = k\pi$, $k = 0, 1, 2, \ldots$. Note that for $x = k\pi$ the Fourier series is zero, whereas $f(x)$ is not defined.

Since the Fourier series is unaltered when $f(x)$ is redefined by putting $f(k\pi) = 0$, this special situation can be corrected. A glance at Figure 12 shows that $f(k\pi) = \frac{1}{2}[f(k\pi +) + f(k\pi -)]$, that is, the value of $f(x)$ at the point of discontinuity is the arithmetic mean of the right- and left-hand limit.

If we redefine $f(x)$ at points of discontinuity by putting $f(x) = \frac{1}{2}[f(x +) + f(x -)]$ which apparently holds also at points where $f(x)$ is continuous, we can prove the following theorem.

7.4-1 Theorem. If the function $f(x)$ with period 2π is piecewise smooth and each point of the interval $-\pi \leq x \leq \pi$ satisfies the equation

$$f(x) = \frac{1}{2}[f(x +) + f(x -)] ,$$

then the Fourier series corresponding to $f(x)$ converges at every point and represents the function $f(x)$.

Proof. We consider the partial sums

$$S_n(x) = \frac{1}{2} a_0 + \sum_{\mu=1}^{n} (a_\mu \cos \mu x + b_\mu \sin \mu x) .$$

If for a_μ, b_μ the integral expressions of relations (2) are substituted and then the order of integration and summation are interchanged, it follows that

$$S_n(x) = \frac{1}{\pi} \int_{-\pi}^{\pi} f(t) \left[\frac{1}{2} + \sum_{\mu=1}^{n} (\cos \mu t \cos \mu x + \sin \mu t \sin \mu x) \right] dt .$$

Further, the familiar formula $\cos \mu t \cos \mu x + \sin \mu t \sin \mu x = \cos \mu(t - x)$ and the relation (see Exercise 35, 4.A)

$$\frac{1}{2} + \sum_{i=1}^{n} \cos i\mu = \frac{\sin (n + \frac{1}{2})\mu}{2 \sin \frac{1}{2} \mu}$$

yield

$$S_n(x) = \frac{1}{\pi} \int_{-\pi}^{\pi} f(t) \frac{\sin (n + \frac{1}{2})(t - x)}{2 \sin \frac{1}{2}(t - x)} dt = \frac{1}{\pi} \int_{-\pi}^{\pi} \lambda(t) dt .$$

If we note that $\lambda(t)$ has a period 2π [$f(t)$ is periodic and the series of the ratio has a period 2π] and, consequently,

$$\int_{-\pi-x}^{\pi-x} \lambda(t)\,dt = \int_{-\pi}^{\pi} \lambda(t)\,dt ,$$

we obtain the more compact form

$$S_n(x) = \frac{1}{\pi}\int_{-\pi}^{\pi} f(\mu + x)\frac{\sin(n+\frac{1}{2})\mu}{2\sin\frac{1}{2}\mu}\,d\mu .$$

We obtain a particularly convenient form for our purposes if we split the integral into an integral from $-\pi$ to 0 and one from 0 to π. In the integral from $-\pi$ to 0 we put $\mu = -s$, so that

$$\int_{-\pi}^{0} f(\mu + x)\frac{\sin(n+\frac{1}{2})\mu}{2\sin\frac{1}{2}\mu}\,d\mu = -\int_{\pi}^{0} f(-s + x)\frac{\sin(n+\frac{1}{2})s}{2\sin\frac{1}{2}s}\,ds$$

$$= \int_{0}^{\pi} f(x - s)\frac{\sin(n+\frac{1}{2})s}{2\sin\frac{1}{2}s}\,ds .$$

Changing the dummy variable s to μ and combining the two parts of the original integral we obtain

$$S_n(x) = \frac{1}{\pi}\int_{0}^{\pi} [f(x + \mu) + f(x - \mu)]\frac{\sin(n+\frac{1}{2})\mu}{2\sin\frac{1}{2}\mu}\,d\mu .$$

Since

$$\frac{2}{\pi}\int_{0}^{\pi}\frac{\sin(n+\frac{1}{2})\mu}{2\sin\frac{1}{2}\mu}\,d\mu = \frac{2}{\pi}\int_{0}^{\pi}\left[\frac{1}{2} + \sum_{i=1}^{n}\cos i\mu\right]d\mu = 1 ,$$

we see that

$$f(x) = \frac{1}{\pi}\int_{0}^{\pi} 2f(x)\frac{\sin(n+\frac{1}{2})\mu}{2\sin\frac{1}{2}\mu}\,d\mu .$$

Hence,

$$S_n(x) - f(x) = \frac{1}{\pi}\int_{0}^{\pi} w(\mu)\sin\left(n + \frac{1}{2}\right)\mu\,d\mu$$

where

$$w(\mu) = \frac{f(x + \mu) + f(x - \mu) - 2f(x)}{2\sin\frac{1}{2}\mu}$$

(for fixed x) is a function of μ.

If we can show that $w(\mu)$ is integrable on $0 \le x \le \pi$ then

$$\lim_{n\to\infty}\int_{0}^{\pi} w(\mu)\sin\left(n + \frac{1}{2}\right)\mu\,d\mu = \lim_{n\to\infty}\int_{0}^{\pi}\left[w(\mu)\cos\frac{\mu}{2}\right]\sin n\mu\,d\mu$$

$$+ \lim_{n\to\infty}\int_{0}^{\pi}\left[w(\mu)\sin\frac{\mu}{2}\right]\cos n\mu\,d\mu$$

$$= 0 + 0 = 0$$

by Corollary 2 of **7.2-1**. Consequently, $\lim_{n \to \infty} [S_n(x) - f(x)] = 0$, whence $\lim_{n \to \infty} S_n(x) = f(x)$, and the proof is complete.

Now $w(\mu)$ is a combination of integrable functions. The only doubt about integrability of $w(\mu)$ arises from the fact that $\sin \frac{1}{2} \mu = 0$ when $\mu = 0$. Thus, to prove that $w(\mu)$ is integrable we have to show that it is bounded from the right as $\mu \to 0$.

By hypothesis $2 f(x) = f(x +) + f(x -)$ and $w(\mu)$ can be written

$$w(\mu) = \left[\frac{f(x + \mu) - f(x +)}{\mu} + \frac{f(x - \mu) - f(x -)}{\mu} \right] \frac{\frac{1}{2} \mu}{\sin \frac{1}{2} \mu} \, .$$

Since the familiar $\lim_{\mu \to \infty} \frac{1}{2} \mu / \sin \frac{1}{2} \mu = 1$ and $f(x)$ is piecewise smooth, that is, $f'(x +)$ and $f'(x -)$ exist, it follows that

$$\lim_{\mu \to 0} w(\mu) = f'(x +) - f'(x -)$$

exists. Consequently $w(\mu)$ is bounded.

It follows that $w(\mu)$ is integrable. This completes the proof.

Since the functions $f(x)$ of Examples 1, 2, and 3 are piecewise smooth on the interval $-\pi \le x \le \pi$, the conditions of **7.4-1** are met if we redefine the functions by requiring that $f(x) = \frac{1}{2}[f(x +) + f(x -)]$ for all x. Under these conditions it follows that the Fourier series generated by these functions:

(a) converge for all x, and

(b) converge pointwise to $f(x)$, that means that the symbol $\sim$ can be replaced by the equality sign $=$. Thus we may write the examples discussed in **6.1** as equalities.

Example 4.

$$f(x) = \sin x + \frac{1}{3} \sin 3 x + \frac{1}{5} \sin 5 x + \cdots$$

$$+ \frac{1}{2 k - 1} \sin (2 k - 1)x + \cdots = - (\pi/4) \, , \quad - \pi < x < 0 \, ,$$

$$= 0 \, , \quad x = 0 \, , \quad x = \pm \pi \, ,$$

$$= \pi/4 \, , \quad 0 < x < \pi \, .$$

We have already mentioned in **7.1** that the series converges uniformly for all x if the neighborhoods of $x = k\pi$, $k = 0, 1, 2, 3, \ldots$ are excluded. It can be shown that the Fourier series of a piecewise smooth function converges uniformly on every closed interval which contains no point of discontinuity of $f(x)$.

Fourier series can be used for evaluating special series in a closed form. For $x = \pi/2$, $\pi/6$, $\pi/3$, the above series yields the remarkable series

$$1 - \frac{1}{3} + \frac{1}{5} - \frac{1}{7} + \cdots + (-1)^{n-1}\frac{1}{2n-1} + \cdots = \frac{\pi}{4},$$

$$1 + \frac{1}{5} - \frac{1}{7} - \frac{1}{11} + \frac{1}{13} + \frac{1}{17} - \cdots = \frac{\pi}{3},$$

$$1 - \frac{1}{5} + \frac{1}{7} - \frac{1}{11} + \frac{1}{13} - \cdots = \frac{\pi}{2\cdot 3^{1/2}},$$

respectively. [Hint: To obtain the second series use $2f(\pi/6) + 2f(\pi/2)$.]

Example 5.

$$\frac{\pi^2}{3} + 4 \sum_{n=1}^{\infty} (-1)^n \frac{\cos nx}{n^2} = x^2, \quad -\pi \leq x \leq \pi, \quad f(x+2\pi) = f(x).$$

Here the periodic function is continuous for all x. Furthermore, it is piecewise smooth and needs no redefinition, since the equality $f(x) = \frac{1}{2}[f(x+) + f(x-)]$ holds for all x.

For $x = \pi$ and $x = 0$ we obtain the familiar series

$$\sum_{n=1}^{\infty} \frac{1}{n^2} = \frac{\pi^2}{6} \quad \text{and} \quad \sum_{n=1}^{\infty} (-1)^{n-1}\frac{1}{n^2} = \frac{\pi^2}{12}.$$

Note that the series converges absolutely and uniformly. This property holds for all functions of this kind.

7.4-2 Theorem. If a piecewise smooth function $f(x)$ with a period 2π is continuous on the interval $-\pi \leq x \leq \pi$, then its Fourier series converges absolutely and uniformly for all x.

Proof. By hypothesis the function $h(x) = f'(x)$ is piecewise continuous. If the Fourier coefficients of $f(x)$ are denoted by a_k, b_k and those of $h(x)$ by c_k, d_k, then, since $f(\pi) = f(-\pi)$, integration by parts yields

$$c_k = \frac{1}{\pi}\int_{-\pi}^{\pi} h(x)\cos kx\,dx = \frac{1}{\pi}f(x)\cos kx\Big|_{-\pi}^{\pi} + \frac{k}{\pi}\int_{-\pi}^{\pi} f(x)\sin kx\,dx = kb_k.$$

Similarly, $d_k = -ka_k$, $c_0 = 0$, $k = 1, 2, \ldots$.

Hence, Bessel's inequality (Corollary 1 of **7.2-1**) applied to $h(x)$ gives

$$\sum_{k=1}^{n} (c_k^2 + d_k^2) = \sum_{k=1}^{n} k^2(a_k^2 + b_k^2) \leq \frac{1}{\pi}\int_{-\pi}^{\pi} h^2(x)\,dx = A^2.$$

If we note further that the maximum value of $a_k\cos kx + b_k\sin kx$ is $(a_k^2 + b_k^2)^{1/2}$, from Cauchy-Schwarz inequality **[1.1-1]** it follows that

$$\sum_{\mu=n+1}^{m} |a_\mu\cos \mu x + b_\mu\sin \mu x| \leq \sum_{\mu=n+1}^{m} (a_\mu^2 + b_\mu^2)^{1/2} = \sum_{\mu=n+1}^{m} \frac{1}{\mu}[\mu(a_\mu^2 + b_\mu^2)^{1/2}]$$

$$\leq \left[\sum_{\mu=n+1}^{m} \frac{1}{\mu^2} \right]^{1/2} \left[\sum_{\mu=n+1}^{m} \mu^2(a_\mu^2 + b_\mu^2) \right]^{1/2}$$

$$\leq A \left[\sum_{\mu=n+1}^{m} \frac{1}{\mu^2} \right]^{1/2}.$$

Since $\sum_{\mu=1}^{\infty} 1/\mu^2$ is convergent, $\sum_{\mu=n+1}^{m} 1/\mu^2$ can be made as small as we please by choosing n and m large enough, so that $A \sum_{\mu=n+1}^{m} 1/\mu^2 < \varepsilon$ where $\varepsilon > 0$ is arbitrarily small. Thus Cauchy's criterion

$$\sum_{\mu=n+1}^{m} |a_\mu \cos \mu x + b_\mu \sin \mu x| < \varepsilon \quad \text{for } n > n_0(\varepsilon), \quad m > n$$

is satisfied for all x. This proves the absolute and uniform convergence of the Fourier series.

Example 6. In this case the Fourier series consists of two trigonometric series, and we have the relation

$$-\frac{\pi}{4} - \frac{2}{\pi} \sum_{k=1}^{\infty} \frac{\cos(2k-1)x}{(2k-1)^2} + \sum_{k=1}^{\infty} \frac{1+(-1)^{k+1}2}{k} \sin kx$$

$$= -\pi, \quad -\pi < x < 0,$$
$$= -(\pi/2), \quad x = 0,$$
$$= 0, \quad x = \pm \pi,$$
$$= x, \quad 0 < x < \pi.$$

The series converges uniformly on any closed interval which does not contain the points of discontinuity $x = k\pi$, $k = 0, \pm 1, \pm 2, \ldots$ (see Fig. 14).

For $x = 0$ and $x = \pi/2$ we obtain

$$\sum_{k=1}^{\infty} \frac{1}{(2k-1)^2} = \frac{\pi^2}{8} \quad \text{and} \quad \sum_{k=1}^{\infty} \frac{(-1)^{k+1}}{2k-1} = \frac{\pi}{4},$$

respectively.

7.5 Change of scale

In many applications the function $F(x)$ is defined on the interval $-l \leq x \leq l$ where $l > 0$ is not equal to π.

One can easily obtain a Fourier series valid on the extended interval by introducing a new variable t so that

$$\frac{t}{\pi} = \frac{x}{l}$$

and by defining $f(t) = F(x)$. Then $f(t)$ is defined on the interval $|t| \leq \pi$.

If $F(x)$ is piecewise smooth then so is $f(t)$ and by the familiar method we obtain

$$f(t) = \frac{1}{2} a_0 + \sum_{n=1}^{\infty} (a_n \cos nt + b_n \sin nt)$$

where

$$a_n = \frac{1}{\pi} \int_{-\pi}^{\pi} f(t) \cos nt\, dt \;, \quad b_n = \frac{1}{\pi} \int_{-\pi}^{\pi} f(t) \sin nt\, dt \;.$$

Now, substituting $f(t) = F(x)$ and $t = \pi x/l$ we have

$$F(x) = \frac{a_0}{2} + \sum_{n=1}^{\infty} \left(a_n \cos \frac{n\pi x}{l} + b_n \sin \frac{n\pi x}{l} \right)$$

with

$$a_n = \frac{1}{l} \int_{-l}^{l} F(x) \cos \frac{n\pi x}{l} dx \;, \quad b_n = \frac{1}{l} \int_{-l}^{l} F(x) \sin \frac{n\pi x}{l} dx \;.$$

The Fourier series has a period $2l$ and $F(x)$ is to be defined accordingly, that is, $F(x + 2l) = F(x)$.

If $F(x)$ is even or odd we obtain a pure cosine or a pure sine series where

$$a_n = \frac{2}{l} \int_{0}^{l} F(x) \cos \frac{n\pi x}{l} dx \;, \quad b_n = 0 \;,$$

or

$$b_n = \frac{2}{l} \int_{0}^{l} F(x) \sin \frac{n\pi x}{l} dx \;, \quad a_n = 0 \;,$$

respectively.

Example 7. Obtain the Fourier series of the function defined by $F(x) = x - [x] - \frac{1}{2}$, when x is not an integer, and $F(k) = 0$, $k = 0, \pm 1, \ldots$, where $[x]$ denotes the largest integer contained in x (Fig. 16).

It is apparent that $F(x + 1) = F(x)$ and $F(- x) = - F(x)$, that is, the function is odd and possesses a period $2l = 1$. Consequently $a_n = 0$ and

$$b_n = \frac{2}{l} \int_{0}^{l} F(x) \sin \frac{n\pi x}{l} dx = 4 \int_{0}^{1/2} \left(x - \frac{1}{2} \right) \sin 2n\pi x\, dx \;.$$

On integration by parts we obtain $b_n = - 1/n\pi$ and it follows that

$$F(x) = - \sum_{n=1}^{\infty} \frac{\sin 2n\pi x}{n\pi} \;.$$

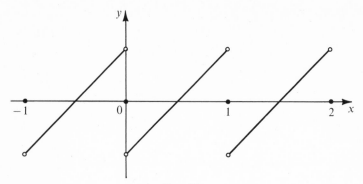

FIG. 16

The series converges uniformly except for integral values of x, that is, in any interval $|x - k| \geq \delta$, $0 < \delta < \frac{1}{2}$, $k = 0, \pm 1, \ldots$.

Example 8. Obtain a Fourier series of the function defined by $F(x) = x$ when $0 < x < 2$.

In this case the values of the function are to be considered only on the interval $0 < x < l$ $(l = 2)$ and what the function may be outside of this interval is completely immaterial. In particular, we may extend the function $F(x)$ to the interval $-l < x < 0$ in any way we please, and then obtain a Fourier series. If the extended function $\bar{F}(x)$ is defined in such a way that it is piecewise smooth and $\bar{F}(x) = \frac{1}{2}[\bar{F}(x+) + \bar{F}(x-)]$ at points of discontinuity, then the Fourier series will of course converge on the whole interval to $\bar{F}(x)$, and irrespective of the extension it will represent the given function $F(x)$ on $0 < x < l$ $(l = 2)$, as required.

Usually the function $\bar{F}(x)$ is defined to be even or odd, and two equally convenient series are obtained. First we consider an even function defined by $\bar{F}(x) = |x|$ when $-2 \leq x \leq 2$ and $\bar{F}(x + 4) = \bar{F}(x)$. Then $b_n = 0$ and

$$a_n = \frac{2}{l} \int_0^l F(x) \cos \frac{n\pi x}{l} dx = \int_0^2 x \cos \frac{n\pi x}{2} dx .$$

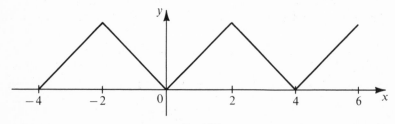

FIG. 17

On integration by parts we obtain

$$a_n = \frac{4}{\pi^2 n^2}(\cos n\pi - 1) \quad \text{if } n \neq 0 , \quad a_0 = \int_0^2 x \, dx = 2 .$$

Thus the Fourier series of $\bar{F}(x)$ follows:

(a) $\bar{F}(x) = 1 + \dfrac{4}{\pi^2} \sum_{n=1}^{\infty} \dfrac{\cos n\pi - 1}{n^2} \cos \dfrac{n\pi x}{2} = 1 - \dfrac{8}{\pi^2} \sum_{k=1}^{\infty} \dfrac{\cos (2k - 1)(\pi x/2)}{(2k - 1)^2} .$

If we define the function $\bar{F}(x)$ to be odd, that is, $\bar{F}(x) = x$ when $-2 < x < 2$, $\bar{F}[2(2k + 1)] = 0$, $k = 0, \pm 1, \ldots$, and $\bar{F}(x + 4) = \bar{F}(x)$, then

$$a_n = 0 , \quad b_n = \frac{2}{l} \int_0^l \bar{F}(x) \sin \frac{n\pi x}{l} \, dx = \int_0^2 x \sin \frac{n\pi x}{2} dx .$$

Similarly, on integration by parts we obtain

$$b_n = -\frac{4 \cos n\pi}{n\pi} .$$

Hence (see Figure 18),

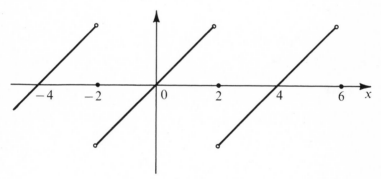

FIG. 18

(b) $$\bar{F}(x) = \frac{4}{\pi} \sum_{k=1}^{\infty} \frac{(-1)^{k+1} \sin (k\pi x/2)}{k}$$

Note that series (a) converges absolutely and uniformly for all x, whereas the sine series (b) converges only conditionally and uniformly on every closed interval not containing any of the points $2(2k + 1)$, $k = 0, \pm 1, \ldots$. However both series represent the function $F(x) = x$ equally well on the interval $0 < x < 2$, as desired.

Exercises 7.C

1. If the Fourier series corresponding to $f(x)$ converges uniformly to $f(x)$ on $-l \leq x \leq l$, prove that Bessel's inequality becomes Parseval's identity

$$\frac{1}{l} \int_{-l}^{l} f^2(x)\,dx = \frac{1}{2}a_0^2 + \sum_{n=1}^{\infty} (a_n^2 + b_n^2) \ .$$

2. In Example 8 we obtained the series

$$|x| = 1 - \frac{8}{\pi^2} \sum_{n=1}^{\infty} \frac{\cos (2k-1)(\pi x/2)}{(2k-1)^2} \ , \quad -2 \leq x \leq 2 \ .$$

Using Parseval's identity (see Exercise 1) first evaluate the series $\sum_{k=1}^{\infty} 1/(2k-1)^4$, then obtain the value of $\sum_{k=1}^{\infty} 1/k^4$.

3. Obtain the Fourier series of $f(x)$ defined by
$$f(x) = x^2 \ , \quad -1 \leq x \leq 1 \ , \quad f(x+2) = f(x) \ .$$

4. Obtain a pure sine and a pure cosine series of $f(x)$ defined as follows
   (a) $f(x) = \pi/4$, when $0 < x < \pi$,
   (b) $f(x) = x$, when $0 < x < 1$,
   (c) $f(x) = x^2$, when $0 < x < 3$.

5. Given $f(x) = x + x^2$ when $-\pi < x < \pi$. Redefine it to satisfy the conditions of **7.4-1**. Then from its Fourier series deduce

$$\sum_{n=1}^{\infty} \frac{1}{n^2} = \frac{\pi^2}{6} \ .$$

6. Show that
   (a) $\cos x = \dfrac{8}{\pi} \displaystyle\sum_{n=1}^{\infty} \dfrac{n \sin 2nx}{4n^2 - 1}$, if $0 < x < \pi$,

   (b) $\sin x = \dfrac{2}{\pi} - \dfrac{4}{\pi} \displaystyle\sum_{n=1}^{\infty} \dfrac{\cos 2nx}{4n^2 - 1}$, if $0 < x < \pi$.

7. The function $f(x)$ is defined as
$$f(x) = \cos ax \ , \quad -\pi \leq x \leq \pi \ .$$
Show that the Fourier expansion is

$$\cos ax = \frac{2a \sin a\pi}{\pi} \left[\frac{1}{a^2} + \sum_{n=1}^{\infty} (-1)^n \frac{\cos nx}{a^2 - n^2} \right]$$

where a is not an integer. Deduce the formulae

$$\frac{1}{\sin a\pi} = \frac{1}{a\pi} + \frac{2a}{\pi} \sum_{n=1}^{\infty} (-1)^{n+1} \frac{1}{n^2 - a^2} \ ,$$

$$\text{ctn } a\pi = \frac{1}{a\pi} + \frac{2a}{\pi} \sum_{n=1}^{\infty} \frac{1}{a^2 - n^2} \ ,$$

valid except for $a = 0, \pm 1, \pm 2, \dots$.

8. In the sciences the complex form of Fourier series is often used. Using the familiar formula
$$e^{i\theta} = \cos \theta + i \sin \theta$$
show that the Fourier series

$$f(x) = \frac{1}{2} a_0 + \sum_{n=1}^{\infty} (a_n \cos nx + b_n \sin nx)$$

can be written in the form

$$f(x) = \sum_{n=-\infty}^{\infty} c_n e^{inx}$$

where $\cos nx = \dfrac{1}{2}(e^{inx} + e^{-inx})$, $\sin nx = \dfrac{1}{2i}(e^{inx} - e^{-inx})$,

$$c_n = \frac{1}{2\pi}\int_{-\pi}^{\pi} f(x)e^{-inx}\,dx\ ,\quad c_0 = a_0\ ,\quad c_n = \frac{1}{2}(a_n - ib_n)\ ,\quad c_{-n} = \frac{1}{2}(a_n + ib_n)\ ,$$

$n = 1, 2, 3, \ldots$.

9. Using Exercise 8, show that the complex form of the Fourier series of $f(x)$ defined by

$$f(x) = e^x\ ,\qquad\qquad \text{when } -\pi < x < \pi\ ,$$
$$= \tfrac{1}{2}(e^\pi + e^{-\pi})\ ,\quad \text{when } x = \pm\pi\ ,\qquad f(x + 2\pi) = f(x)$$

is

$$f(x) = \frac{e^\pi - e^{-\pi}}{2\pi}\sum_{n=-\infty}^{\infty}(-1)^n\frac{1 + ni}{1 + n^2}e^{inx}$$

and rewrite it in the real form

$$f(x) = \frac{e^\pi - e^{-\pi}}{\pi}\left[\frac{1}{2} - \frac{1}{1 + 1^2}(\cos x - \sin x) + \frac{1}{1 + 2^2}(\cos 2x - 2\sin 2x)\right.$$
$$\left. + \cdots + (-1)^n\frac{1}{1 + n^2}(\cos nx - n\sin nx) + \cdots\right].$$

10. Using Exercise 9, evaluate the series

   (a) $\displaystyle\sum_{n=1}^{\infty}\frac{1}{1 + n^2}\ ,$ (b) $\displaystyle\sum_{n=1}^{\infty}\frac{(-1)^{n+1}}{1 + n^2}\ .$

7.6 Integration of Fourier series

In **5.5** we have seen that an infinite series can be integrated term by term if it is uniformly convergent; otherwise term by term integration might lead to incorrect results. One of the remarkable properties of Fourier series is that not only do we not require that the Fourier series corresponding to $f(x)$ shall uniformly converge, but we need not even assume that it converges at all in order to integrate it termwise.

7.6-1 Theorem. If $f(x)$ is piecewise continuous on the interval $-\pi \le x \le \pi$ and the corresponding Fourier series is

$$f(x) \sim \frac{1}{2}a_0 + \sum_{\mu=1}^{\infty}(a_\mu \cos \mu x + b_\mu \sin \mu x)\ ,$$

then the series can be integrated term by term between any two limits c and x lying on the interval $-\pi \le x \le \pi$, that is,

$$\int_c^x f(t)\,dt = \int_c^x \frac{1}{2}a_0\,dt + \sum_{\mu=1}^{\infty}\left[\int_c^x a_\mu \cos \mu t\,dt + \int_c^x b_\mu \sin \mu t\,dt\right]$$

with " $\sim$ " replaced by " $=$ ".

Furthermore, for every fixed value of c the series on the right converges absolutely and uniformly in x.

Proof. Consider the function

$$F(x) = \int_{-\pi}^{x} \left[f(t) - \frac{1}{2} a_0 \right] dt .$$

This function is clearly continuous on the interval and, since $f(x)$ is piecewise continuous, possesses a piecewise continuous derivative $F'(x) = f(x) - \frac{1}{2} a_0$. Consequently, $F(x)$ is piecewise smooth. Furthermore,

$$F(\pi) - F(-\pi) = \int_{-\pi}^{\pi} \left[f(t) - \frac{1}{2} a_0 \right] dt$$

$$= \int_{-\pi}^{\pi} f(t)\, dt - \frac{1}{2} a_0 \int_{-\pi}^{\pi} dt = \pi a_0 - \pi a_0 = 0 .$$

Thus, if follows that $F(\pi) = F(-\pi)$ and consequently $F(x)$ can be extended continuously with a period of 2π for all x.

Now by **7.4-1** and **7.4-2** it follows that

$$F(x) = \frac{1}{2} A_0 + \sum_{\mu=1}^{\infty} (A_\mu \cos \mu x + B_\mu \sin \mu x) ;$$

the series converges absolutely and uniformly and represents $F(x)$ for all x. If we note further that

$$A_\mu = \frac{1}{\pi} \int_{-\pi}^{\pi} F(x) \cos \mu x\, dx , \qquad B_\mu = \frac{1}{\pi} \int_{-\pi}^{\pi} F(x) \sin \mu x\, dx ,$$

on integrating by parts, as in **7.4-2**, we obtain the relations

$$A_\mu = -\frac{b_\mu}{\mu} , \qquad B_\mu = \frac{a_\mu}{\mu} \quad (\mu > 0) .$$

Hence,

$$F(x) - F(c) = \sum_{\mu=1}^{\infty} [A_\mu(\cos \mu x - \cos \mu c) + B_\mu(\sin \mu x - \sin \mu c)]$$

$$= \sum_{\mu=1}^{\infty} \left[\frac{a_\mu}{\mu}(\sin \mu x - \sin \mu c) - \frac{b_\mu}{\mu}(\cos \mu x - \cos \mu c) \right] .$$

If $F(x)$ is replaced by its definition, it follows that

$$\int_{c}^{x} f(t)\, dt - \int_{c}^{x} \frac{1}{2} a_0\, dt = \sum_{\mu=1}^{\infty} \left[a_\mu \int_{c}^{x} \cos \mu t\, dt + b_\mu \int_{c}^{x} \sin \mu t\, dt \right] ,$$

and this is the relation we started out to prove. Note that the series on the right side converges absolutely and uniformly.

If in addition $f(x + 2\pi) = f(x)$, integration term by term can be carried out over any interval whatever.

Theorem **7.6-1** has not only theoretical value but is handy in obtaining new Fourier series and in evaluating special infinite series. This is illustrated by the following examples.

Example 9. The trigonometric series

$$\sum_{n=1}^{\infty} \frac{\sin nx}{\log (1 + n)}$$

which converges for all x and by **5.7-3** even converges uniformly on any closed interval not containing any of the points $x = 2k\pi$, $k = 0, \pm 1, \ldots$ is not a Fourier series. For if the series were a Fourier series the term by term integrated series

$$- \sum_{n=1}^{\infty} \frac{\cos nx}{n \log (1 + n)}$$

would converge absolutely and uniformly (**7.6-1**). But the series diverges for $x = 0$ (see Chapter 3, Example 14).

Example 10. By integrating the relation

$$f_1(x) = x - \frac{1}{2} = - \sum_{n=1}^{\infty} \frac{\sin 2n\pi x}{n\pi} , \quad 0 < x < 1$$

(Example 7) term by term we obtain a new series

$$\frac{x^2}{2} - \frac{x}{2} + C = \sum_{n=1}^{\infty} \frac{\cos 2n\pi x}{2\pi^2 n^2} , \quad 0 \le x \le 1 ,$$

which by **7.6-1** converges on the closed interval $0 \le x \le 1$ absolutely and uniformly. (Note that the original series does not converge uniformly on $0 < x < 1$.)

To determine C we may substitute for x a special value, say, $x = 0$ or $x = 1$. Then

$$C = \frac{1}{2\pi^2} \sum_{n=1}^{\infty} \frac{1}{n^2} = \frac{1}{2\pi^2} \cdot \frac{\pi^2}{6} = \frac{1}{12} .$$

If the value of the series $\sum_{n=1}^{\infty} 1/n^2$ is not readily available we may obtain C by observing that the constant C of the Fourier series

$$x^2 - \frac{x}{2} = - C + \sum_{n=1}^{\infty} \frac{\cos 2n\pi x}{2\pi^2 n^2}$$

is $- C = \frac{1}{2} a_0$, where

$$a_0 = \frac{2}{l} \int_0^l f(x)\,dx = 2 \int_0^1 \left(\frac{x^2}{2} - \frac{x}{2} \right) dx = -\frac{1}{6} \, ,$$

whence $C = 1/12$. Consequently,

$$f_2(x) = \frac{x^2}{2} - \frac{x}{2} + \frac{1}{12} = \sum_{n=1}^{\infty} \frac{\cos 2n\pi x}{2\pi^2 n^2} \, .$$

By integrating the last series once more we have

$$\frac{x^3}{6} - \frac{x^2}{4} + \frac{x}{12} + C = \sum_{n=1}^{\infty} \frac{\sin 2n\pi x}{2^2 \pi^3 n^3} \, .$$

Substitution of $x = 0$ yields at once $C = 0$. Thus

$$f_3(x) = \frac{x^3}{6} - \frac{x^2}{4} + \frac{x}{12} = \sum_{n=1}^{\infty} \frac{\sin 2n\pi x}{2^2 \pi^3 n^3} \, .$$

By repeating the procedure we can obtain $f_1(x)$, $f_2(x)$, $f_3(x)$, $\ldots$, $f_n(x)$, $\ldots$, the "Bernoulli polynomials" which play an important part in many investigations. (see K. Knopp, *Infinite Series*, p. 623.)

These relations can be used for evaluation of special series. For instance, putting $x = \frac{1}{4}$ in $f_3(x)$ we obtain at once

$$\frac{\pi^3}{32} = 1 - \frac{1}{3^3} + \frac{1}{5^3} - \frac{1}{7^3} + \cdots + (-1)^{n+1} \frac{1}{(2n-1)^3} + \cdots .$$

Exercises 6.D

1. Integrating the relation (Example 5)
$$\sum_{n=1}^{\infty} (-1)^n \frac{\cos nx}{n^2} = \frac{1}{4}\left(x^2 - \frac{\pi^2}{3} \right), \quad -\pi \le x \le \pi \, ,$$
obtain the series
$$\sum_{n=1}^{\infty} (-1)^n \frac{\sin nx}{n^3} = \frac{1}{12}(x^2 - \pi^2)x$$
and then by using Parseval's identity (Exercises 6.C, Problem 1) evaluate $\sum_{n=1}^{\infty} 1/n^6$.

2. Integrating term by term the series
$$\sum_{n=1}^{\infty} \frac{\sin nx}{n} = \frac{\pi - x}{2}, \quad 0 < x < 2\pi$$
obtain successively

(a) $\displaystyle \sum_{n=1}^{\infty} \frac{\cos nx}{n^2} = \frac{\pi^2}{6} - \frac{\pi}{2}x + \frac{x^2}{4}$,   (b) $\displaystyle \sum_{n=1}^{\infty} \frac{\sin nx}{n^3} = \frac{\pi^2}{6}x - \frac{\pi}{4}x^2 + \frac{x^3}{12}$,

(c) $\displaystyle \sum_{n=1}^{\infty} \frac{\cos nx}{n^4} = \frac{\pi^4}{90} - \frac{\pi^2}{12}x^2 + \frac{\pi}{12}x^3 - \frac{x^4}{48}$,

all valid on $0 \le x \le 2\pi$. Then evaluate the series

$$\sum_{n=1}^{\infty} \frac{(-1)^{n+1}}{n^2}, \quad \sum_{n=1}^{\infty} \frac{(-1)^{n+1}}{(2n-1)^3}, \quad \sum_{n=1}^{\infty} \frac{(-1)^{n+1}}{n^4}.$$

3. Is the trigonometric series

$$\sum_{n=1}^{\infty} \frac{\cos nx}{\log(1+n)}$$

a Fourier series?

4. Using Example 1 for $k = 1$,

$$\sin x + \frac{1}{3}\sin 3x + \frac{1}{5}\sin 5x + \cdots + \frac{1}{2k-1}\sin(2k-1)x + \cdots$$
$$= -(\pi/4), \quad -\pi < x < 0,$$
$$= 0, \quad x = 0, \quad x = \pm\pi,$$
$$= \pi/4, \quad 0 < x < \pi,$$

evaluate the series

$$1 + \frac{1}{3^2} + \frac{1}{5^2} + \cdots + \frac{1}{n^2} + \cdots.$$

7.7 Remarks

Sufficient conditions for representation of a function by its Fourier series, as stated in **7.4-1**, cover almost any conceivable application in the natural sciences. The theorem holds under less stringent conditions, but to date necessary and sufficient conditions are not known. Efforts to deduce necessary and sufficient conditions from continuity, monotony, differentiability, integrability, and so on, have failed. For instance, a conjecture that a continuous function can be represented by its Fourier series was refuted by a counterexample given by du Bois-Reymond (Abhand. Akad. München, XII, 1876).

On the other hand, a continuous function need not be differentiable, as is shown by Weierstrass' example of a uniformly convergent trigonometric series

$$f(x) = \sum_{n=1}^{\infty} a^n \cos(b^n \pi x), \quad 0 < a < 1, \quad b \text{ an integer} > 0, \quad ab > 1 + \frac{3}{2}\pi.$$

This series represents a continuous function which is nowhere differentiable. And yet it possesses a Fourier series.

Since $f(x)$ is even and has a period $2l = 2$ it follows that $b_k = 0$ and

$$a_k = \frac{2}{l}\int_0^l f(x)\cos k\pi x\,dx = 2\sum_{n=1}^{\infty} a^n \int_0^l \cos(b^n \pi x)\cos k\pi x\,dx = 0, \quad \text{if } k \neq b^m,$$
$$= a^m, \quad \text{if } k = b^m,$$

$m = 1, 2, 3, \ldots$. Consequently the Fourier series of $f(x)$ is identical with the given trigonometric series.

It is easily seen that the following theorem holds:

If a trigonometric series converges uniformly on $-\pi \leq x \leq \pi$ (consequently, for all x) it is the Fourier series of the function represented by it, and this function admits no other representation by a trigonometric series converging uniformly on $-\pi \leq x \leq \pi$.

In Chapter 5 we have seen that the limiting function $f(x)$ of a sequence $\{f_n(x)\}$ may not be represented by the limiting curve C of the sequence $\{C_n\}$, where C_n denotes the curve $y = f_n(x)$, if the sequence does not converge uniformly. The same phenomenon occurs if the Fourier series does not converge uniformly. The limiting curves $y = S_n(x)$ do not represent the function $f(x)$, where $S_n(x)$ is the partial sum. This phenomenon in Fourier series, first accurately described by G. W. Gibbs, is known as Gibbs' phenomenon.

Let us consider an example (see Example 4).

$$f(x) = \sin x + \frac{\sin 3x}{3} + \cdots + \frac{\sin (2n-1)x}{2n-1} + \cdots$$

$$= -\pi/4 , \quad -\pi < x < 0 ,$$
$$= 0 , \quad x = 0 , \quad x = \pm \pi ,$$
$$= \pi/4 , \quad \pi < x < \pi .$$

Clearly, the limiting function $f(x)$ is discontinuous at $x = 0$, and consequently the series does not converge uniformly on every interval containing zero.

Differentiation of

$$y = S_{2n-1}(x) = \sin x + \frac{\sin 3x}{3} + \cdots + \frac{\sin (2n-1)x}{2n-1} ,$$

which represents the approximating curves, yields

$$y' = \cos x + \cos 3x + \cdots + \cos (2n-1)x = \frac{\sin 2nx}{2 \sin x}$$

which shows that the maxima of y occur at $2nx = \pi, 3\pi, 5\pi, \ldots$ and the minima at $2nx = 2\pi, 4\pi, 6\pi, \ldots$.

It is easily seen that

$$S_{2n-1}\left(\frac{\pi}{2n}\right) = \frac{1}{2} h \sum_{k=1}^{n} \frac{\sin (2k-1)(h/2)}{(2k-1)(h/2)} ,$$

where $h = \pi/n$, converges to the Riemann integral

$$\lim_{n \to \infty} S_{2n-1}\left(\frac{\pi}{2n}\right) = \frac{1}{2} \int_{0}^{\pi} \frac{\sin x}{x} dx \approx 1.179 \frac{\pi}{4} .$$

This shows that the first maximum of the approximation curves to the right of 0 tends to the segment $0 \le y \le 1.179(\pi/4)$. Similarly the first minimum of the approximation curves to the left of the origin tends to the segment $-1.179(\pi/4) \le y \le 0$.

Consequently, the approximation curves on the right of zero do not approach $\pi/4$ as we should expect, but tend to a value $1.179(\pi/4)$, which is greater that $\pi/4$.

Thus the continuous limiting approximation curve C contains, besides the graph of the function, the segment $-1.179(\pi/4) \le y \le 1.179(\pi/4)$ which exceeds the jump $\pi/2$ of the limiting function.

It can be shown that the Fourier series of every piecewise continuous function $f(x)$ exhibits the same behavior at points of discontinuity.

7.8 Fourier integrals

If a function is initially defined on a finite interval, say $-l < x < l$, we can always extend the definition of $f(x)$ outside this interval by imposing a periodicity condition, that is, by requiring the equation $f(x + 2l) = f(x)$ to hold for every x. Thus the function is defined everywhere on $-\infty < x < \infty$, and one can obtain the Fourier series corresponding to $f(x)$.

However, if the function is already defined everywhere on $-\infty < x < \infty$ and is not periodic, it cannot be represented by a Fourier series for all x. In this case the function can sometimes be represented by infinite integrals which are in many ways analogous to Fourier series. These integrals, known as Fourier integrals, play an important role in many applications.

The following discussion is heuristic. We shall start with the Fourier series of an arbitrary function defined on the interval $-l < x < l$ and see what happens to the representation when $l \to \infty$.

First let us consider the function of period $2l$ defined as follows:

$$
\begin{aligned}
f_l(x) &= 0 , && \text{when } -l < x < -1 , \\
&= 1 , && \text{when } -1 < x < 1 , \\
&= \tfrac{1}{2} , && \text{when } |x| = 1 , \\
&= 0 , && \text{when } 1 < x < l , \qquad f_l(x + 2l) = f_l(x) .
\end{aligned}
$$

Then the graph of $f_2(x)$ is given in Figure 19 and $f_4(x)$ in Figure 20.

As $l \to \infty$ we obtain the function (see Fig. 21)

$$
\begin{aligned}
f(x) &= \lim_{l \to \infty} f_l(x) = 1 , && |x| < 1 , \\
&= \tfrac{1}{2} , && |x| = 1 , \\
&= 0 , && \text{otherwise} .
\end{aligned}
$$

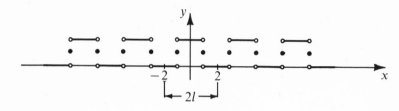

FIG. 19

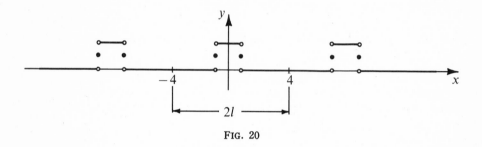

FIG. 20

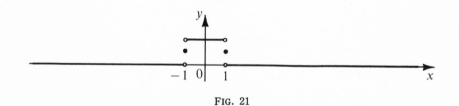

FIG. 21

Assume that $f(x)$ is piecewise smooth, periodic and satisfies the condition $f(x) = \frac{1}{2}[f(x+) + f(x-)]$ for all x. Then if in its Fourier series

$$f_l(x) = \frac{1}{2} a_0 + \sum_{n=1}^{\infty} \left(a_n \cos \frac{n\pi x}{l} + b_n \sin \frac{n\pi x}{l} \right)$$

the Fourier integral formulas for a_n, b_n are inserted (**7.5**) and the familiar relation

$$\cos \frac{n\pi t}{l} \cos \frac{n\pi x}{l} + \sin \frac{n\pi t}{l} \sin \frac{n\pi x}{l} = \cos n\pi \left(\frac{t-x}{l} \right)$$

is used, it follows that

$$f_l(x) = \frac{1}{2l} \int_{-l}^{l} f_l(t)\, dt + \frac{1}{l} \sum_{n=1}^{\infty} \int_{-l}^{l} f_l(t) \cos \frac{n\pi(t-x)}{l}\, dt .$$

Furthermore, if we assume that the integral

$$A = \int_{-\infty}^{\infty} |f(x)|\, dx$$

exists, then

$$\left| \frac{1}{2l} \int_{-l}^{l} f_l(t)\, dt \right| \le \frac{1}{2l} \int_{-l}^{l} |f_1(t)|\, dt \le \frac{A}{2l} \ .$$

Consequently, $\lim_{l \to \infty} a_0 = 0$.

If $\pi/l = h$, we obtain

$$f_l(x) = \frac{1}{2l} \int_{-l}^{l} f_l(t)\, dt + \frac{1}{\pi} \lim_{n \to \infty} h \sum_{k=1}^{n} \int_{-l}^{l} f_l(t) \cos nh(t-x)\, dt \ .$$

By choosing l large enough we can make h arbitrarily small. Since the first term on the right approaches 0, as l increases, and the second term is analogous to the definition of the definite integral in the sense of Riemann, we may conjecture that

$$\lim_{l \to \infty} f_l(x) = f(x) = \frac{1}{\pi} \int_{0}^{\infty} ds \int_{-\infty}^{\infty} f(t) \cos s(t-x)\, dt$$

which turns out to be a valid representation of the function $f(x)$. (A rigorous proof can be found in H. S. Carslaw, *Fourier's Series and Integrals*. pp. 283-294, Macmillan Co., New York, 1921.)

If the notation

$$A(s) = \int_{-\infty}^{\infty} f(t) \cos st\, dt \ , \quad B(s) = \int_{-\infty}^{\infty} f(t) \sin st\, dt$$

is introduced, the Fourier integral representation of $f(x)$ takes the form

$$f(x) = \frac{1}{\pi} \int_{0}^{\infty} [A(s) \cos sx + B(s) \sin sx]\, ds \ .$$

Similarly, as in the case of Fourier series, if $f(x)$ is an even function, then $B(s) = 0$, and

$$A(s) = 2 \int_{0}^{\infty} f(t) \cos st\, dt \ , \quad f(x) = \frac{1}{\pi} \int_{0}^{\infty} A(s) \cos sx\, ds \ .$$

If $f(x)$ is an odd function, then $A(s) = 0$, and

$$B(s) = 2 \int_{0}^{\infty} f(t) \sin st\, dt \ , \quad f(s) = \frac{1}{\pi} \int_{0}^{\infty} B(s) \sin sx\, ds \ .$$

Example 11. Obtain the Fourier integral representation of the function defined as follows

$$f(x) = 1, \quad \text{when } |x| < 1,$$
$$= \tfrac{1}{2}, \quad \text{when } |x| = 1,$$
$$= 0, \quad \text{when } |x| > 1.$$

Since $f(x)$ is even, $B(s) = 0$ and

$$A(s) = 2 \int_0^\infty f(t) \cos st \, dt = 2 \int_0^1 \cos st \, dt = \frac{2 \sin s}{s}.$$

Thus

$$f(x) = \frac{2}{\pi} \int_0^\infty \frac{\cos sx \sin s}{s} \, ds$$

which can be written in the form

$$\int_0^\infty \frac{\cos sx \sin s}{s} \, ds = \pi/2, \quad \text{when } |x| < 1,$$
$$= \pi/4, \quad \text{when } |x| = 1,$$
$$= 0, \quad \text{when } |x| > 1.$$

This integral, known as Dirichlet's discontinuous factor is used in many applications.

A particular case, when $x = 0$, yields the familiar integral

$$\int_0^\infty \frac{\sin s}{s} \, ds = \frac{\pi}{2}.$$

Example 12. Find the Fourier integral representation of
(a) $f(x) = e^{-k|x|}$, $-\infty < x < \infty$, $k > 0$. Since $f(x)$ is even, $B(s) = 0$ and

$$A(s) = 2 \int_0^\infty e^{-kt} \cos ts \, dt = \frac{2k}{k^2 + s^2}.$$

(It is easily obtained by integration by parts.) It follows that

$$f(x) = e^{-k|x|} = \frac{2k}{\pi} \int_0^\infty \frac{\cos sx}{k^2 + s^2} \, ds.$$

Hence,

$$\int_0^\infty \frac{\cos sx}{k^2 + s^2} \, ds = \frac{\pi}{2k} e^{-k|x|}, \quad k > 0.$$

144

(b)
$$f(x) = e^{-k|x|}, \qquad \text{when } x > 0 ,$$
$$= 0 , \qquad \text{when } x = 0 ,$$
$$= - e^{-k|x|}, \qquad \text{when } x < 0 .$$

Since the function is odd, $A(s) = 0$ and

$$B(s) = 2 \int_0^\infty e^{-kt} \sin st\, dt = \frac{s \sin sx}{k^2 + s^2} ,$$

$$f(x) = \frac{2}{\pi} \int_0^\infty \frac{s \sin sx}{k^2 + s^2}\, ds .$$

Hence,

$$\int_0^\infty \frac{s \sin sx}{k^2 + s^2}\, ds = (\pi/2) e^{-kx} , \quad x > 0 ,$$

$$= 0 , \quad x = 0 ,$$

$$= - (\pi/2) e^{-k|x|} , \quad x < 0 , \quad k > 0 .$$

These examples show that Fourier integral representation of a function may be used for evaluating integrals.

Exercises 7.E

1. Find the Fourier integral representation of
$$f(x) = 1 - |x| , \quad \text{when } |x| \le 1 ,$$
$$= 0 , \qquad \text{when } |x| > 1 ,$$
then evaluate the integral
$$\int_0^\infty \frac{1 - \cos s}{s^2} \cos (sx)\, ds .$$

2. As a special case of Problem 1 show that
$$\int_0^\infty \frac{\sin^2 s}{s^2}\, ds = \frac{\pi}{2} .$$

3. Show that the integral representation of the function
$$f(x) = 0 , \qquad \text{when } x < 0 ,$$
$$= \tfrac{1}{2} , \qquad \text{when } x = 0 ,$$
$$= e^{-x} , \qquad \text{when } x > 0 ,$$
which is neither even nor odd, is
$$f(x) = \frac{1}{\pi} \int_0^\pi \frac{\cos xs + s \sin xs}{1 + s^2}\, ds .$$

In Exercises 4-6 obtain Fourier integral representations if $f(x)$ is given as follows.

4. $f(x) = e^{-|x|} + e^{-2|x|} .$

5. $f(x) = |x| , \qquad \text{when } |x| \le 1 ,$

$$= 2 - |x| , \quad \text{when } 1 < |x| \le 2 ,$$
$$= 0 , \quad \text{when } |x| > 2 .$$

6. $f(x) = e^{-x} \cos x , \quad \text{when } x > 0 ,$
   $= - e^{x} \cos x , \quad \text{when } x < 0 ,$
   $= 0 , \quad \text{when } x = 0 .$

7. Show that

$$\int_{-\infty}^{\infty} ds \int_{-\infty}^{\infty} f(t) \sin s(x - t) \, dt = 0 .$$

Then using the formula $e^{i\theta} = \cos \theta + i \sin \theta$ obtain the so called complex form of the Fourier integral

$$f(x) = \frac{1}{2\pi} \int_{-\infty}^{\infty} ds \int_{-\infty}^{\infty} f(t) e^{is(x-t)} \, dt .$$

$$\left[\text{Hint:} \quad \text{Use} \quad f(x) = \frac{1}{\pi} \int_{0}^{\infty} ds \int_{-\infty}^{\infty} f(t) \cos s(t - x) \, dt \right.$$

$$\left. = \frac{1}{2\pi} \int_{-\infty}^{\infty} ds \int_{-\infty}^{\infty} f(t) \cdot \cos s(t - x) \, dt . \right]$$

7.9 Orthogonal functions

A sequence $\{\lambda_\mu(x)\}$ of functions is said to be orthogonal on an interval $a \le x \le b$ if the integral

$$\int_{a}^{b} \lambda_n(x) \lambda_m(x) \, dx = 0 \quad \text{if } m \ne n \ (m, n = 0, 1, 2, 3, \ldots) .$$

When $m = n$ the integral $N(\lambda_n)$

$$N(\lambda_n) = \int_{a}^{b} \lambda_n^2(x) \, dx$$

is called the norm of $\lambda_n(x)$.

The sequence of functions is called orthonormal if

$$\int_{a}^{b} \lambda_n(x) \lambda_m(x) \, dx = 0 , \quad \text{when } m \ne n ,$$

$$= 1 , \quad \text{when } m = n ,$$

that is, the norm of an orthonormal sequence is 1.

Example 13. We have already seen that the sequence of functions

$$1 , \quad \cos x , \quad \sin x , \quad \cos 2x , \quad \sin 2x , \ldots , \quad \cos nx , \quad \sin nx , \ldots$$

is orthogonal on the interval $-\pi \le x \le \pi$ (or on any interval of length 2π, that is, $-\pi \pm c \le x \le \pi \pm c, \ c > 0$).

Since $N(1) = 2\pi$, $N(\sin nx) = N(\cos nx) = \pi$, it is apparent that one obtains an orthonormal sequence by dividing each function by the square root of its norm, that is,

$$\frac{1}{(2\pi)^{1/2}}, \quad \frac{\cos x}{\pi^{1/2}}, \quad \frac{\sin x}{\pi^{1/2}}, \quad \frac{\cos 2x}{\pi^{1/2}}, \quad \frac{\sin 2x}{\pi^{1/2}}, \dots, \quad \frac{\cos nx}{\pi^{1/2}}, \quad \frac{\sin nx}{\pi^{1/2}}, \dots$$

is an orthonormal sequence.

Example 14. Similarly the sequence

$$\left(\frac{2}{\pi}\right)^{1/2} \sin x, \quad \left(\frac{2}{\pi}\right)^{1/2} \sin 2x, \dots, \quad \left(\frac{2}{\pi}\right)^{1/2} \sin nx, \dots$$

is orthonormal on $0 \le x \le \pi$.

Example 15. Another example of an orthonormal sequence on $0 \le x \le \pi$ is

$$\frac{1}{\pi^{1/2}}, \quad \left(\frac{2}{\pi}\right)^{1/2} \cos x, \quad \left(\frac{2}{\pi}\right)^{1/2} \cos 2x, \dots, \quad \left(\frac{2}{\pi}\right)^{1/2} \cos nx, \dots .$$

Note that the sequence of Example 13 is not orthogonal on $0 \le x \le \pi$, since, for instance,

$$\int_0^\pi \sin 2x \cos x\, dx = \frac{1}{2}\int_0^\pi (\sin 3x + \sin x)\, dx = \frac{4}{3} \ne 0 .$$

Example 16. The sequence

$$\{P_\mu(x)\}, \quad P_\mu(x) = \frac{1}{2^\mu \mu!}\frac{d^\mu}{dx^\mu}(x^2 - 1)^\mu$$

of so called Legendre polynomials is orthogonal on $-1 \le x \le 1$.

It is easily checked that $P_0(x) = 1$, $P_1(x) = x$, $P_2(x) = \frac{1}{2}(3x^2 - 1)$, $P_3(x) = \frac{1}{2}(5x^3 - 3x)$, $P_4(x) = \frac{1}{8}(35x^4 - 30x^2 + 3)$, $P_5(x) = \frac{1}{8}(63x^5 - 70x^3 + 15x), \dots$ satisfy the orthogonality condition

$$\int_{-1}^1 P_n(x)P_m(x)\, dx = 0, \quad \text{if } m \ne n .$$

Orthogonality is easily proved if the Legendre equations

$$[(1 - x^2)P_m']' = - m(m + 1)P_m, \quad [(1 - x^2)P_n']' = - n(n + 1)P_n$$

which define these polynomials are used. If the first equation is multiplied by P_n, the last by $- P_m$ and added, if follows that

$$[(1 - x^2)P_m']'P_n - [(1 - x^2)P_n']'P_m = [n(n + 1) - m(m + 1)]P_m P_n ,$$

which can be written in the form

147

$$[(1 - x^2)(P_n P_m' - P_n' P_m)]' = (n - m)(m + n + 1)P_m P_n .$$

Integration over x from -1 to 1, yields

$$[(1 - x^2)(P_n P_m' - P_n' P_m)]_{-1}^{1} = 0 = (n - m)(m + n + 1)\int_{-1}^{1} P_m P_n \, dx$$

whence orthogonality of the sequence follows.

Integration by parts μ times of $N(P_\mu)$ yields

$$N(P_\mu) = \int_{-1}^{1} P_\mu(x) P_\mu(x) \, dx = \frac{2}{2\mu + 1} .$$

Thus the sequence $\{((2\mu + 1)/2)^{1/2} P_\mu(x)\}$ is orthonormal.

Orthonormal sequences simplify proofs of theorems. In **7.1** only orthogonality of the sequence (a) was used to obtain a Fourier series corresponding to $f(x)$. This procedure suggests the attempt to represent given functions in terms of any orthogonal sequence $\{\lambda_\mu(x)\}$. Thus, if we assume that such a representation as

$$f(x) = \sum_{n=0}^{\infty} c_n \lambda_n(x)$$

is possible and the series converges uniformly on $a \leq x \leq b$, then multiplication by $\lambda_m(x)$ and integration yield

$$\int_a^b f(x) \lambda_m(x) \, dx = \sum_{n=0}^{\infty} c_n \int_a^b \lambda_n(x) \lambda_m(x) \, dx .$$

Since all integrals on the right are zero if $m \neq n$, it follows that

$$\int_a^b f(x) \lambda_m(x) \, dx = c_m N(\lambda_m) .$$

Thus the desired formula

$$c_m = \frac{1}{N(\lambda_m)} \int_a^b f(x) \lambda_m(x) \, dx$$

is obtained. The coefficients c_m are called Fourier constants of $f(x)$ with respect to the orthogonal sequence $\{\lambda_\mu(x)\}$, and the series so obtained is called the generalized Fourier series. Note that if the sequence of Example 13 is used, c_m becomes identical with Fourier coefficients obtained in **7.1**.

If $f(x)$ is defined on $0 \leq x \leq \pi$, sequences 14 and 15 yield at once Fourier coefficient formulas obtained in Example 8 for $l = \pi$. But here we do not need to define $f(x)$ for $-\pi \leq x < 0$ and think of another function $F(x)$ defined on $-\pi \leq x \leq \pi$ which coincides with $f(x)$ on

$0 \le x \le \pi$. Similarly,

$$\int_a^b \left[f(x) - \sum_{\mu=0}^{n} c_\mu \lambda_\mu(x) \right]^2 dx \ge 0$$

yields

$$\sum_{\mu=0}^{n} c_\mu^2 \le \int_a^b f^2(x)\, dx \quad \text{for all } n.$$

Consequently $\sum_{\mu=0}^{\infty} c_\mu^2$ converges and therefore $\lim_{\mu \to \infty} c_\mu = 0$.

Thus Fourier series are but a special case of series of orthogonal sequences.

CHAPTER 8

IMPROPER INTEGRALS

The Riemann integral, or the definite integral of $f(x)$ from $x = a$ to $x = b$, denoted by $\int_a^b f(x)\,dx$, is defined under the assumption that a and b are finite numbers and $f(x)$ is bounded on the closed interval $[a, b]$, There are definite integrals of great importance in analysis which do not satisfy these assumptions.

If one or both limits of integration are infinite and $f(x)$ is integrable on every finite interval of integration, then the integral is called an improper integral of the first kind. We have already used such integrals while discussing convergence of infinite series (**3.5-3**) and representing a function by Fourier integrals (7.8). The "gamma function" $\Gamma(x)$ defined by

$$\Gamma(x) = \int_0^\infty e^{-t} t^{x-1}\,dt\ , \quad x \geq 1$$

and the Laplace transform

$$F(x) = \int_0^\infty e^{-xt} f(t)\,dt\ , \quad x > 0$$

are two more examples of improper integrals of the first kind.

If the interval of integration is finite but the integrand is not bounded on the interval $[a, b]$, then the integral is called an improper integral of the second kind. Examples of this sort are the "beta function" $\beta(p, q)$ defined by

$$\beta(p, q) = \int_0^1 x^{p-1}(1 - x)^{q-1}\,dx\ , \quad 0 < p < 1,\ 0 < q < 1$$

where the integrand is not bounded in the neighborhood of $x = 0$ and of $x = 1$, and the elliptic integral

$$K = \int_0^1 \frac{dx}{[(1 - x^2)(1 - k^2 x^2)]^{1/2}} \ , \quad k^2 < 1$$

where the integrand becomes infinite when x approaches one.

It may happen that both kinds of improper integrals are contained in the same integral, for example,

$$\Gamma(x) = \int_0^\infty e^{-t} t^{x-1} dt \ , \quad 0 < x < 1$$

where the interval of integration is infinite and the integrand is not bounded at $t = 0$. Such mixed types can easily be split into integrals of the first and the second kind by writing

$$\Gamma(x) = \int_0^1 e^{-t} t^{x-1} dt + \int_1^\infty e^{-t} t^{x-1} dt$$

where the first integral is of the second kind and the second integral is of the first kind.

In this chapter we shall discuss convergence and divergence of improper integrals. It turns out that the tests and proofs of theorems bear close analogy to convergence and divergence tests and corresponding theorems for infinite series.

8.1 Improper integrals of the first kind

The improper integrals of the first kind are defined as follows:

$$\int_a^\infty f(x)\,dx = \lim_{b\to\infty} \int_a^b f(x)\,dx \ , \quad \int_{-\infty}^b f(x)\,dx = \lim_{a\to-\infty} \int_a^b f(x)\,dx \ ,$$

$$\int_{-\infty}^\infty f(x)\,dx = \lim_{a\to-\infty} \int_a^c f(x)\,dx + \lim_{b\to\infty} \int_c^b f(x)\,dx \ , \quad -\infty < c < \infty \ .$$

When the limits exist, the corresponding integral is said to converge to the value of this limit. When the limit does not exist, the integral is said to diverge.

When a primitive function $F(x)$ is known, then by extension of the fundamental theorem one can determine convergence or divergence of thesei ntegrals and, in case of convergence, find the value to which the improper integral converges. If the limits

$$\lim_{b\to\infty} F(b) = F(\infty) \ , \quad \lim_{a\to-\infty} F(a) = F(-\infty)$$

exist, then it follows that the corresponding integrals converge to the values

$$\int_a^\infty f(x)\,dx = F(\infty) - F(a) , \qquad \int_{-\infty}^b f(x)\,dx = F(b) - F(-\infty) .$$

Example 1. Since

$$\int_0^b \frac{dx}{1 + x^2} = \tan^{-1} b$$

and $\lim\limits_{b\to\infty} \tan^{-1} b = \pi/2$, it follows that the integral $\int_0^\infty dx/(1 + x^2)$ converges to the value $\pi/2$.

Example 2. The integral $\int_{-\infty}^\infty \sin x\,dx$ does not converge, for by definition

$$\int_{-\infty}^\infty \sin x\,dx = \int_{-\infty}^c \sin x\,dx + \int_c^\infty \sin x\,dx$$

and $\lim\limits_{a\to-\infty} (\cos a - \cos c)$ as well as $\lim\limits_{b\to\infty} (\cos b - \cos c)$ do not exist.

Warning! It does not follow from

$$\int_{-\infty}^\infty \sin x\,dx = \lim_{a\to\infty} \int_{-a}^a \sin x\,dx = \lim_{a\to\infty} (\cos a - \cos a) = 0$$

that the integral exists. Note that the definition requires the existence of $\int_{-\infty}^c \sin x\,dx$ and of $\int_c^\infty \sin x\,dx$.

If the integrals $\int_{-\infty}^c f(x)\,dx$ and $\int_c^\infty f(x)\,dx$ exist, then

$$\int_{-\infty}^\infty f(x)\,dx = F(\infty) - F(-\infty) .$$

Another way of proving convergence or divergence of improper integrals is to use infinite series.

We have already seen that if $f(x)$ is a positive decreasing function defined for $x \geq 1$, then the integral and the series

$$\int_1^\infty f(x)\,dx \quad \text{and} \quad \sum_{\mu=1}^\infty f(\mu)$$

both converge or both diverge (**3.5-3**). We have obtained a more general equation between series and improper integrals (see § 4.6, Euler's summation formula). One can define convergence of improper integrals by infinite series in the following way.

If the interval of integration is partitioned by a sequence of numbers $x_0 = a < x_1 < x_2 < \cdots < x_n < \cdots$, then it is clear that a convergent improper integral can be written as a series in the form

$$\int_a^\infty f(x)\, dx = a_1 + a_2 + \cdots + a_n + \cdots$$

where

$$a_1 = \int_a^{x_1} f(x)\, dx\,, \quad a_2 = \int_{x_1}^{x_2} f(x)\, dx\,, \dots, \quad a_n = \int_{x_{n-1}}^{x_n} f(x)\, dx\,, \dots.$$

This shows that the idea of convergence of an improper integral can be reduced to that of an infinite series in many ways. This leads to a definition:

If

$$\sum_{\mu=0}^{\infty} \int_{x_\mu}^{x_{\mu+1}} f(x)\, dx$$

converges for all strictly monotonic sequences $\{x_n\}$ with $\lim_{n\to\infty} x_n = \infty$, then the improper integral $\int_a^\infty f(x)\, dx$ is convergent; and conversely.

If we choose the points x_μ in such a way that the integrand does not change sign within any individual sub-interval, we obtain a series possibly having both positive and negative terms. The series $\sum_{\mu=1}^{\infty} |a_\mu|$ will then correspond to the integral $\int_a^\infty |f(x)|\, dx$. This again quite naturally leads to the concept of absolute convergence of improper integrals.

If both integrals $\int_a^\infty f(x)\, dx$ and $\int_a^\infty |f(x)|\, dx$ converge, we say that $\int_a^\infty f(x)\, dx$ converges absolutely. If the integral $\int_a^\infty f(x)\, dx$ converges, but $\int_a^\infty |f(x)|\, dx$ diverges, we say that the integral converges conditionally. Since an infinite series converges, if it converges absolutely, the above definition infers that the existence of $\int_a^\infty |f(x)|\, dx$ implies convergence of $\int_a^\infty f(x)\, dx$.

Example 3. Using infinite series, show that the integral

$$\int_0^\infty \frac{\sin x}{x^p}\, dx\,, \quad 0 < p \le 1$$

converges conditionally.

Solution. If b is any real number on the interval $0 \le x < \infty$, we divide $T = [0, b]$ by $x_\mu = \mu\pi$ $(\mu = 0, 2, 3, \dots, k_b)$, where k_b is the largest possible integer such that $k_b\pi \le b$. Then

$$\int_0^b \frac{\sin x}{x^p}\, dx = \int_0^\pi \frac{\sin x}{x^p}\, dx + \int_\pi^{2\pi} \frac{\sin x}{x^p}\, dx + \cdots + \int_{k_b\pi}^b \frac{\sin x}{x^p}\, dx$$

where $0 \le b - k_b\pi < \pi$. [Since $\int_0^b (\sin x\, dx)/x^p$ exists, any other partition of T would give the same result.]

It is clear that the terms

$$a_\mu = \int_{(\mu-1)\pi}^{\mu\pi} \frac{\sin x}{x^p} \, dx$$

are alternately positive and negative (positive for odd μ and negative for even μ) and that $\lim_{\mu\to\infty} a_\mu = 0$.

Substitution of $x = t - \pi$ into

$$a_\mu = \int_{(\mu-1)\pi}^{\mu\pi} \frac{\sin x}{dx} \, dx$$

yields

$$|a_\mu| = \int_{(\mu-1)\pi}^{\mu\pi} \frac{|\sin x|}{x^p} \, dx = \int_{\mu\pi}^{(\mu+1)\pi} \frac{|\sin(t-\pi)|}{(t-\pi)^p} \, dt = \int_{\mu\pi}^{(\mu+1)\pi} \frac{|\sin t|}{(t-\pi)^p} \, dt$$

$$> \int_{\mu\pi}^{(\mu+1)\pi} \frac{|\sin t|}{t^p} \, dt = |a_{\mu+1}| \ .$$

Thus $|a_\mu| > |a_{\mu+1}|$ and by Leibnitz's test the alternating series $\sum_{\mu=1}^{\infty} a_\mu$ converges (4.2-1). It remains to be shown that the improper integral is equal to this series.

Since the remainder R_b of the equality

$$\int_0^b \frac{\sin x}{x^p} \, dx = \sum_{\mu=1}^{kq} a_\mu + R_b$$

satisfies the inequality

$$|R_b| = \left| \int_{k_b\pi}^b \frac{\sin x}{x^p} \, dx \right| \le \int_{k_b\pi}^b \frac{|\sin x|}{x^p} \, dx \le \frac{1}{k_b^p \pi^p} \int_{k_b\pi}^{(k_b+1)\pi} |\sin x| \, dx = \frac{2}{k_b^p \pi^p}$$

and $k_b^p \to \infty$ as $b \to \infty$, it follows that $|R_b| \to 0$ and

$$\int_0^\infty \frac{\sin x}{x^p} \, dx = \sum_{\mu=1}^{\infty} a_\mu \ .$$

This proves that the integral converges.

From the relation

$$|a_\mu| = \int_{(\mu-1)\pi}^{\mu\pi} \frac{|\sin x|}{x^p} \, dx > \int_{(\mu-1)\pi}^{\mu\pi} \frac{|\sin x| \, dx}{(\mu\pi)^p} = \frac{2}{(\mu\pi)^p}$$

it follows that

$$\int_0^\infty \frac{|\sin x|}{x^p} \, dx = \sum_{\mu=1}^{\infty} |a_\mu| > \frac{2}{\pi} \sum_{\mu=1}^{\infty} \frac{1}{\mu^p}, \quad 0 < p \le 1 \ .$$

Since the harmonic series diverges, it follows that the integral

154

$$\int_0^\infty \frac{|\sin x|}{x^p}\,dx$$

diverges, and this proves conditional convergence of the original integral. Note that

$$\lim_{x \to 0} \frac{\sin x}{x^p} = \lim_{x \to 0} \frac{\sin x}{x} x^{1-p} = 0 \ , \quad \text{if } p < 1 \ ,$$

$$= 1 \ , \quad \text{if } p = 1 \ .$$

8.1-1 Theorem (Cauchy's criterion). If $f(t)$ is defined for $t \geq a$ and integrable over $a \leq t \leq x$, for every x, then $\int_a^\infty f(t)\,dt$ converges if and only if, given an arbitrary $\varepsilon > 0$, a number $x_0 > a$ can be determined so that

$$\left| \int_{x_1}^{x_2} f(t)\,dt \right| < \varepsilon$$

for every $x_2 > x_1 > x_0$.

Proof. From the relations

$$\int_a^\infty f(t)\,dt = \sum_{\mu=1}^\infty a_\mu \ , \quad a_\mu = \int_{t_{\mu-1}}^{t_\mu} f(t)\,dt \ , \quad t_0 = a \ , \quad t_\mu > t_{\mu-1} \ , \quad \lim_{\mu \to \infty} t_\mu = \infty$$

and

$$|a_{n+1} + a_{n+2} + \cdots + a_{n+k}| = \left| \int_{t_n}^{t_{n+k}} f(t)\,dt \right| \ ,$$

the statement follows immediately if Cauchy's criterion for infinite series (**3.3-1**) is used and $x_1 = t_n$, $x_2 = t_{n+k}$.

Cauchy's criterion is often handy in proving theorems. An example is the following theorem.

8.1-2 Theorem. If $\int_a^\infty |f(t)|\,dt$ converges, then $\int_a^\infty f(t)\,dt$ converges.

Proof. By hypothesis, Cauchy's criterion

$$\int_{x_1}^{x_2} |f(t)|\,dt < \varepsilon$$

is satisfied for $x_2 > x_1 > x_0$. Since

$$\left| \int_{x_1}^{x_2} f(t)\,dt \right| \leq \int_{x_1}^{x_2} |f(t)|\,dt < \varepsilon \ ,$$

the statement follows.

Example 4. $\int_0^\infty [(\sin x)/x^p]\,dx$, $0 < p \leq 1$ converges.

Integration by parts yields

$$\int_{x_1}^{x_2} \frac{\sin x}{x^p} \, dx = \frac{\cos x_1}{x_1^p} - \frac{\cos x_2}{x_2^p} + p \int_{x_1}^{x_2} \frac{\cos x}{x^{p+1}} \, dx \, , \quad x_1 > 0 \, .$$

Hence,

$$\left| \int_{x_1}^{x_2} \frac{\sin x}{x^p} \, dx \right| \le \frac{|\cos x_1|}{x_1^p} + \frac{|\cos x_2|}{x_2^p} + p \int_{x_1}^{x_2} \frac{dx}{x^{p+1}} \le \frac{1}{x_1^p} + \frac{1}{x_2^p} + \frac{1}{x_1^p} - \frac{1}{x_2^p} = \frac{2}{x_1^p} \, .$$

It follows that

$$\left| \int_{x_1}^{x_2} \frac{\sin x}{x^p} \, dx \right| < \varepsilon$$

if $2/x_1^p < \varepsilon$, that is, if $x_2 > x_1 > x_0 = (2/\varepsilon)^{1/p}$. This proves the statement.

Though there is great analogy between series and improper integrals, there are also differences. One of these worth noting is the following.

If an infinite series is convergent, then $\lim_{n \to \infty} a_n = 0$. But if an integral $\int_0^\infty f(x) \, dx$ is convergent it does not necessarily follow that $\lim_{x \to \infty} f(x) = 0$.

In fact, an improper integral can exist even when the integrand is unbounded. For example, the integrand of

$$\int_0^\infty t \sin (t^4) \, dt$$

is unbounded since if $t = [(2n + 1)\pi/2]^{1/4}$, n a positive integer, then

$$\lim_{n \to \infty} \left| [(2n + 1)\pi/2]^{1/4} \sin \frac{(2n + 1)\pi}{2} \right| = \lim_{n \to \infty} [(2n + 1)\pi/2]^{1/4} = \infty \, .$$

And yet the integral converges. For by putting $t^4 = x$ we obtain

$$\int_0^\infty t \sin (t^4) \, dt = \frac{1}{4} \int_0^\infty \frac{\sin x}{x^{1/2}} \, dx \, ,$$

which is a special case of Example 4 for $p = 1/2$.

8.2 Integrals of the first kind with positive integrands

First we shall discuss improper integrals with positive integrands for the same reasons that make it useful to study series of positive terms before taking up more general types of series.

If $f(t) \ge 0$ on the interval $a \le t \le x$, then for every x

$$F(x) = \int_a^x f(t) \, dt$$

is a non-decreasing function as x increases.

If $F(x)$ is not bounded, then for each M, no matter how large, there exists some x such that $F(x) > M$, and consequently $\lim\limits_{x \to \infty} F(x) = \infty$. This means that the integral diverges.

If $F(x) \leq M$ for all $x \geq a$, that is, $F(x)$ is bounded, then it can be proved that $\lim\limits_{x \to \infty} F(x) = F(\infty)$ exists. The proof follows the very same lines as in the case of monotonic sequences, and it is left to the reader. Since for $n \leq x < n + 1$ the inequality

$$F(n) \leq F(x) < F(n + 1)$$

holds, where n is a positive integer, it follows that

$$F(\infty) \leq \lim\limits_{x \to \infty} F(x) \leq F(\infty)$$

that is, $\lim\limits_{x \to \infty} F(x)$ exists, if and only if, the sequence $\{F(n)\}$ possesses a limit.

In consequence of this remark we may at once formulate counterparts of **3.4-1, 3.4-2** and **3.4-3**.

8.2-1 Theorem. If $f(t)$ is a non-negative integrable function when $t \geq a$ and $\int_a^x f(t)\, dt$ is bounded above for all x, then $\int_a^\infty f(t)\, dt$ converges; otherwise it diverges to ∞.

8.2-2 Theorem (Comparison test). If $f(x)$ and $g(x)$ are integrable functions when $x \geq a$ and $0 \leq f(x) \leq g(x)$, then

$$\int_a^\infty f(x)\, dx \quad \text{converges} \qquad \text{if} \quad \int_a^\infty g(x)\, dx \quad \text{converges}$$

$$\int_a^\infty g(x)\, dx \quad \text{diverges} \qquad \text{if} \quad \int_a^\infty f(x)\, dx \quad \text{diverges}.$$

Example 5. The integral $\int_1^\infty dx/(1 + x^4)^{1/2}$ converges by comparison, since

$$\int_1^\infty \frac{dx}{(1 + x^4)^{1/2}} < \int_1^\infty \frac{dx}{(x^4)^{1/2}} = \int_1^\infty \frac{dx}{x^2} = 1 \, .$$

8.2-3 Theorem (Limit comparison test). If $f(x)$ and $g(x)$ are non-negative integrable functions when $x \geq a$ and

$$\lim\limits_{x \to \infty} \frac{f(x)}{g(x)} = c \neq 0$$

exists, then either both integrals

157

$$\int_a^\infty f(x)\,dx \quad \text{and} \quad \int_a^\infty g(x)\,dx$$

converge, or both diverge.

If $c = 0$ and $\int_a^\infty g(x)\,dx$ converges, then $\int_a^\infty f(x)\,dx$ also converges.
If $c = \infty$ and $\int_a^\infty g(x)\,dx$ diverges, then $\int_a^\infty f(x)\,dx$ also diverges.

Corollary. If we choose $g(x) = 1/x^p$ and note that $\int_a^\infty dx/x^p$ converges if $p > 1$ and diverges for $p \leq 1$, it follows that the integral $\int_a^\infty f(x)\,dx$ converges if $\lim_{x\to\infty} x^p f(x) = c$, $p > 1$ and diverges if $\lim_{x\to\infty} x^p f(x) = c \neq 0$ or ∞ and $p \leq 1$.

This test is often very useful in applications.

Example 6. $\int_1^\infty (\log x\,dx)/x^2$ converges by the Corollary, since for $p = 3/2$, $\lim_{x\to\infty} f(x)/g(x) = \lim_{x\to\infty} \log x/x^{1/2} = 0$.

Exercises 8.A

1. If $f(x) \geq 0$, then $\int_a^b f(x)\,dx \geq 0$. If $a = -1$, $b = 1$, $f(x) = 1/x^2 > 0$, then $\int_{-1}^1 dx/x^2 = (-1/x)\big|_{-1}^1 = (-1) - 1 = -2$ is not ≥ 0. What is wrong with this evaluation?

2. Express the integral $\int_{-\infty}^\infty dx/[(x+2)(x-1)]$ as a sum of improper integrals of the first and second kind.

In problems 3–12 determine which of the integrals exist by first finding a primitive function.

3. $\displaystyle\int_0^\infty \frac{dx}{(x^2+1)(x^2+4)}$

4. $\displaystyle\int_0^\infty \frac{dx}{(x^2+1)^2}$

5. $\displaystyle\int_{-\infty}^\infty \frac{x^4\,dx}{(x^2+1)^2(x^2+4)}$

6. $\displaystyle\int_a^\infty e^{-ax}\sin bx\,dx, \quad a > 0$

7. $\displaystyle\int_a^\infty e^{-ax}\cos bx\,dx, \quad a > 0$

8. $\displaystyle\int_0^\infty e^{ax^2}x\,dx, \quad a > 0$

9. $\displaystyle\int_{-\infty}^\infty \frac{e^{x/3}}{1+e^x}\,dx$

10. $\displaystyle\int_0^\infty e^{-x}x^3\,dx$

11. $\displaystyle\int_2^\infty \frac{dx}{x(\log x)^k}$

12. $\displaystyle\int_0^\infty \frac{dx}{(e^x)^{1/2}}.$

In problems 13–20 establish convergence or divergence by using tests. (Do not evaluate.)

13. $\displaystyle\int_1^\infty \frac{x^2\,dx}{2x^4 - x + 1}$

14. $\displaystyle\int_1^\infty x^p e^{-x}\,dx$

15. $\displaystyle\int_1^\infty \frac{dx}{(1+x^3)^{1/2}}$

16. $\displaystyle\int_{-\infty}^\infty e^{-x^2}\,dx$

17. $\displaystyle\int_1^\infty \frac{x^{p-1}}{x+1}\,dx, \quad 0 < p < 1$

18. $\displaystyle\int_1^\infty \frac{x\,dx}{e^x - 1}$

19. $\displaystyle\int_1^\infty e^{-x^2} x^2\, dx$
20. $\displaystyle\int_0^\infty \frac{x^3\, dx}{(4 + x^8)^{1/2}}$.

21. If the integral $\int_a^\infty f(x)\, dx$ converges where $f(x)$ is a positive function which decreases steadily to zero, prove that $\lim_{x \to \infty} x f(x) = 0$. [Hint: If m denotes an integer $\geq a$, apply **3.5-2** to the series $\sum_{n=m}^\infty \int_n^{n+1} f(x)\, dx$.]

22. Show that the integral $\int_1^\infty t^{x-1} (\log t)^n e^{-t}\, dt$ is convergent for $n = 1, 2, 3$. Is it convergent for every positive integer n?

8.3 Conditional convergence of improper integrals of the first kind

Since the integrand $|f(x)|$ is non-negative, we can apply the methods of 8.2 to test whether an integral is absolutely convergent. If an integral is conditionally convergent, more delicate tests are needed. In many of the instances of practical importance, the technique of integration by parts reduces the integral to a new one which is absolutely convergent. First let us consider an example.

Example 7. Using "∞" as an abbreviation for the limit operation, we integrate $\int_2^\infty (\cos x / \log x)\, dx$ by parts

$$\int_2^\infty \frac{\cos x}{\log x}\, dx = \frac{\sin x}{\log x}\Bigg|_2^\infty + \int_2^\infty \frac{\sin x}{x(\log x)^2}\, dx = -\frac{\sin 2}{\log 2} + \int_2^\infty \frac{\sin x\, dx}{x(\log x)^2}\, .$$

Since $\int_2^\infty dx/x(\log x)^2$ converges, it follows that the new integral on the right converges absolutely. Consequently the original integral converges.

It is easily seen that the integral does not converge absolutely. If we write

$$\int_2^\infty \frac{|\cos x|}{\log x}\, dx = \int_2^\pi \frac{|\cos x|}{\log x}\, dx + \int_\pi^{2\pi} \frac{|\cos x|}{\log x}\, dx + \cdots + \int_{(k-1)\pi}^{k\pi} \frac{|\cos x|}{\log x}\, dx + \cdots$$

$$> \frac{1}{\log \pi} \int_2^\pi |\cos x|\, dx + \frac{1}{\log 2\pi} \int_\pi^{2\pi} |\cos x|\, dx + \cdots$$

$$+ \frac{1}{\log k\pi} \int_{(k-1)\pi}^{k\pi} |\cos x|\, dx + \cdots$$

$$= \frac{1}{\log \pi} \int_2^\pi |\cos x|\, dx + 2 \sum_{k=2}^\infty \frac{1}{\log k\pi}\, ,$$

it follows that the integral diverges, since $\sum_{k=2}^\infty 1/\log k\pi$ diverges.

The same procedure can be used to prove convergence of a more general class of improper integrals.

8.3-1 Theorem (Dirichlet test). If f, g, g' are continuous, $\lim_{x \to \infty} g(x) = 0$, $\int_a^\infty g'(x)\, dx$ is absolutely convergent, and $F(x) = \int_a^x f(t)\, dt$ is bounded for all $x \geq a$, then the integral

$$\int_a^\infty f(x)g(x)\,dx$$

converges.

Proof. Integrating by parts and noting that $F(a) = 0$ we obtain

$$\int_a^x f(t)g(t)\,dt = F(x)g(x) - \int_a^x F(t)g'(t)\,dt\ .$$

Note that $|F(x)| \le M$ and $|F(x)g(x)| \le M|g(x)|$. Consequently $\lim_{x\to\infty} F(x)g(x) = 0$, and it follows that

$$\int_a^\infty f(t)g(t)\,dt = -\int_a^\infty F(t)g'(t)\,dt\ .$$

Since $|\int_a^\infty F(t)g'(t)\,dt| \le M \int_a^\infty |g'(t)|\,dt$, it follows that the integral on the right of the equality converges absolutely. Consequently the original integral converges.

A more general test can be obtained without the assumption that g is continuously differentiable. The proof is simple if the second mean value theorem for Riemann integrals based on the concept of the Riemann–Stieltjes interal is used. (See J. M. H. Olmsted, *Advanced Calculus*, Appleton-Century-Crofts, Inc., New York, 1959, p. 465.)

Corollary. In particular the conditions of Dirichlet's test are satisfied for $g(x) = 1/x^p$, $p > 0$. That is, the integral

$$\int_a^\infty \frac{f(x)}{x^p}\,dx$$

converges if $F(x) = \int_a^x f(t)\,dt$ is bounded and $p > 0$, $a > 0$.

Example 8. To show that the integral

$$\int_1^\infty \cos(x^2)\,dx$$

is convergent we set $x = t^{1/2}$, obtaining the improper integral

$$\frac{1}{2}\int_1^\infty \frac{\cos t}{t^{1/2}}\,dt\ .$$

This integral converges by the Corollary where $p = 1/2$. That the integral does not converge absolutely can be shown exactly as in Example 7. The original integral shows that $\int_a^\infty f(t)\,dt$ can converge without having $\lim_{t\to\infty} f(t) = 0$.

Exercises 8.B

1. Assume that $f(x)$ is continuous on $a \leq x < \infty$ and decreases steadily to zero as $x \to \infty$. Prove that the integral

$$G = \int_a^\infty f(x) \sin x \, dx$$

converges conditionally if the series $\sum_{k=m}^\infty f(k\pi)$, $(m\pi \geq a)$ diverges.

2. Show that if the integral G in Problem 1 is approximated by $\int_a^{n\pi} f(x) \sin x \, dx$, that is,

$$G \approx \int_a^{n\pi} f(x) \sin nx \, dx$$

then the error of the approximation $|\int_{n\pi}^\infty f(x) \sin nx \, dx|$ is less than $2 f(n\pi)$.

In Exercises 3–12, determine whether the integral converges or diverges and, in case of convergence, whether it converges absolutely or conditionally.

3. $\int_0^\infty \dfrac{x \cos x}{a^2 + x^2} \, dx$, $(a \neq 0)$

4. $\int_0^\infty \dfrac{\sin x}{1 + x^2} \, dx$

5. $\int_2^\infty \dfrac{\log (\log x)}{\log x} \cos x \, dx$

6. $\int_{-\infty}^\infty \dfrac{x \sin x}{1 + x^2} \, dx$

7. $\int_0^\infty \dfrac{\sin x \sin ax}{x} \, dx$

8. $\int_0^\infty \dfrac{e^{-x} \sin x}{x} \, dx$

9. $\int_0^\infty x \cos (x^4) \, dx$

10. $\int_1^\infty t \sin (e^t) \, dt$

11. $\int_1^\infty \sin \left(\dfrac{1}{x^2}\right) dx$

12. $\int_0^\infty \dfrac{1 - \cos x}{x^2} \, dx$.

13. Show that $\int_0^\infty (\sin^2 x \, dx)/x^2$ converges and is equal to $\int_0^\infty (\sin x \, dx)/x$ (hint: integrate by parts).

14. If $f(x) = \int_2^x dt/\log t$ and $g(x) = x/\log x$, prove that $\lim_{x \to \infty} f(x)/g(x) = 1$.

15. Show that $0 < \int_0^x (\sin t \, dt)/t < \pi$ for $x > 0$.

8.4   Improper integrals of the second kind

If the integrand of an integral

$$\int_a^b f(x) \, dx$$

with finite limits becomes unbounded at a finite number of points $x_0 = a < x_1 < x_2 < \cdots < x_n = b$, we call it an improper integral of the second kind. Such integrals can be written as a sum of integrals containing but one of these points as lower or upper limit. For example, the integrand of

$$\beta(p, q) = \int_0^1 x^{p-1}(1 - x)^{q-1}\, dx \,, \quad 0 < p < 1 \,, \quad 0 < q < 1$$

is not bounded as $x \to 0$ and as $x \to 1$. We can write

$$\beta(p, q) = \int_0^c x^{p-1}(1 - x)^{q-1}\, dx + \int_c^1 x^{p-1}(1 - x)^{q-1}\, dx \,, \quad 0 < c < 1$$

and consider these two integrals separately.

Thus we shall consider integrals with finite limits where the integrand $f(x)$ is integrable either on $a < x \leq b$ or on $a \leq x < b$, that is, $f(x)$ becomes unbounded either as $x \to a$ or as $x \to b$, but not both.

If the integral is improper at the lower limit, we define it to be

$$\int_a^b f(x)\, dx = \lim_{\varepsilon \to 0+} \int_{a+\varepsilon}^b f(x)\, dx \,.$$

If this limit exists, we say the improper integral converges.

Similarly, when the integral is improper at b, we write

$$\int_a^b f(x)\, dx = \lim_{\varepsilon \to 0+} \int_a^{b-\varepsilon} f(x)\, dx \,.$$

If these limits do not exist, the corresponding integral is said to diverge.

When a primitive function $F(x)$ is known we shall write, respectively,

$$\int_a^b f(x)\, dx = \lim_{\varepsilon \to 0+} [F(b) - F(a + \varepsilon)] = F(b) - F(a +) \,,$$

$$\int_a^b f(x)\, dx = \lim_{\varepsilon \to 0+} [F(b - \varepsilon) - F(a)] = F(b -) - F(a) \,.$$

When these exist, the corresponding integral is said to converge to this value.

If $f(x)$ becomes infinite at a and b, we write

$$\int_a^b f(x)\, dx = \lim_{\varepsilon \to 0+} \int_{a+\varepsilon}^{b-\varepsilon} f(x)\, dx = \lim_{\varepsilon \to 0+} \int_{a+\varepsilon}^c f(x)\, dx + \lim_{\varepsilon \to 0+} \int_c^{b-\varepsilon} f(x)\, dx$$

$$= \lim_{\varepsilon \to 0+} [F(c) - F(a + \varepsilon)] + \lim_{\varepsilon \to 0+} [F(b - \varepsilon) - F(c)] \,.$$

If both limits exist independently of each other, we may write

$$\int_a^b f(x)\, dx = F(b -) - F(a +) \,.$$

Example 9. Since the integrand of

$$\int_0^1 \frac{dx}{(1 - x^2)^{1/2}}$$

becomes infinite as $x \to 1$, we write

$$\int_0^1 \frac{dx}{(1 - x^2)^{1/2}} = \lim_{\varepsilon \to 0+} \int_0^{1-\varepsilon} \frac{dx}{(1 - x^2)^{1/2}} = \lim_{\varepsilon \to 0+} [\sin^{-1}(1 - \varepsilon) - \sin^{-1}(0)]$$

$$= \sin^{-1} 1 = \frac{\pi}{2},$$

that is, the integral converges to the value $\pi/2$.

It is worth noting that there are other ways of showing that an improper integral converges.

Change of variable according to $x = \sin t$ converts the integral

$$\int_0^1 \frac{dx}{(1 - x^2)^{1/2}} = \int_0^{\pi/2} \frac{\cos t \, dt}{(1 - \sin^2 t)^{1/2}} = \int_0^{\pi/2} dt = \frac{\pi}{2}$$

into a proper integral.

Another change of variable $x = 1 - 1/t$ transforms the integral into an improper integral of the first kind

$$\int_0^1 \frac{dx}{(1 - x^2)^{1/2}} = \int_1^\infty \frac{dt}{t(2t - 1)^{1/2}}$$

which converges (**8.2-3**).

Example 10. The integrand of

$$\int_0^1 \frac{dx}{x \log x}$$

is not bounded as $x \to 0$ and $x \to 1$. By definition we consider separately

$$\int_0^c \frac{dx}{x \log x} = \lim_{\varepsilon \to 0+} \int_\varepsilon^c \frac{dx}{x \log x} = \lim_{\varepsilon \to 0+} \log |\log x| \Big|_\varepsilon^c = -\infty \quad (\varepsilon < c < 1)$$

$$\int_c^1 \frac{dx}{x \log x} = \lim_{\varepsilon \to 0+} \int_c^{1-\varepsilon} \frac{dx}{x \log x} = \lim_{\varepsilon \to 0+} \log |\log x| \Big|_0^{1-\varepsilon} = -\infty .$$

Since these limits do not exist, the original integral diverges.

Exercises 8.C

Find a primitive function and determine convergence or divergence of the following integrals.

1. $\displaystyle\int_0^{\pi/2} \cot x \, dx$

2. $\displaystyle\int_{-1}^1 \frac{dx}{x^2 - 1}$

3. $\displaystyle\int_0^1 \log x \, dx$

4. $\displaystyle\int_0^1 \frac{1 - x^7}{1 - x} dx$

5. $\displaystyle\int_0^1 x^3 \log x \, dx$

6. $\displaystyle\int_{-1}^1 \frac{dx}{(1 - x^2)^{1/2}}$

7. By setting $t = (1 - x)^{-1}$, transform the improper integral
$$\int_0^1 \log\left(\frac{1}{1-x}\right) dx$$
into an improper integral of the first kind and then determine whether the original integral converges.

8. By setting $t = - \log x$ transform the integral
$$\int_0^1 \left(\log \frac{1}{x}\right)^3 dx$$
into an integral of the first kind and then test its convergence.

8.5 Improper integrals of the second kind with positive integrands

If we assume that $f(x) \geq 0$ and integrable on $a \leq x < b$, then

$$F(x) = \int_a^x f(t)\, dx$$

is a non-decreasing function as x increases. If $f(x)$ is unbounded at b, then the improper integral

$$\int_a^b f(t)\, dt$$

converges if and only if $F(x)$ is bounded. It follows that $F(x)$ converges to $\lim_{x \to b-} F(x)$ if $F(x)$ is bounded and to ∞ if $F(x)$ is not bounded. In case $\lim_{x \to b-} F(x) = \infty$ we say that the integral diverges. This result leads directly to analogues to **8.2-1**, **8.2-2**, and **8.2-3**; wordings differ but slightly from the statements of these theorems. Similarly, the same results are obtained for integrals of the second kind which are improper at the lower limit a. The proofs are left to the reader.

One can use infinite series to obtain tests for convergence just as it has been done in case of improper integrals of the first kind. If $\{a_n\}$ is an arbitrary strictly monotonic sequence with $\lim_{n \to \infty} a_n = a$ and $f(x)$ is un-bounded at $x = a$, then the improper integral

$$\int_a^b f(x)\, dx = \int_{a_1}^b f(x)\, dx + \int_{a_2}^{a_1} f(x)\, dx + \cdots + \int_{a_n}^{a_{n-1}} f(x)\, dx + \cdots$$

by definition converges if the series converges for all sequences; and conversely. Similarly, if $f(x)$ is unbounded at $x = b$.

There is still another way of proving these tests. If $f(x)$ is not bounded at $x = a$, then the substitution $x = a + t^{-1}$ yields

$$\int_{a+\varepsilon}^b f(x)\, dx = \int_{(b-a)^{-1}}^{\varepsilon^{-1}} \frac{1}{t^2} f\left(a + \frac{1}{t}\right) dt \, .$$

Passing to the limit as $\varepsilon \to 0+$ yields

$$\int_a^b f(x)\, dx = \int_{(b-a)^{-1}}^\infty \frac{1}{t^2} f\left(a + \frac{1}{t}\right) dt \, ,$$

that is, the integral is reduced to an improper integral of the first kind. Similarly, if $\lim_{x \to b-} f(x) = \infty$, the substitution $x = b - t^{-1}$ yields

$$\int_a^b f(x)\, dx = \int_{(b-a)^{-1}}^\infty \frac{1}{t^2} f\left(b + \frac{1}{t}\right) dt \, .$$

Thus, if the improper integral of the first kind converges, then the corresponding improper integral of the second kind converges; and conversely. Consequently, by suitable transformations the entire theory of integrals of the first kind can be carried over to integrals of the second kind.

As an example we prove the comparison test by this transformation.

8.5-1 Theorem. If $f(x)$ and $g(x)$ are integrable on $a < x \leq b$ (or $a \leq x < b$) and such that

$$0 \leq f(x) \leq g(x) \, ,$$

then

$$\int_a^b f(x)\, dx \quad \text{converges} \qquad \text{if} \quad \int_a^b g(x)\, dx \quad \text{converges} \, ,$$

$$\int_a^b g(x)\, dx \quad \text{diverges} \qquad \text{if} \quad \int_a^b f(x)\, dx \quad \text{diverges} \, .$$

Proof. In case $\lim_{x \to a+} f(x) = \infty$, the transformation $x = a + 1/t$ yields

$$\int_a^b f(x)\, dx = \int_{(b-a)^{-1}}^\infty \frac{1}{t^2} f\left(a + \frac{1}{t}\right) dt \, .$$

Since by hypothesis $0 \leq f[a + (1/t)] \leq g[a + (1/t)]$, $a \leq a + (1/t) \leq b$, it follows that

$$0 \leq \frac{1}{t^2} f\left(a + \frac{1}{t}\right) \leq \frac{1}{t^2} g\left(a + \frac{1}{t}\right), \quad \frac{1}{b-a} \leq t < \infty \, .$$

If now **8.2-2** is applied to the transform, the statement follows.

If $\lim_{x \to b-} f(x) = \infty$, the transformation $x = b - t^{-1}$ yields the same results.

In the very same way, **8.2-3** and its Corollary carry over to the following.

8.5-2 Theorem. If $f(x)$ and $g(x)$ are positive integrable functions on $a < x \le b$ and if

$$\lim_{x \to a+} \frac{f(x)}{g(x)} = c \ne 0$$

exists, then the integrals

$$\int_a^b f(x)\, dx \quad \text{and} \quad \int_a^b g(x)\, dx$$

both converge or both diverge.

If $\lim\limits_{x \to a+} f(x)/g(x) = 0$ and $\int_a^b g(x)\, dx$ converges, then $\int_a^b f(x)\, dx$ converges.

If $\lim\limits_{x \to a+} f(x)/g(x) = \infty$ and $\int_a^b g(x)\, dx$ diverges, then $\int_a^b f(x)\, dx$ diverges.

Corollary. If we choose $g(x) = 1/(x - a)^q$ and note that

$$\int_a^b \frac{dx}{(x-a)^q} = \lim_{\varepsilon \to 0+} \int_{a+\varepsilon}^b \frac{dx}{(x-a)^q} = \frac{(b-a)^{1-q}}{1-q}, \quad q < 1,$$

$$= \infty, \qquad q \ge 1,$$

then it follows by **8.5-2** that the integral

$$\int_a^b f(x)\, dx$$

converges if

$$\lim_{x \to a+} (x - a)^q f(x) = c, \quad 0 < q < 1$$

and diverges if

$$\lim_{x \to a+} (x - a)^q f(x) = c \ne 0 \text{ (or } c = \infty), \quad q \ge 1.$$

Similarly, if $\lim\limits_{x \to b-} f(x) = \infty$, we obtain the same results by choosing $g(x) = 1/(b - x)^q$.

Example 11. Since the integrand of the integral

$$\int_0^1 x^{p-1}(1 - x)^{q-1}\, dx, \quad 0 < p, \quad q < 1$$

is not bounded as $x \to 0+$ and as $x \to 1-$, we write

$$\int_0^1 x^{p-1}(1 - x)^{q-1}\, dx = \int_0^c x^{p-1}(1 - x)^{q-1}\, dx + \int_c^1 x^{p-1}(1 - x)^{q-1}, \quad 0 < c < 1.$$

It is easily seen that $\lim\limits_{x\to 0+} x^{1-p} f(x) = 1$ and $\lim\limits_{x\to 0-}(1-x)^{1-q} f(x) = 1$, consequently by the Corollary the first integral on the right converges for $0 < 1 - p < 1$ and the second for $0 < 1 - q < 1$, that is, for $0 < p, q < 1$. For $p, q \leq 0$ the improper integral diverges; for $p, q \geq 1$ the integral is proper.

Example 12. $\int_1^4 (x^{1/2}/\log x)\, dx$ diverges, since by L'Hospital's rule

$$\lim_{x\to 1+} (x - 1)\frac{x^{1/2}}{\log x} = \lim_{x\to 1+}\frac{\frac{3}{2}x^{1/2} - \frac{1}{2}x^{-1/2}}{1/x} = 1\,,$$

that is, $q = 1$.

8.6 Conditional convergence of improper integrals of the second kind

In order to test improper integrals of the second kind for conditional convergence we reduce them to the first kind by changing the variable

$$x = a + t^{-1} \quad \text{or} \quad x = b - t^{-1}\,,$$

as the case may be (see § 8.5) and apply **8.3-1**.

Example 13. Consider the improper integral

$$\int_0^1 \frac{\sin 1/x}{x^p}\, dx\,, \quad p > 0\,.$$

The change of variable $x = t^{-1}$ yields

$$\int_\varepsilon^1 \frac{\sin x^{-1}}{x^p}\, dx = \int_1^{\varepsilon^{-1}} \frac{\sin t}{t^{2-p}}\, dt\,.$$

As $\varepsilon \to 0+$ we have

$$\int_0^1 \frac{\sin x^{-1}}{x^p}\, dx = \int_1^\infty \frac{\sin t}{t^{2-p}}\, dt\,.$$

The integral on the right converges when $2 - p > 0$ by the Corollary of **8.3-1**, that is, for $p < 2$. That the integral converges absolutely for $2 - p > 1$ or $0 < p < 1$ is obvious. In Example 3, we have shown that the integral diverges absolutely for $1 \leq p < 2$. Consequently the original integral converges absolutely for $0 < p < 1$, conditionally for $1 \leq p < 2$, and diverges for $p \geq 2$.

Exercises 8.D

Test the following integrals for convergence.

1. $\displaystyle\int_0^1 \frac{\log x}{x^{1/2}}\,dx$

2. $\displaystyle\int_1^2 \frac{x^{1/2}}{\log x}\,dx$

3. $\displaystyle\int_0^1 \frac{\cos 1/x}{x}\,dx$

4. $\displaystyle\int_0^1 \frac{\sin x^{-1}}{x^2 \log\left[1 + (1/x)\right]}\,dx$

5. $\displaystyle\int_0^\pi \frac{\log x}{1 + x}\,dx$

6. $\displaystyle\int_0^{\pi/2} \frac{x^2}{(\sin x)^3}\,dx$

7. $\displaystyle\int_0^{\pi/2} \log \sin x\,dx$

8. $\displaystyle\int_0^\pi \frac{dx}{(\cos^2 x)^{1/3}}$

9. $\displaystyle\int_0^\pi \frac{dx}{(\sin x)^p}\,, \quad 0 < p < 1$

10. $\displaystyle\int_\pi^{4\pi} \frac{\sin x}{(x - \pi)^\alpha}\,dx\,, \quad 0 < \alpha < 2\,.$

8.7 Some Remarks

We have seen that

$$\int_a^x f(t)\,dt \quad \text{corresponds to} \quad S_n = \sum_{k=1}^n a_k$$

and we have found certain analogies between the tests for infinite series and the tests for improper integrals. Since the variable t and x vary continuously, whereas the variables k and n vary through the integers only, some important differences in the two cases are to be expected.

The natural analogue for convergence of series and improper integrals

$$\lim_{n\to\infty} a_n \quad \text{and} \quad \lim_{x\to\infty} f(x) = 0$$

has been disproved by counter-examples (see § 8.2 and Example 8). One might conjecture that this analogue holds if $f(x)$ is continuous and, in addition, $f(x) \geq 0$. The following example shows that this conjecture is false. Define

$$h(x) = 1 - |x|\,, \quad \text{for} \quad |x| \leq 1\,,$$
$$= 0\,, \quad \text{otherwise}\,.$$

Then $h(k^2(x - k))$, where $k = 2, 3, 4, \ldots, n, \ldots$ determines a triangular graph shown in Figure 22. Note that the area of the triangle is $1/k^2$.

Define $f(x) = \sum_{k=2}^\infty h(k^2(x - k))$. Then it follows that $\int_1^\infty f(x)\,dx$ is the sum of the areas of these triangles, that is,

$$\int_1^\infty f(x)\,dx = \sum_{k=2}^\infty \frac{1}{k^2}\,,$$

where the series converges to the value $(\pi^2/6) - 1$ (see Chapter 7, Example 5). Consequently, the integral converges. However, $f(k) = 1 \neq 0$ for $k = 1, 2, 3, \ldots, n, \ldots$ that is, $\lim_{x\to\infty} f(x) \neq 0$.

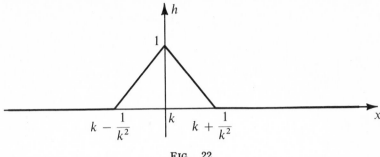

FIG. 22.

Furthermore, if the triangle in Figure 22 is altered in such a way that its height and base are $k^{1/2}$ and $2/(k^5)^{1/2}$, respectively, then the area of the triangle is unchanged (equals $1/k^2$). However, the corresponding function is not bounded on the interval of integration, even though the integral converges.

The reader will have noted that there are fewer tests for convergence of integrals than there are for series. For instance, there is no counterpart to the ratio test, for there is no simple way of expressing it for improper integrals.

If one considers such simple examples as the improper integral of the first kind

$$\int_{-\infty}^{\infty} \sin x \, dx$$

which according to the definition of convergence diverges, even though

$$\lim_{a \to \infty} \left[\int_{-a}^{0} \sin x \, dx + \int_{0}^{a} \sin x \, dx \right] = 0$$

exists; and the improper integral of the second kind

$$\int_{-1}^{1} \frac{1}{x} \, dx \, ,$$

which by the definition diverges, even though

$$\lim_{\varepsilon \to 0+} \left[\int_{-1}^{-\varepsilon} \frac{dx}{x} + \int_{\varepsilon}^{1} \frac{dx}{x} \right] = 0$$

exists.

From a certain point of view it might be convenient to think of the area under the curve $y = 1/x$ from -1 to 1 as being zero, and one might be tempted to revise the definition of convergence in order to include these cases. This has been done.

If the integral $\int_{-a}^{a} f(x)\, dx$ and its limit exist as $a \to \infty$, then the improper integral $\int_{-\infty}^{\infty} f(x)\, dx$ is called Cauchy's principal value and is denoted by

$$\mathscr{P} \int_{-\infty}^{\infty} f(x)\, dx = \lim_{a \to \infty} \int_{-a}^{a} f(x)\, dx \, .$$

Similarly, if $f(x)$ is not bounded at c and $\int_{a}^{b} f(x)\, dx$ does not exist, but

$$\lim_{\varepsilon \to 0+} \left[\int_{a}^{c-\varepsilon} f(x)\, dx + \int_{c+\varepsilon}^{b} f(x)\, dx \right]$$

does exist, we call this the Cauchy principal value and write

$$\mathscr{P} \int_{a}^{b} f(x)\, dx = \lim_{\varepsilon \to 0+} \left[\int_{a}^{c-\varepsilon} f(x)\, dx + \int_{c+\varepsilon}^{b} f(x)\, dx \right].$$

Exercises 8.E

1. Does the relation

$$\int_{0}^{\infty} \cos x \, dx = \int_{0}^{\pi} \cos x \, dx + \int_{\pi}^{2\pi} \cos x \, dx + \cdots + \int_{k\pi}^{(k+1)\pi} \cos x \, dx + \cdots$$

hold? Does the relation

$$\int_{0}^{\infty} f(x)\, dx = \sum_{k=0}^{\infty} \int_{k\pi}^{(k+1)\pi} f(x)\, dx$$

always hold if $f(x) \geq 0$?

2. If we choose $x_1 = n\pi$, $x_2 = m\pi$, m, n positive integers and $m > n$, then Cauchy's convergence criterion

$$\left| \int_{x_1}^{x_2} \cos x \, dx \right| = 0 < \varepsilon$$

is satisfied (see **8.1-1**). Consequently the integral $\int_{0}^{\infty} \cos x \, dx$ should converge, but it diverges. What is wrong here?

In Exercises 3–9 establish convergence or divergence.

3. $\int_{1}^{3} \dfrac{dx}{\log\,(\log x)}$

4. $\int_{0}^{3} \dfrac{dx}{1 - x}$

5. $\int_{-\infty}^{\infty} \dfrac{x\, dx}{e^{x} + x^{4}}$

6. $\int_{0}^{\infty} \dfrac{dx}{(1 + x)x^{1/2}}$

7. $\int_{-\infty}^{\infty} x^{2} e^{-|x|} \, dx$

8. $\int_{1}^{\infty} \dfrac{dx}{(x - 1)^{1/2}(3 - x)^{2/3}}$

9. $\int_{0}^{\infty} \dfrac{(e^{-x} - 1)^{2}}{x^{3}} \, dx$.

In the following exercises determine all values of the parameter a

for which the integral converges.

10. $\displaystyle\int_0^\infty \frac{e^{-x}-1}{x^a}\, dx$

11. $\displaystyle\int_0^\infty \frac{x^{a-1}}{1+x}\, dx$

12. $\displaystyle\int_0^\infty \frac{\sin x\,(1-\cos x)}{x^a}\, dx$

13. $\displaystyle\int_0^\infty x^a \cos (x^4)\, dx$

14. $\displaystyle\int_{-\infty}^\infty \frac{\cos x}{x^a}\, dx$

15. $\displaystyle\int_0^\infty \frac{e^{-ax}\sin x}{x}\, dx$.

8.8   Functions defined by improper integrals

Many important functions in analysis appear as improper integrals. These functions are of great value in applied sciences. Before discussing special functions of this sort, we shall study some general properties of improper integrals. Let us first consider some examples.

Example 14.   The integral

$$\int_0^\infty e^{-xy}\sin x\, dx$$

determines a function $F(y)$ for each y for which the integral converges. It is easily seen that the integral converges for all $y > 0$ and diverges for $y \le 0$. Using integration by parts twice we obtain

$$F(y) = \int_0^\infty e^{-xy}\sin x\, dx = \frac{1}{1+y^2}, \quad y > 0 .$$

The integral is said to converge pointwise to $F(y)$ on the interval $0 < y < \infty$. The function $F(y)$ is continuous on its domain.

Example 15.   The function defined for positive values of y by the improper integral

$$\Gamma(y) = \int_0^\infty e^{-x}x^{y-1}\, dx , \quad y > 0$$

is called the gamma function. If $y \ge 1$, the integral is of the first kind. If $0 < y < 1$ we write

$$\Gamma(y) = \int_0^1 e^{-x}x^{y-1}\, dx + \int_1^\infty e^{-x}x^{y-1}\, dx ,$$

and it follows that $\Gamma(y)$ consists of improper integrals of the second and of the first kind. Since the first integral converges by **8.5-2** and the second by **8.2-3**, the original integral defines a function.

If the integral

$$F(y) = \int_a^\infty f(x, y)\, dx$$

converges pointwise to $F(y)$ on an interval T, then in practice it is important to know whether $F'(y)$ is continuous and whether the equations

$$F'(y) = \int_a^\infty \frac{\partial f}{\partial y}\, dx\,, \qquad \int_c^d F(y)\, dy = \int_a^\infty dx \int_c^d f(x, y)\, dy$$

hold.

If we, for instance, could differentiate and integrate the function $F(y)$ defined in Example 14 in this way, we would at once obtain the formulas

$$F'(y) = -\int_0^\infty xe^{-xy} \sin x\, dx = \frac{-2y}{(1 + y^2)^2}\,,$$

or

$$\int_0^\infty xe^{-xy} \sin x\, dx = \frac{2y}{(1 + y^2)^2}\,, \quad y > 0$$

$$\int_0^y F(y)\, dy = \int_0^\infty dx \int_0^y e^{-xy} \sin x\, dx = \tan^{-1} y\,,$$

or

$$\int_0^\infty \frac{1 - e^{-xy}}{x} \sin x\, dx = \tan^{-1} y\,, \quad y > 0\,,$$

which give the values of the corresponding improper integrals.

Just as in the case of sequences and infinite series, continuity, differentiability, and integrability of $F(y)$ depend on uniform convergence of the improper integral. Here again uniform convergence plays a fundamental role.

8.9 Uniform convergence of improper integrals

A reader who thoroughly understands uniform convergence of sequences and series will easily follow the parallel between uniform convergence of series and improper integrals.

If we use the relation

$$\int_a^\infty f(x, y)\, dx = \int_a^{x_1} f(x, y)\, dx + \int_{x_1}^{x_2} f(x, y)\, dx + \cdots + \int_{x_{n-1}}^{x_n} f(x, y)\, dx + \cdots$$

(see § 8.1), the definition of uniform convergence of improper integrals of the first kind can be based on that of infinite series.

If, for every strictly monotonically increasing sequence $\{x_n\}$ with $\lim\limits_{n \to \infty} x_n = \infty$, the series converges uniformly, that is,

$$|R_n(y)| = \left| \int_{x_n}^{x_{n+1}} f(x, y)\, dx + \int_{x_{n+1}}^{x_{n+2}} f(x, y)\, dx + \cdots \right| = \left| \int_{x_n}^\infty f(x, y)\, dx \right| < \varepsilon$$

for $n > n_0$ and all y on T, then the improper integral is said to converge uniformly; and conversely. In other words, the integral

$$F(y) = \int_a^\infty f(x, y)\, dx$$

converges uniformly on T when for a given $\varepsilon > 0$ there exists a number A such that for every $b > A$ the inequality

$$\left| \int_b^\infty f(x, y)\, dx \right| < \varepsilon$$

holds for all y on T.

Example 16. The integral

$$\int_0^\infty e^{-xy} \sin x\, dx$$

converges uniformly on $T = [c, \infty)$, $c > 0$.
Since

$$\left| \int_b^\infty e^{-xy} \sin x\, dx \right| \leq \int_b^\infty e^{-cx}\, dx = \frac{e^{-bc}}{c},$$

it follows that $|\int_b^\infty e^{-xy} \sin x\, dx| < \varepsilon$ if $e^{-bc}/c < \varepsilon$, that is, if $b > \log(1/c\varepsilon)/c = A$. Thus, for every given $\varepsilon > 0$, there exists a number A such that for $b > A$ the inequality holds. Consequently the integral converges uniformly. That the integral does not converge uniformly on $0 \leq y < \infty$ is evident, since for $y = 0$ the integral $\int_0^\infty \sin x\, dx$ diverges.

Similarly, from the equation

$$\int_a^b f(x, y)\, dx = \int_{a_1}^b f(x, y)\, dx + \int_{a_2}^{a_1} f(x, y)\, dx + \cdots + \int_{a_n}^{a_{n-1}} f(x, y)\, dx + \cdots$$

(see § 8.6), where the integral is improper at $x = a$, we state the following definition:

If the infinite series converges uniformly on T for all strictly monotonically decreasing sequences $\{a_n\}$ with $\lim_{n \to \infty} a_n = a$, that is,

$$|R_n(y)| = \left| \int_{a_{n+1}}^{a_n} f(x, y)\, dx + \int_{a_{n+2}}^{a_{n+1}} f(x, y)\, dx + \cdots \right| = \left| \int_a^{a_n} f(x, y)\, dx \right| < \varepsilon$$

for $n > n_0$ and all y on T, then the improper integral of the second kind is said to converge uniformly on T; and conversely.

In other words, the integral of the second kind,

$$\int_a^b f(x, y)\, dx\ ,$$

converges uniformly on T if for a given $\varepsilon > 0$ there exists a number $\delta > 0$ such that

$$\left| \int_a^{a+h} f(x, y)\, dx \right| < \varepsilon$$

for $0 < h < \delta$ and all y on T.

If the integral is improper at $x = b$, then the inequality is

$$\left| \int_{b-h}^{b} f(x, y)\, dx \right| < \varepsilon$$

for $0 < h < \delta$ and all y on T.

Example 17. The integral

$$F(y) = \int_0^1 e^{-x} x^{y-1}\, dx , \quad 0 < y < 1 ,$$

improper at $x = 0$, converges uniformly to $F(y)$ on $T = [c, 1]$, $c > 0$.

Since $x^{y-1} \leq x^{c-1}$ on T and consequently

$$\left| \int_0^h e^{-x} x^{y-1}\, dx \right| < \int_0^h x^{c-1}\, dx = \frac{h^c}{c} ,$$

it follows that $|\int_0^h e^{-x} x^{y-1}\, dx| < \varepsilon$ if $h^c/c < \varepsilon$, that is, if $0 < h < (c\varepsilon)^{1/c} = \delta$. This means that for every $\varepsilon > 0$ there exists a number $\delta = (c\varepsilon)^{1/c}$ such that for every $0 < h < \delta$ the inequality holds for all y on $T = [c, 1]$. This proves that the integral converges uniformly on T.

Tests for uniform converges of improper integrals are similar to those of infinite series.

Theorem **8.1-1** (Cauchy's criterion) can be restated as follows:

8.9-1 Theorem. (Cauchy's criterion). If $f(x, y)$ is continuous on the region R: $a \leq x < \infty$, $c \leq y \leq d$, then the integral $\int_a^\infty f(x, y)\, dx$ converges uniformly on $T = [c, d]$ if and only if, given an arbitrary $\varepsilon > 0$, a number $x_0 > a$ can be determined such that

$$\left| \int_{x_1}^{x_2} f(x, y)\, dx \right| < \varepsilon$$

for every $x_2 > x_1 > x_0$ and y on T.

Weierstrass' M-test, the theorems on continuity, integration, and differentiation are precisely analogues of **5.5-3**, **5.4-1**, **5.5-1** and **5.5-2**, respectively.

8.9-2 Theorem (Weierstrass' M-test). If $f(x, y)$ is continuous on the region R: $a \leq x < \infty$, $c \leq y \leq d$, and there is a function $M(x)$ such that $|f(x, y)| \leq M(x)$ on R and $\int_a^\infty M(x)\, dx$ converges, then the integral

$$F(y) = \int_a^\infty f(x, y)\, dx$$

converges absolutely and uniformly on $T = [c, d]$.

8.9-3 Theorem (Weierstrass' M-test). If $f(x, y)$ is continuous on the region R: $a < x < b$, $c \leq y \leq d$, and there is a function $M(x)$ such that $|f(x, y)| \leq M(x)$ on R and $\int_a^b M(x)\, dx$ converges, then the improper integral of the second kind

$$\int_a^b f(x, y)\, dx$$

converges absolutely and uniformly on $T = [c, d]$.

The proof of these theorems (using the definition or Cauchy's criterion) is trivial and is left to the reader.

For brevity we shall limit our discussion to improper integrals of the first kind. The theorems for integrals of the second kind can be easily formulated by using transformations (8.5).

If the improper integral converges conditionally, Weierstrass' M-test cannot be applied. The following tests are often useful.

8.9-4 Theorem (Abel's test). If $f(x, y)$ and $g(x, y)$ are continuous functions on the region R: $a \leq x < \infty$, $c \leq y \leq d$, and if $|\int_a^\infty f(x, y)\, dx| < M$ on R, $\int_a^\infty |\partial g(x, y)/\partial x|\, dx$ converges uniformly on $T = [c, d]$, and $g(x, y)$ converges uniformly to zero as $x \to \infty$, then

$$\int_a^\infty f(x, y) g(x, y)\, dx \quad \text{converges uniformly on } T.$$

Proof. Denote

$$\Phi(t, y) = \int_a^t f(x, y)\, dx \, .$$

By hypothesis $|\Phi(t, y)| < M$ for all $t \geq a$. Integrating by parts we obtain

$$\int_{x_1}^{x_2} f(x, y) g(x, y)\, dx = \Phi(x_2, y) g(x_2, y) - \Phi(x_1, y) g(x_1, y)$$

$$- \int_{x_1}^{x_2} \Phi(x_1, y) \frac{\partial g}{\partial x}\, dx \, .$$

It follows that

$$\left| \int_{x_1}^{x_2} f(x, y)g(x, y)\, dx \right| \leq |\Phi(x_2, y)||g(x_2, y)| + |\Phi(x_1, y)||g(x_1, y)|$$

$$+ \int_{x_1}^{x_2} |\Phi(x, y)| \left| \frac{\partial g}{\partial x} \right| dx$$

$$< M \left| |g(x_2, y)| + |g(x_1, y)| \right| + M \int_{x_1}^{x_2} \left| \frac{\partial g}{\partial x} \right| dx \, .$$

Since, by hypothesis, $g(x, y)$ converges uniformly to zero as $x \to \infty$, and $\int_a^\infty |\partial g/\partial x|\, dx$ converges uniformly on T, it follows that we can choose x_0 such that for $x_2 > x_1 > x_0$ the sum $|g(x_2, y)| + |g(x_1, y)| < \varepsilon/2M$ and $\int_{x_1}^{x_2} |\partial g/\partial x|\, dx < \varepsilon/2M$. Consequently,

$$\left| \int_{x_1}^{x_2} f(x, y)g(x, y)\, dx \right| < M \frac{\varepsilon}{2M} + M \frac{\varepsilon}{2M} = \varepsilon$$

for $x_2 > x_1 > x_0$. Thus, by Cauchy's criterion (**8.9-1**), the integral converges uniformly on T.

8.9-5 Theorem (Dirichlet test). If $f(x, y)$ and $\partial g(x, y)/\partial x$ are continuous on R: $a \leq x < \infty$, $c \leq y \leq d$ and if

$$\int_a^\infty f(x, y)\, dx \quad \text{converges uniformly on} \quad T = [c, d] \, ,$$

$$\int_a^\infty \left| \frac{\partial g}{\partial x} \right| dx < M \quad \text{on} \quad T \, , \quad \text{and} \quad |g(x, y)| < M \quad \text{on} \quad T \, ,$$

then the integral $\int_a^\infty f(x, y)g(x, y)\, dx$ converges uniformly on T.

The proof follows the very same lines as in **8.9-4** and is left as an exercise. $\Big($Hint: Note that

$$\int_{x_1}^{x_2} f(x, y)g(x, y)\, dx = \Phi(x, y)g(x, y) \Big|_{x_1}^{x_2} - \int_{x_1}^{x_2} \Phi(x, y) \frac{\partial g}{\partial x}\, dx$$

$$= [\Phi(x, y) - K]g(x, y) \Big|_{x_1}^{x_2} - \int_{x_1}^{x_2} [\Phi(x, y) - K] \frac{\partial g}{\partial x}\, dx$$

where K is any constant with respect to x. For the proof use $K = \int_a^\infty f(x, y)dx$, that is,

$$\Phi(t, y) - K = \int_a^t f(x, y)\, dx - \int_a^\infty f(x, y)\, dx = - \int_t^\infty f(x, y)\, dx \, . \Big)$$

8.9-6 Theorem. If $f(x, y)$ is continuous on the region R: $a \leq x < \infty$, $c \leq y \leq d$, then the function $F(y)$ defined by

$$F(y) = \int_a^\infty f(x, y)\, dx$$

is continuous on $T = [c, d]$ if the integral converges uniformly on T.

Proof. We have to show that given $\varepsilon > 0$ there exists a number $\delta > 0$ such that for y_0 and $y_0 + h$ on T and $|h| < \delta$ the inequality

$$|F(y_0 + h) - F(y_0)| < \varepsilon$$

holds.

Since

$$
\begin{aligned}
F(y_0 + h) - F(y_0) &= \int_a^\infty [f(x, y_0 + h) - f(x, y_0)]\, dx \\
&= \int_a^b [f(x, y_0 + h) - f(x, y_0)]\, dx + \int_b^\infty f(x, y_0 + h)\, dx \\
&\quad - \int_b^\infty f(x, y_0)\, dx\, ,
\end{aligned}
$$

it follows that

$$
\begin{aligned}
|F(y_0 + h) - F(y_0)| &\leq \int_a^b |f(x, y_0 + h) - f(x, y_0)|\, dx \\
&\quad + \left|\int_b^\infty f(x, y_0 + h)\, dx\right| + \left|\int_b^\infty f(x, y_0)\, dx\right| .
\end{aligned}
$$

Now, $f(x, y)$ is uniformly continuous on the rectangle $a \leq x \leq b$, $c \leq y \leq d$; consequently we can determine a number δ so that

$$|f(x, y_0 + h) - f(x, y_0)| < \frac{1}{3}\,\frac{\varepsilon}{b - a} \quad \text{for} \quad |h| < \delta\, .$$

Furthermore, since the integral is uniformly convergent, we can find a number A such that

$$\left|\int_b^\infty f(x, y)\, dx\right| < \frac{\varepsilon}{3} \quad \text{for} \quad b > A\, .$$

It follows that

$$|F(y_0 + h) - F(y_0)| < \frac{\varepsilon}{3} + \frac{\varepsilon}{3} + \frac{\varepsilon}{3} = \varepsilon \quad \text{for} \quad |h| < \delta\, .$$

This proves that $F(y)$ is continuous on T, that is,

$$\lim_{y \to y_0} F(y) = F(y_0)\, ,$$

or

$$\lim_{y \to y_0} \int_a^\infty f(x, y)\, dx = \int_a^\infty \lim_{y \to y_0} f(x, y)\, dx = \int_a^\infty f(x, y_0)\, dx\, .$$

177

In other words, if the integral converges uniformly, then limit and integration may be interchanged.

Example 18. The function $F(y)$ represented by the improper integral

$$F(y) = \int_0^\infty \frac{\cos(xy)}{x^{1/2}} \, dx$$

is continuous for all $|y| \geq \delta > 0$.

If we write

$$F(y) = \int_0^1 \frac{\cos(xy)}{x^{1/2}} \, dx + \int_1^\infty \frac{\cos(xy)}{x^{1/2}} \, dx \, ,$$

then the first improper integral on the right converges absolutely and uniformly for all y by **8.9-3** with $M(x) = 1/x^{1/2}$; the second improper integral converges by **8.9-4** with $f(x, y) = \cos xy$ and $g(x, y) = 1/x^{1/2}$. Consequently by **8.9-6** both integrals represent continuous functions for all $|y| \geq \delta > 0$, and so does their sum $F(y)$.

Exercises 8.F

Show the integrals of Exercises 1–13 uniformly convergent on the intervals indicated.

1. $\int_0^\infty \frac{y \, dx}{x^2 + y^2}$, $1 \leq y \leq 2$

2. $\int_0^\infty \frac{\cos xy}{1 + x^2} \, dx$, $a \leq y \leq b$

3. $\int_0^\infty e^{-x^2 y^2} \, dx$, $0.1 < y < 10$

4. $\int_0^1 (\log xy)^{1/3} \, dx$, $1 \leq y \leq 3$

5. $\int_1^\infty \frac{\sin x}{x^y} \, dx$, $y \geq a > 0$

6. $\int_0^\infty \frac{e^{-xy} \sin x}{x} \, dx$, $y \geq 0$

7. $\int_0^1 e^{-x} x^{y-1} \, dx$, $0.1 \leq y \leq 1$

8. $\int_1^\infty \frac{\cos x}{(x^2 + y^2)^{1/2}} \, dx$, for all y

9. $\int_1^\infty \frac{x \cos(xy)}{1 + x^2} \, dx$, $|y| \geq \delta > 0$

10. $\int_1^\infty \frac{x \sin(xy)}{1 + x^2} \, dx$, $|y| \geq \delta > 0$

11. $\int_1^\infty \frac{\sin xy}{x} \, dx$, $|y| \geq \delta > 0$

12. $\int_a^\infty e^{-xy} \frac{\cos x}{x} \, dx$, $0 \leq y \leq A$, $a > 0$

13. $\int_a^\infty e^{-xy} \frac{\sin x}{x} \, dx$, $a > 0$, $0 \leq y \leq A$.

14. Prove that

$$F(y) = \int_0^\infty y e^{-yx} \, dx$$

converges uniformly to $F(y)$ on $0 < a \leq y \leq b$ and does not converge uniformly on $0 \leq y \leq b$.

15. The function $F(y)$ defined by the integral

$$F(y) = \int_0^\infty \frac{y\,dx}{x^2 + y^2}$$

is non-uniformly convergent in any interval containing the origin. Show this by evaluating the integral. It converges to $\pi/2$ uniformly on $0 < a \le y \le b$.

8.10 Integration of improper integrals

8.10-1 Theorem. If $f(x, y)$ is continuous on the region $R: c \le y \le d$, $a \le x < \infty$ and the integral

$$F(y) = \int_a^\infty f(x, y)\,dx$$

converges uniformly on $T = [c, d]$, then the improper integral

$$\int_c^d F(y)\,dy = \int_a^\infty dx \int_c^d f(x, y)\,dy$$

converges uniformly on T.

Proof. From the hypothesis of uniform convergence it follows that

$$\left| \int_b^\infty f(x, y)\,dx \right| < \frac{\varepsilon}{d - c}, \quad b > A.$$

Hence the inequality

$$(\alpha) \qquad \left| \int_c^d dy \int_b^\infty f(x, y)\,dx \right| < \varepsilon, \quad b > A$$

holds. If the obvious relation

$$\int_b^\infty f(x, y)\,dx = F(y) - \int_a^b f(x, y)\,dx$$

is used it follows that

$$\left| \int_c^d dy \int_b^\infty f(x, y)\,dx \right| = \left| \int_c^d dy \left[F(y) - \int_a^b f(x, y)\,dx \right] \right| < \varepsilon, \quad b > A.$$

Hence, as $b \to \infty$, we have

$$\int_c^d F(y)\,dy = \lim_{b \to \infty} \int_c^d dy \int_a^b f(x, y)\,dx.$$

Now, $f(x, y)$ is continuous on the rectangle $a \le x \le b$, $c \le y \le d$, consequently a reversal of order of integration is permissible, and passing to the limit, as $b \to \infty$, yields

$$\lim_{b\to\infty} \int_c^d dy \int_a^b f(x, y)\, dx = \lim_{b\to\infty} \int_a^b dx \int_c^d f(x, y)\, dy \, ,$$

or

$$(\beta) \qquad \int_c^d F(y)\, dy = \int_c^d dy \int_a^\infty f(x, y)\, dx = \int_a^\infty dx \int_c^d f(x, y)\, dy \, .$$

From (β) and (α) it follows that

$$\left| \int_c^d dy \int_b^\infty f(x, y)\, dx \right| = \left| \int_b^\infty dx \int_c^d f(x, y)\, dy \right| < \varepsilon \, , \quad b > A \, .$$

The last inequality shows that the last integral on the right of (β) is uniformly convergent. This completes the proof.

Example 19. Since the integral $\int_0^\infty e^{-xy} \sin x\, dx$ converges uniformly on $T = [c, d]$, $c > 0$ (see Example 16), we may integrate it with respect to y from c to d under the integral sign

$$\int_0^\infty \sin x\, dx \int_c^d e^{-xy}\, dy = \int_c^d \frac{dy}{1 + y^2} \, .$$

This yields the remarkable formula

$$\int_0^\infty \frac{e^{-cx} - e^{-dx}}{x} \sin x\, dx = \tan^{-1} d - \tan^{-1} c \, .$$

Some special cases:
As $d \to \infty$ we obtain

$$\int_0^\infty e^{-cx} \frac{\sin x}{x}\, dx = \frac{\pi}{2} - \tan^{-1} c \, .$$

As $c \to 0$, the last relation yields the familiar integral (see Chapter 7, Example 11)

$$\int_0^\infty \frac{\sin x}{x}\, dx = \frac{\pi}{2} \, .$$

This example shows how **8.10-1** can lead to ingenious methods for evaluating improper integrals.

Exercises 8.G

1. From the relation

$$\int_0^\infty e^{-x} \cos xy \, dx = \frac{1}{1+y^2}, \quad y > 0$$

obtain the formula

$$\int_0^\infty e^{-x} \frac{1 - \cos yx}{x^2} \, dx = y \tan^{-1} y - \frac{1}{2} \log(1 + y^2), \quad y > 0.$$

2. Evaluate the integral

$$\int_0^\infty \frac{e^{-ax} - e^{-bx}}{x} \, dx.$$

(Hint: Integrate $\int_0^\infty e^{-yx} dx = 1/y$ with respect to y from $0 < a \le y \le b$.)

3. Evaluate the integral

$$\int_0^\infty \frac{e^{-ax} \sin yx}{x} \, dx, \quad a \ge 0.$$

4. Evaluate the integral

$$\int_0^\infty \frac{e^{-bx} - e^{-ax}}{x} \cos x \, dx.$$

(Hint: Start with $y/1 + y^2 = \int_0^\infty e^{-yx} \cos x \, dx$.)

5. Show that

$$\int_0^\infty e^{-x} \frac{1 - \cos xy}{x} \, dx = \frac{1}{2} \log(1 + y^2).$$

8.11 Differentiation of improper integrals

8.11-1 Theorem. If $f(x, y)$ and $f_y(x, y)$ are continuous on $R: a \le x < \infty, \ c \le y \le d$; and if the integral

$$F(y) = \int_a^\infty f(x, y) \, dx$$

converges and the integral

$$\int_a^\infty f_y(x, y) \, dx$$

converges uniformly on $T = [a, b]$, then

$$F'(y) = \int_a^\infty f_y(x, y) \, dx$$

on T.

Proof. By **8.9-6** the function

$$\lambda(y) = \int_a^\infty f_y(x, y) \, dx$$

is continuous on T and may be integrated under the integral sign (**8.10-1**). Thus

$$\int_a^y \lambda(t)\, dt = \int_a^\infty dx \int_a^y f_t(x, t)\, dt = \int_a^\infty [f(x, y) - f(x, a)]\, dx = F(y) - F(a)\ .$$

On differentiating this equation we obtain

$$\lambda(y) = F'(y)\ ,$$

which proves the theorem.

Example 20. We shall evaluate the integral

$$F(y) = \int_0^\infty e^{-a^2 x^2} \cos(2yx)\, dx\ .$$

In order to justify the differentiation

$$F'(y) = -2\int_0^\infty e^{-a^2 x^2} x \sin(2yx)\, dx$$

we must show that $F(y)$ converges and $F'(y)$ converges uniformly on $T = [0, \infty)$. If we note that the integrands are absolutely less than $M_1(x) = e^{-a^2 x^2}$ and $M_2(x) = xe^{-a^2 x^2}$, respectively, and $\int_a^\infty M_k(x)\, dx$ converges ($k = 1, 2$), it follows by **8.9-2** that both integrals converge uniformly.

On integrating by parts we obtain

$$F'(y) = \frac{1}{a^2}\int_0^\infty \sin(2yx)\, d(e^{-a^2 x^2}) = \frac{-2y}{a^2}\int_0^\infty e^{-a^2 x^2} \cos(2yx)\, dx = -\frac{2y}{a^2}F(y)$$

which yields

$$F(y) = c\, e^{-y^2/a^2}$$

where c is a constant of integration independent of y.

The constant is determined by putting $y = 0$. It follows that

$$c = F(0) = \int_0^\infty e^{-a^2 x^2}\, dx = \frac{1}{a}\int_0^\infty e^{-t^2}\, dt = \frac{\pi^{1/2}}{2a} \quad (ax = t)$$

where $\int_0^\infty e^{-t^2}\, dt = \pi^{1/2}/2$ is the so-called probability integral.

Consequently,

$$F(y) = \frac{\pi^{1/2}}{2a} e^{-y^2/a^2}\ .$$

Example 21. Evaluate

$$\int_0^\infty \frac{dx}{(x^2 + 1)^{n+1}}$$

182

where n is a positive integer.

We shall consider a somewhat more general case:

$$\int_0^\infty \frac{dx}{(x^2 + y)^{n+1}}, \quad y \geq 1.$$

We start with the case $n = 0$.

$$F(y) = \int_0^\infty \frac{dx}{x^2 + y} = \frac{\pi}{2} y^{-1/2}.$$

Differentiating the relation n times we find

$$F^{(n)}(y) = (-1)(-2) \cdots (-n) \int_0^\infty \frac{dx}{(x^2 + y)^{n+1}}$$

$$= \left(-\frac{1}{2}\right)\left(-\frac{3}{2}\right)\left(-\frac{5}{2}\right) \cdots \left(-\frac{2n-1}{2}\right) \frac{\pi}{2} y^{-(2n+1)/2}.$$

Since $1/(x^2 + y)^{n+1} \leq M(x) = 1/(x^2 + 1)$ and $\int_0^\infty M(x)\, dx$ converges, $F(y)$ and $F^{(n)}(y)$ converge uniformly by **8.9-2**. Thus we obtain

$$\int_0^\infty \frac{dx}{(x^2 + y)^{n+1}} = \frac{1 \cdot 3 \cdot 5 \cdots (2n-1)}{2^n n!} \frac{\pi}{2} y^{-(2n+1)/2}$$

$$= \frac{1 \cdot 3 \cdot 5 \cdots (2n-1)}{2 \cdot 4 \cdot 6 \cdots 2n} \frac{\pi}{2} y^{-(2n+1)/2}.$$

For $y = 1$ we obtain

$$\int_0^\infty \frac{dx}{(x^2 + 1)^{n+1}} = \frac{1 \cdot 3 \cdot 5 \cdots (2n-1)}{2 \cdot 4 \cdot 6 \cdots 2n} \frac{\pi}{2}.$$

By putting $x = \tan \theta$ we obtain the familiar integral

$$\int_0^{\pi/2} \cos^{2n} \theta \, d\theta = \frac{1 \cdot 3 \cdot 5 \cdots (2n-1)}{2 \cdot 4 \cdot 6 \cdots 2n} \frac{\pi}{2}.$$

Example 22. The integral

$$F(c, d) = \int_0^\infty \frac{e^{-cx} - e^{-dx}}{x},$$

which has been evaluated by the method of integration (Example 19), can easily be found by diffentiating with respect to c (or d).

Since F and

$$\frac{\partial F}{\partial c} = -\int_0^\infty e^{-cx} \sin x \, dx = -\frac{1}{c^2 + 1}$$

converge uniformly for $c > 0$, integration with respect to c yields

$$F(c, d) = -\tan^{-1} c + A$$

where A is a constant of integration independent of c. A is easily found if we put $c = d$. Since $F(d, d) = 0$, it follows that $A = \tan^{-1} d$. Consequently

$$F(c, d) = \tan^{-1} d - \tan^{-1} c .$$

Exercises 8.H

Evaluate the integrals 1–4 by the method of differentiation. Justify differentiation under the integral sign.

1. $\displaystyle\int_0^\infty \frac{1 - e^{-yx^2}}{x^2} \, dx$, $\quad y \geq 0$

2. $\displaystyle\int_0^\infty \frac{e^{-ax} \sin yx}{x} \, dx$, $\quad a > 0$

3. $\displaystyle\int_0^\infty \frac{e^{-ax} - e^{-bx}}{x} \cos x \, dx$, $\quad a, b > 0$

4. $\displaystyle\int_0^\infty e^{-x} \frac{1 - \cos xy}{x} \, dx$.

5. Give reasons why $\int_0^\infty ((\sin xt)/t) \, dt$ cannot be evaluated by the method of differentiation.

6. Show that
$$\int_0^\infty t^{2n} e^{-at^2} \, dt = \frac{\pi^{1/2}}{2} \frac{1 \cdot 3 \cdot 5 \cdots (2n - 1)}{2^n} \alpha^{(-n-(1/2))} .$$
(Hint: Start with $\int_0^\infty e^{-at^2} \, dt = (\frac{1}{2}\pi^{1/2})a^{-1/2}$.)

7. Evaluate
$$\int_{-\infty}^\infty \frac{\cos bx - \cos ax}{x^2} \, dx .$$

8.12 Gamma Function.

The function $\Gamma(y)$ defined by the improper integral

$$\Gamma(y) = \int_0^\infty e^{-t} t^{y-1} \, dt , \quad y > 0$$

is called the gamma function. It plays an important role in sciences. Furthermore, many definite integrals can be represented in terms of gamma functions or are special cases of it. For example, by setting $t = x^2$ in

$$\Gamma\left(\frac{1}{2}\right) = \int_0^\infty e^{-t} t^{-1/2} \, dt = 2 \int_0^\infty e^{-x^2} \, dx = \pi^{1/2}$$

where $\int_0^\infty e^{-x^2} \, dx = \frac{1}{2}\pi^{1/2}$ is the so-called probability integral.

If $0 < y < 1$, both integrals

$$\Gamma(y) = \int_0^1 e^{-t} t^{y-1} \, dt + \int_1^\infty e^{-t} t^{y-1} \, dt$$

are improper (see Example 15).

By Weierstrass' *M*-test (**8.9-3** and **8.9-2**) where $M_1(t) = e^{-t}t^{a-1}$ and $M_2(t) = e^{-t}t^{b-1}$, respectively, it follows that both integrals converge absolutely and uniformly, and consequently $\Gamma(y)$ is a continuous function on every interval $0 < a \le y \le b$.

In the very same way one can show that the *n*th derivative of $\Gamma(y)$

$$\Gamma^{(n)}(y) = \int_0^\infty e^{-t} (\log t)^n t^{y-1} \, dt$$

is also continuous on the same interval.

From the inequality

$$\Gamma(y) > \int_0^1 e^{-t}t^{y-1} \, dt > e^{-1} \int_0^1 t^{y-1} \, dt = \frac{1}{ey}$$

it follows that $\lim_{y \to 0+} \Gamma(y) = \infty$, that is, for $y = 0$ the integral diverges.

The gamma function has several important functional properties. Integrating by parts we obtain

$$\int_\varepsilon^b e^{-t}t^{y-1} \, dt = \frac{t^y}{y}e^{-t}\Big|_\varepsilon^b + \frac{1}{y}\int_\varepsilon^b e^{-t}t^y \, dt \; .$$

As $\varepsilon \to 0+$ and $b \to \infty$, the first term on the right vanishes and we have

$$\int_0^\infty e^{-t}t^{y-1} \, dt = \frac{1}{y}\int_0^\infty e^{-t}t^y \, dt$$

or

$$\Gamma(y + 1) = y\Gamma(y) \; .$$

If we note that $\Gamma(1) = \int_0^\infty e^{-t} \, dt = 1$, we obtain

$$\Gamma(2) = 1\Gamma(1) = 1$$
$$\Gamma(3) = 2\Gamma(2) = 2 \cdot 1 = 2!$$
$$\Gamma(4) = 3\Gamma(3) = 3 \cdot 2 \cdot 1 = 3!$$
$$\vdots$$
$$\Gamma(n + 1) = n\Gamma(n) = n(n - 1) \cdots 1 = n! \; .$$

Usually the factorial $n!$ is defined for positive integers. The above functional relation of the gamma function may be used for defining factorials of positive and negative fractions. For example, $0! = \Gamma(1) = 1$, $(-\frac{1}{2})! = \Gamma(\frac{1}{2}) = \pi^{1/2}$, $(\frac{1}{2})! = \frac{1}{2}\Gamma(\frac{1}{2}) = \frac{1}{2}\pi^{1/2}$, $(\frac{3}{2})! = \frac{3}{2}\Gamma(\frac{3}{2}) = \frac{3}{4}\Gamma(\frac{1}{2}) = \frac{3}{4}\pi^{1/2}$, and so on.

Similarly, we may extend $\Gamma(y)$ to negative nonintegral values of y

$$\Gamma(y) = \frac{\Gamma(y+1)}{y}, \quad -1 < y < 0$$

$$\Gamma(y) = \frac{\Gamma(y+2)}{y(y+1)}, \quad -2 < y < -1$$

$$\vdots$$

$$\Gamma(y) = \frac{\Gamma(y+n)}{y(y+1)\cdots(y+n-1)}, \quad -n < y < -n+1 .$$

Thus, we may define $\Gamma(y)$ for all y except $y = 0, -1, -2, \ldots$. Note that the right-hand side of the above relations depends entirely on the values of $\Gamma(y)$ on the interval $0 < y < 1$. It follows that one needs tabulate $\Gamma(y)$ only on an interval of length 1. This has been done (*Short Table of Integrals*, B. O. Peirce and R. M. Foster, New York, Ginn and Co., 1955).

Since

$$\Gamma''(y) = \int_0^\infty e^{-t} (\log t)^2 t^{y-1}\, dt > 0 , \quad y > 0 ,$$

the curve of $\Gamma(y)$ is convex. Since $\Gamma(y) > 0$ for $y > 0$ and $\Gamma(1) = \Gamma(2) = 1$, $\Gamma(y)$ has just one minimum between 1 and 2. The general character of the graph of $\Gamma(y)$ is given in Figure 23.

Some definite integrals can be expressed in terms of the gamma function.

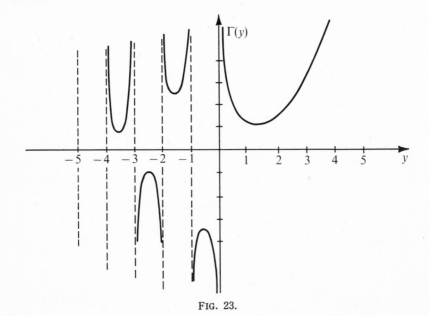

FIG. 23.

Example 23. Represent the function defined by the integral

$$\beta(y, n) = \int_0^1 t^{y-1}(1 - t)^{n-1} \, dt \, ,$$

where $y > 0$ and n is a positive integer in terms of gamma functions.
When $n = 1$, we have

$$\beta(y, 1) = \int_0^1 t^{y-1} \, dt = \frac{1}{y} \, .$$

When $n > 1$ we integrate by parts to get

$$\beta(y, n) = \frac{n - 1}{y} \int_0^1 t^y (1 - t)^{n-2} \, dt = \frac{n - 1}{y} \beta(y + 1, \, n - 1) \, .$$

Repeating integration we obtain

$$\beta(y, n) = \frac{(n - 1)(n - 2)}{y(y + 1)} \beta(y + 2, \, n - 2) \, .$$

This procedure leads to

$$\beta(y, n) = \frac{(n - 1)(n - 2) \cdots 2 \cdot 1}{y(y + 1) \cdots (y + n - 2)} \beta(y + n - 2, \, 1) = \frac{(n - 1)!}{y(y + 1) \cdots (y + n - 1)} \, .$$

Thus,

$$\beta(y, n) = \frac{(n - 1)!}{y(y + 1) \cdots (y + n - 1)} = \frac{\Gamma(y)(n - 1)!}{y(y + 1) \cdots (y + n - 1)\Gamma(y)} \, .$$

Using the functional relation of the gamma function we obtain the relation

$$\beta(y, n) = \frac{\Gamma(y)\Gamma(n)}{\Gamma(y + n)} \, .$$

It can be proved that the above relation holds if n is not an integer.
If we put $t = \sin^2 \theta$, we obtain

$$\beta(y, n) = 2 \int_0^{\pi/2} \sin^{2y-1} \theta \cos^{2n-1} \theta \, d\theta \, .$$

Hence

$$\frac{1}{2}\beta\left(\frac{1}{2}, \, n + \frac{1}{2}\right) = \frac{\Gamma(\frac{1}{2})\Gamma(n + \frac{1}{2})}{2\Gamma(n + 1)} = \int_0^{\pi/2} \cos^{2n} \theta \, d\theta = S_{2n} \, ,$$

$$\frac{1}{2}\beta\left(\frac{1}{2}, \, n + 1\right) = \frac{\Gamma(\frac{1}{2})\Gamma(n + 1)}{2\Gamma(n + \frac{3}{2})} = \int_0^{\pi/2} \cos^{2n+1} \theta \, d\theta = S_{2n+1} \, .$$

If we note that $\cos^k \theta > \cos^p \theta$ for $k < p$, $0 < \theta < \pi/2$, it follows that

$$0 < S_{2n+1} < S_{2n} < S_{2n-1}$$

or

$$1 < \frac{S_{2n}}{S_{2n+1}} < \frac{S_{2n-1}}{S_{2n+1}} = 1 + \frac{1}{2n} .$$

Hence

$$\lim_{n \to \infty} \frac{S_{2n}}{S_{2n+1}} = \lim_{n \to \infty} \left[\frac{\Gamma(n + \frac{1}{2})}{\Gamma(n + 1)} \right]^2 \left(n + \frac{1}{2} \right) = 1 .$$

Substitution of $\Gamma(n + \frac{1}{2}) = (n - \frac{1}{2})(n - \frac{3}{2}) \cdots \frac{1}{2}\Gamma(\frac{1}{2})$, $\Gamma(\frac{1}{2}) = \pi^{1/2}$, and $\Gamma(n + 1) = n!$ yields the infinite product of Wallis

$$\frac{\pi}{2} = \lim_{n \to \infty} \left[\frac{2 \cdot 4 \cdot 6 \cdots 2n}{1 \cdot 3 \cdot 5 \cdots (2n - 1)} \right]^2 \frac{1}{2n + 1}$$

which may be written in the form

$$\pi^{1/2} = \lim_{n \to \infty} \frac{2 \cdot 4 \cdot 6 \cdots 2n}{1 \cdot 3 \cdot 5 \cdots (2n - 1)} \cdot \frac{1}{n^{1/2}[1 + (1/2n)]^{1/2}} = \lim_{n \to \infty} \frac{(n!)^2 2^{2n}}{(2n)! n^{1/2}} .$$

The gamma function has many more useful properties. For example, it can be proved that

$$\Gamma(y)\Gamma(1 - y) = \frac{\pi}{\sin \pi y} , \quad 0 < y < 1 .$$

For $a > 0$

$$\int_0^\infty e^{-at} t^{y-1} \, dt = \frac{\Gamma(y)}{a^y} ,$$

as is easily seen by making the substitution $at = x$.

Exercises 8.I

1. Show that $\Gamma(\alpha)$ can be written in the form
$$\Gamma(\alpha) = \int_0^1 \left(\ln \frac{1}{x} \right)^{\alpha-1} dx , \quad \alpha > 0 .$$

2. Compute (a) $\Gamma(5/2)$, (b) $\Gamma(7/2)$, (c) $\Gamma(-1/2)$, (d) $\Gamma(-5/2)$

3. Evaluate

(a) $\displaystyle\int_0^\infty e^{-t} t^{1/2} \, dt$ (c) $\displaystyle\int_0^\infty e^{-\alpha t} t^{1/2} \, dt$ (e) $\displaystyle\int_0^\infty e^{-t} t^{(n-(1/2))} \, dt$.

(b) $\displaystyle\int_0^\infty e^{-t} t^{3/2} \, dt$ (d) $\displaystyle\int_0^1 \left(\log \frac{1}{t} \right)^n \, dt$

(Note: In (d) and (e) n is a positive integer.)

4. Show that

$$\int_0^1 \frac{dt}{(1 - t^{1/4})^{1/2}} = 4\beta\left(4, \frac{1}{2}\right) = \frac{128}{35} .$$

(Hint: Set $x = t^{1/4}$.)

5. Show that $\Gamma(\frac{1}{2} + n) = [(2n)!/4^n n!]\pi^{1/2}$ (n positive integer).

6. $\beta(4, 4) = \int_0^1 t^3 (1 - t)^3 \, dt$. Evaluate the integral by integration and by using gamma functions.

7. Show that

$$\int_0^{\pi/2} \sin^{2n} t \, dt = \frac{1}{2}\beta\left(\frac{1}{2}, n + \frac{1}{2}\right) = \frac{\Gamma(\frac{1}{2})\Gamma(n + \frac{1}{2})}{2\Gamma(n + 1)} .$$

8. Show that

$$\int_0^1 \frac{dt}{(1 - t^p)^{1/2}} = \frac{\pi^{1/2}\Gamma(1/p)}{p\Gamma[(1/p) + \frac{1}{2}]} , \quad p > 0 .$$

9. Show that

$$\int_0^1 \left[\frac{\log (1/t)}{t}\right]^{1/2} dt = (2\pi)^{1/2} .$$

8.13 Approximation of infinite series

In §4.6 we derived the remarkable formula

$$\sum_{\mu=0}^{n} f(\mu) = \int_0^n f(x) \, dx + \frac{1}{2}[f(0) + f(n)] + \int_0^n f_1(x)f'(x) \, dx ,$$

where $f_1(x) = x - |x| - \frac{1}{2}$, known as Euler's summation formula. The formula has been used to prove convergence of certain infinite series (Example 16 and 18, Chapter 4); it can be used to approximate infinite series, or, conversely, to estimate values of improper integrals. In the following we shall illustrate the use of the formula in approximating series, in particular, slowly convergent infinite series.

In order to write Euler's summation formula in a somewhat more refined form we first consider the following. Integrating the Fourier series of $f_1(x)$

$$f_1(x) = x - |x| - \frac{1}{2} = -\sum_{\mu=1}^{\infty} \frac{\sin 2\pi\mu x}{\pi\mu} ,$$

we obtained the following Fourier series (Chapter 7, Example 10) valid on $0 \leq x \leq 1$:

$$f_2(x) = \frac{x^2}{2} - \frac{x}{2} + \frac{1}{12} = \sum_{\mu=1}^{\infty} \frac{2 \cos 2\pi\mu x}{(2\pi\mu)^2} ,$$

$$f_3(x) = \frac{x^3}{6} - \frac{x^2}{4} + \frac{x}{12} = \sum_{\mu=1}^{\infty} \frac{2 \sin 2\pi\mu x}{(2\pi\mu)^3} ,$$

$$f_4(x) = \frac{x^4}{24} - \frac{x^3}{12} + \frac{x^2}{24} - \frac{1}{720} = -\sum_{\mu=1}^{\infty} \frac{2 \cos 2\pi\mu x}{(2\pi\mu)^4} .$$

It is easily seen how this procedure leads to the general formulas

(1)
$$f_{2k}(x) = (-1)^{k-1} \sum_{\mu=1}^{\infty} \frac{2\cos 2\pi\mu x}{(2\pi\mu)^{2k}} ,$$

$$f_{2k+1}(x) = (-1)^{k-1} \sum_{\mu=1}^{\infty} \frac{2\sin 2\pi\mu x}{(2\pi\mu)^{2k+1}} .$$

If the Bernoulli numbers

$$\beta_1 = -\frac{1}{2} , \quad \beta_2 = \frac{1}{6} , \quad \beta_3 = 0 , \quad \beta_4 = \frac{1}{30} , \quad \beta_5 = \beta_7 = \beta_9 = \beta_{11} = \beta_{13} = \beta_{15} = 0 ,$$

$$\beta_6 = \frac{1}{42} , \quad \beta_8 = -\frac{1}{30} , \quad \beta_{10} = \frac{5}{66} , \quad \beta_{12} = -\frac{691}{2730} , \quad \beta_{14} = \frac{7}{6} , \quad \ldots$$

are used (see Chapter 6, Example 17), the polynomials $f_n(x)$, $n = 2, 3, 4, \ldots$, can be put in the form

$$f_2(x) = \frac{x^2}{2!} + \frac{\beta_1}{1!}\frac{x}{1!} + \frac{\beta_2}{2!} , \quad f_3(x) = \frac{x^3}{3!} + \frac{\beta_1}{1!}\frac{x^2}{2!} + \frac{\beta_2}{2!}\frac{x}{1!} ,$$

etc., and by induction

(2)
$$f_k(x) = \frac{x^k}{k!} + \frac{\beta_1}{1!}\frac{x^{k-1}}{(k-1)!} + \frac{\beta_2}{2!}\frac{x^{k-2}}{(k-2)!} + \cdots + \frac{\beta_k}{k!}$$

$$= \frac{1}{k!}\left[\binom{k}{0}x^k + \binom{k}{1}\beta_1 x^{k-1} + \binom{k}{2}\beta_2 x^{k-2} + \cdots \right.$$

$$\left. + \binom{k}{k-1}\beta_{k-1}x + \binom{k}{k}\beta_k \right].$$

Sometimes $f_k(x)$ is expressed by the symbolical formula

$$f_k(x) = \frac{1}{k!}(x + \beta)^k .$$

From (1) and (2) for $x = 0$ it follows that

(3)
$$\frac{\beta_{2k}}{(2k)!} = (-1)^{k-1} \sum_{\mu=1}^{\infty} \frac{2}{(2\pi\mu)^{2k}}$$

whence

$$\sum_{\mu=1}^{\infty} \frac{1}{\mu^{2k}} = (-1)^{k-1} \frac{\beta_{2k}(2\pi)^{2k}}{2(2k)!} , \quad k = 1, 2, 3, \ldots .$$

Integrating by parts and using the above properties $f_k(x + n) = f_k(x)$, $f_2(n) = f_2(0) = \beta_2/2!$, $f_3(n) = f_3(0) = 0$, we obtain

$$\int_0^n f_1(x)f'(x)\,dx = f_2(x)f'(x)\Big|_0^n - \int_0^n f_2(x)f''(x)\,dx$$

$$= \frac{\beta_2}{2!}[f'(n) - f'(0)] - f_3(x)f''(x)\Big|_0^n + \int_0^n f_3(x)f'''(x)\,dx$$

$$= \frac{\beta_2}{2!}[f'(n) - f'(0)] + \int_0^n f_3(x)f'''(x)\,dx\ ,$$

and in general

$$\int_0^n f_{2k-1}(x)f^{(2k-1)}(x)\,dx = \frac{\beta_{2k}}{(2k)!}[f^{(2k-1)}(n) - f^{(2k-1)}(0)] + \int_0^n f_{2k+1}(x)f^{(2k+1)}(x)\,dx\ .$$

Using these relations we can write Euler's summation formula in the following form:

$$(4)\quad f(0) + f(1) + \cdots + f(n) = \int_0^n f(x)\,dx + \frac{1}{2}[f(n) + f(0)] + \frac{\beta_2}{2!}[f'(n) - f'(0)]$$

$$+ \frac{\beta_4}{4!}[f'''(n) - f'''(0)] + \cdots$$

$$+ \frac{\beta_{2k}}{(2k)!}[f^{(2k-1)}(n) - f^{(2k-1)}(0)] + P_k\ ,$$

where

$$P_k = \int_0^n f_{2k+1}(x)f^{(2k+1)}(x)\,dx = - \int_0^n f_{2k}(x)f^{(2k)}(x)\,dx\ .$$

$\Big($ Note that

$$- \int_0^n f_{2k}(x)f^{(2k)}(x)\,dx = - \Big[f_{2k+1}(x)f^{(2k)}(x)\Big]_0^n + \int_0^n f_{2k+1}(x)f^{(2k+1)}(x)\,dx$$

and the first term on the right vanishes. $\Big)$

If $\lim\limits_{k\to\infty} P_k = 0$, then the sum on the left-hand side has been transformed into the infinite series on the right-hand side. It turns out that for almost all the functions which occur in applications the series on the right diverges as $k \to \infty$. The reason for this is that the Bernoulli numbers increase very rapidly.

If the series $\sum_{x=0}^{\infty} f(x)$ is convergent, $f(x)$ and $f^{(k)}(x)$, $k = 1, 2, 3, \ldots, p$, tend to zero as $x = n$ and $n \to \infty$, Euler's summation formula takes the form

$$(5)\qquad \sum_{x=0}^{\infty} f(x) = \int_0^{\infty} f(x)\,dx + \frac{1}{2}f(0) - \frac{\beta_2}{2!}f'(0) - \frac{\beta_4}{4!}f'''(0) - \cdots$$

$$- \frac{\beta_{2k}}{(2k)!}f^{(2k-1)}(0) + P_k\ ,$$

where

$$P_k = \int_0^\infty f_{2k+1}(x) f^{(2k+1)}(x)\, dx\ .$$

If formula (5) is applied to the remainder R_k, then

$$R_k = \sum_{x=k+1}^\infty f(x) = \int_{k+1}^\infty f(x)\, dx + \frac{1}{2} f(k+1) - \frac{\beta_2}{2!} f'(k+1)$$

$$- \frac{\beta_4}{4!} f'''(k+1) - \cdots - \frac{\beta_{2\mu}}{(2\mu)!} f^{(2\mu-1)}(k+1) + P_{k,R}\ ,$$

where

$$P_{k,R} = \int_{k+1}^\infty f_{2\mu+1}(x) f^{(2\mu+1)}(x)\, dx\ .$$

Using $P_{k,R}$ to obtain the upper and lower estimate of the remainder R_k, we proceed exactly as in Chapter 3, Example 17. This leads to the following theorem.

8.13-1 Theorem. If $S = \sum_{x=0}^\infty f(x)$ is a convergent series where $f(x)$, defined for $x \geq 0$, is $2\mu + 1$ times continuously differentiable, then the error $P_{k,R}$ of the approximation

(6)
$$S \approx S_k + \int_{k+1}^\infty f(x)\, dx + \frac{1}{2} f(k+1) - \frac{\beta_2}{2!} f'(k+1)$$

$$- \frac{\beta_4}{4!} f'''(k+1) - \cdots - \frac{\beta_{2\mu}}{(2\mu)!} f^{(2\mu-1)}(k+1)$$

is given by

$$P_{k,R} = \int_{k+1}^\infty f_{2\mu+1}(x) f^{(2\mu+1)}(x)\, dx\ .$$

If the improper integral converges absolutely, by (3) we have

(7)
$$|P_{k,R}| \leq \int_{k+1}^\infty |f_{2\mu+1}(x)||f^{(2\mu+1)}(x)|\, dx \leq \sum_{n=1}^\infty \frac{2}{(2\pi n)^{2\mu+1}} \int_{k+1}^\infty |f^{(2\mu+1)}(x)|\, dx$$

$$< \frac{2}{(2\pi)^{2\mu+1}} \sum_{n=1}^\infty \frac{1}{n^{2\mu}} \int_{k+1}^\infty |f^{(2\mu+1)}(x)|\, dx$$

$$= \frac{2}{(2\pi)^{2\mu+1}} \frac{|\beta_{2\mu}|(2\pi)^{2k}}{2(2\mu)!} \int_{k+1}^\infty |f^{(2\mu+1)}(x)|\, dx$$

$$= \frac{|\beta_{2\mu}|}{2\pi(2\mu)!} \int_{k+1}^\infty |f^{(2\mu+1)}(x)|\, dx\ .$$

This is an estimate of the error of the approximation (6).

Example 24. Approximate $S = \sum_{n=1}^{\infty} 1/n^2$.
For $f(x) = 1/(x + 1)^2$ and $\mu = 3$, (7) yields

$$|P_{k,R}| < \frac{7}{2\pi(42)(k+1)^8} \cdot$$

If we choose, say, $k = 4$, we obtain the approximation

$$S \approx 1 + \frac{1}{2^2} + \frac{1}{3^2} + \frac{1}{4^2} + \frac{1}{5} + \frac{1}{2}\frac{1}{5^2} + \frac{1}{6}\frac{1}{5^3} - \frac{1}{30}\frac{1}{5^5} + \frac{1}{42}\frac{1}{5^7}$$

with an error $|P_{4,R}| < 7/2\pi(42)5^8 < 10^{-7}$.

For more refined scientific needs one can increase the accuracy considerably by putting $k = 9$ and $\mu = 4$, that is, adding 9 terms of the series and 6 additional terms. In this case, (6) and (7) yield

$$S \approx S_9 + \frac{1}{10} + \frac{1}{2}\frac{1}{10^2} + \frac{1}{6}\frac{1}{10^3} - \frac{1}{30}\frac{1}{10^5} + \frac{1}{42}\frac{1}{10^7} - \frac{1}{30}\frac{1}{10^9}$$

with an error less than 10^{-11}. If the three terms $\beta_{10}10^{-11} + \beta_{12}10^{-13} + \beta_{14}10^{-15}$ were added to the displayed series, the sum would have an error less than 10^{-16}, giving $\pi^2/6 = 1.644\,934\,066\,848\,232\,3\ldots$ [by (3), $\sum_{n=1}^{\infty} 1/n^2 = \pi^2/6$]. Incidentally, the latter approximation shows that greater accuracy does not necessarily require more effort if a suitable k yields easily calculated terms.

Recall that an approximation to six decimal places by standard method requires addition of 10^6 terms, the method of upper and lower estimates of the remainder based on Cauchy's integral requires addition of 10^3 terms (see Chapter 3, Example 17), whereas the approximation (6) requires addition of 9 terms with an error less than 10^{-7}.

Example 25. Obtain an estimate of the divergent sum

$$S_{n+1} = 1 + \frac{1}{2} + \frac{1}{3} + \cdots + \frac{1}{n+1}$$

as n increases.

Solution. Putting $f(x) = 1/(1 + x)$ in (4) and choosing $\mu = 3$ we obtain

$$S_{n+1} = 1 + \frac{1}{2} + \frac{1}{3} + \cdots + \frac{1}{n+1} = \ln(n+1) + \frac{1}{2}\left[\frac{1}{n+1} + 1\right]$$
$$+ \frac{\beta_2}{2}\left[1 - \frac{1}{(n+1)^2}\right] + \frac{\beta_4}{4}\left[1 - \frac{1}{(n+1)^4}\right] + \frac{\beta_6}{6}\left[1 - \frac{1}{(n+1)^6}\right]$$
$$- 7!\int_0^n f_7(x)\frac{dx}{(1+x)^8} \cdot$$

Hence,

$$\lim_{n \to \infty} [S_{n+1} - \ln(n+1)] = \gamma = \frac{1}{2} + \frac{\beta_2}{2} + \frac{\beta_4}{4} + \frac{\beta_6}{6} - 7! \int_0^\infty f_7(x) \frac{dx}{(1+x)^8} .$$

This shows that the partial sum S_{n+1} of the harmonic series increases as $\ln(n+1)$ in such a way that their difference approaches a constant γ, the so-called Euler's constant, which can be evaluated by the formula

$$\gamma = \frac{1}{2} + \frac{1}{12} - \frac{1}{120} + \frac{1}{252} - 7! \int_0^\infty f_7(x) \frac{dx}{(1+x)^8} .$$

To approximate the integral we proceed as follows. By (7) we obtain as an estimate

$$7! \int_3^\infty f_7(x) \frac{dx}{(1+x)^8} < \frac{|\beta_6| 7!}{2\pi (6!) 7 (4^7)} = \frac{|\beta_6|}{2\pi \cdot 4^7} = \frac{1}{2\pi \cdot 42 \cdot 4^7} < 10^{-6} .$$

Consequently,

$$\gamma = \frac{1459}{2520} - 7! \int_0^\infty f_7(x) \frac{dx}{(1+x)^8} + \frac{\delta}{10^6} , \quad \text{where} \quad |\delta| < 1 .$$

To evaluate the integral we use (4) putting $n = 3$, $k = 3$:

$$1 + \frac{1}{2} + \frac{1}{3} + \frac{1}{4} = \log 4 + \frac{1459}{2520} + \frac{1}{2} \frac{1}{4} - \frac{1}{12} \frac{1}{4^2} + \frac{1}{120} \frac{1}{4^4} - \frac{1}{252} \frac{1}{4^6}$$
$$- 7! \int_0^3 f_7(x) \frac{dx}{(1+x)^8} .$$

If the value of the integral obtained from this last relation is substituted in the formula for γ, we have

$$\gamma \approx 1 + \frac{1}{2} + \frac{1}{3} + \frac{1}{4} - \ln 4 - \frac{1}{2} \frac{1}{4} + \frac{1}{12} \frac{1}{4^2} - \frac{1}{120} \frac{1}{4^4} + \frac{1}{252} \frac{1}{4^6}$$
$$= 0.57721\ldots$$

correct to at least 5 decimal places. We assume here that the natural logarithm of 4 is known. Otherwise it can be easily calculated by adding some additional terms (see Chapter 6, Example 7).

Example 26. For $f(x) = \log x$ theorem **4.6-1** yields

$$\ln n! = \left(n + \frac{1}{2}\right) \ln n - (n-1) + \int_1^n f(x) \frac{dx}{x} .$$

Integration by parts

$$\int_1^n f_1(x)\frac{dx}{x} = \left[\frac{f_2(x)}{x}\right]_1^n + \int_1^n \frac{f_2(x)}{x^2}\,dx$$

shows that the integral converges as $n \to \infty$ (see 8.13). Consequently, we may write

$$\ln n! = \left(n + \frac{1}{2}\right)\ln n - n + \gamma_n$$

where $\gamma_n = 1 + \int_1^n f_1(x)(dx/x)$ and $\lim_{n\to\infty}\gamma_n = \gamma$ exist.

To evaluate γ we proceed as follows:
If the equalities

$$2\ln(2^n n!) = 2n\ln 2 + 2\ln n! = 2n\ln 2 + 2\left[\left(n + \frac{1}{2}\right)\ln n - n + \gamma_n\right],$$

$$\ln(2n+1)! = \left(2n + \frac{3}{2}\right)\ln(2n+1) - (2n+1) + \gamma_{2n+1},$$

are subtracted and $\frac{1}{2}\log(2n+1)$ is added to both sides, easy calculation yields

$$\ln\frac{2\cdot 4\cdot 6\cdots 2n}{1\cdot 3\cdot 5\cdots(2n-1)}\frac{1}{(2n+1)^{1/2}} = (2n+1)\ln\left(1 - \frac{1}{2n+1}\right)$$
$$+ 1 - \ln 2 + 2\gamma_n - \gamma_{2n+1}.$$

Hence, as $n \to \infty$

$$\ln\left(\frac{\pi}{2}\right)^{1/2} = -1 + 1 - \ln 2 + \gamma$$

or

$$\gamma = \frac{1}{2}\ln 2\pi.$$

Note that Wallis' product has been used (8.12, Example 23). (The limit of $(2n+1)\ln[1 - 1/(2n+1)]$ is easily found if the series of $\ln(1+x)$ for $x = -1/(2n+1)$ is used, Chapter 6, Example 9.)

Thus we obtained the remarkable result

$$\lim_{n\to\infty}\ln\frac{n!}{(n/e)^n n^{1/2}} = \lim_{n\to\infty}\gamma_n = \frac{1}{2}\ln 2\pi$$

or

$$\lim_{n\to\infty}\frac{n!}{(n/e)^n(2\pi n)^{1/2}} = 1,$$

known as Stirling's formula.

In words, the expressions $n!$ and $(n/e)^n(2\pi n)^{1/2}$ differ only by a small percentage when n is large, and we say that the two expressions are asymptotically equal.

The formula is useful in many applications, especially in statistics and in the theory of probability.

If we note that

$$\lim_{n \to \infty} \gamma_n = \gamma = 1 + \int_1^\infty f_1(x) \frac{dx}{x} \,,$$

Stirling's formula may be written in the form

$$\ln n! = \left(n + \frac{1}{2}\right) \ln n - n + \gamma - \int_n^\infty f_1(x) \frac{dx}{x}$$

where the integral gives us an estimate of the degree of accuracy of the approximation.

8.14 Remark

If $f(x)$ is positive and possesses continuous derivatives tending monotonically to 0, as $x \to \infty$, one can easily obtain a more accurate estimate of the error of the approximation (6). Note first, that all derivatives $f^{(2\mu+1)}(x)$, $\mu = 0, 1, 2, \ldots$, are negative; secondly, the Bernoulli numbers have alternating signs. If $|P_{k,R}|$ in (7) is less than

$$\left| \frac{\beta_{2\mu}}{(2\mu)!} f^{(2\mu-1)}(k+1) \right| \,,$$

then (6), from the fourth term on, is a finite alternating series and the error is less than the first term omitted, that is, is less than

$$\left| \frac{\beta_{2\mu+2}}{(2\mu+2)!} f^{(2\mu+1)}(k+1) \right| .$$

Exercises 8.J

1. Abel's series

$$S = \sum_{n=1}^\infty \frac{1}{(n+1)[\ln(n+1)]^2}$$

converges more slowly than the series $\sum_{n=1}^\infty 1/n^2$. Obtain an estimate of the error of the approximation when $\mu = 3$ and $k = 8$. How many terms are to be added so that the error of the approximation is less than 10^{-7}?

2. Approximate the series

$$\sum_{n=1}^{\infty} \frac{1}{n^2}$$

correct to six decimals.

3. Approximate the alternating series

$$\sum_{n=1}^{\infty} \frac{(-1)^{n-1}}{n}$$

correct to six or more decimal places. [Hint: Apply (6) to the series $\sum_{n=1}^{\infty} 1/(2n-1)2n = \sum_{n=1}^{\infty} (-1)^{n-1}/n.$]

4. How many terms are to be added if the error of the approximation of the series

$$\sum_{n=2}^{\infty} \frac{1}{n (\ln n)^3}$$

is to be less than 10^{-8}?

5. Show that

$$\ln 1 + \ln 2 + \cdots + \ln n = \ln n! = (n + \tfrac{1}{2}) \ln n - n + \delta_n$$

where δ_n is a function of n. Prove that $\lim_{n \to \infty} \delta_n = \delta$ exists and estimate δ_{20}. [Hint: Put $f(x) = \ln (1 + x)$ in (4).]

APPENDIX:

ANSWERS AND HINTS TO ODD-NUMBERED EXERCISES

Exercises 1.A

3. Hint: Consider $[(x + y)/2] - x$ and $y - [(x + y)/2]$.

5. (a) $x > -\dfrac{9}{7}$; (b) $-4 < x < 4$; (c) $x \geq -\dfrac{3}{2} + \dfrac{1}{2}5^{1/2}$ or $x \leq -\dfrac{3}{2} - \dfrac{1}{2}$

$5^{1/2}$; in set notation $S_1 \cup S_2$, $S_1 = \left\{x \middle| x \geq -\dfrac{3}{2} + \dfrac{1}{2}5^{1/2}\right\}$, $S_2 = \left\{x \middle| x \right.$

$\left. \leq -\dfrac{3}{2} - \dfrac{1}{2}5^{1/2}\right\}$; (d) $x > 0$; (e) $x < 0$; (f) all x.

7. (a) 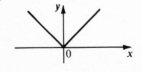   (b)

   (c)   (d)

   (e)   (f)

   (g)   (h) The whole x-axis.

   (i)

9. $S_1 = \left\{x \middle| -1 \leq x \leq \dfrac{11}{3}\right\}$, $S_2 = \left\{x \middle| -\dfrac{1}{5} < x < 1\right\}$; Solution $S = S_1 \cap S_2$,

   $S = \left\{x \middle| -\dfrac{1}{5} < x < 1\right\}$.

11. $a = \pm b$

13. (a)   (b)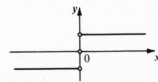

(c)

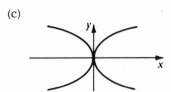

(d)

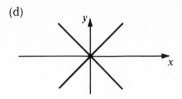

(e)

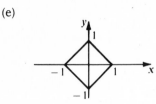

(f) Inside of graph *e*.

15. $|x + y - (a + b)| < \dfrac{5}{6}$, $|x - y - (a - b)| < \dfrac{5}{6}$; $-2 < xy - ab < \dfrac{7}{3}$.

17. Hint: Consider $(ab)^{1/2} - 2ab/(a + b)$.

19. Hint: Consider $x/y + y/x - 2$.

Exercises 2.A

1. (a) 1; (b) $\frac{1}{3}$; (c) 0; (d) ∞; (e) 1; (f) no limit; (g) $\frac{3}{4}$; (h) 0; (i) $0.69\ldots$.

3. $|a_n - 1| \leq \dfrac{1}{31}$; 5. $n_0 \geq 10^6$; 7. 0; 9. $\dfrac{a_0}{b_0}$; 11. $a_n = \dfrac{a + b + (ab/n)}{[(1 + (a/n))(1 + (b/n))]^{1/2}}$

$\rightarrow \dfrac{a + b}{2}$; 13. 1; 15. a; 17. 1; 19. $\dfrac{1}{c}$; 21. 0; 23. $\dfrac{3}{4}$; 25. 0; 27. $\dfrac{13}{30}$;

29. no limit; 31. 0; 33. $\dfrac{4}{3}$; 35. ∞; 37. $a_n = \dfrac{10^{10}}{10!} \dfrac{10}{11} \dfrac{11}{12} \cdots \dfrac{10}{n - 1} \dfrac{10}{n}$,

$0 < a_n < \dfrac{10^{10}}{10!} \dfrac{10}{n} \rightarrow 0$ as $n \rightarrow \infty$.

Exercises 2.B

1. (a) $a_{n+k} - a_n = \dfrac{1}{(n + 1)^2} + \dfrac{1}{(n + 2)^2} + \cdots + \dfrac{1}{(n + k)^2}$

$< \dfrac{1}{n(n + 1)} + \dfrac{1}{(n + 1)(n + 2)} + \cdots + \dfrac{1}{(n + k - 1)(n + k)}$

$= \dfrac{1}{n} - \dfrac{1}{n + k}$.

$|a_{n+k} - a_n| < 1/n$ and $|a_{n+k} - a| < \varepsilon$ for $n > n_0 = [1/\varepsilon]$, $k = 1, 2, 3, \ldots$.

(b) $a_n = \frac{1}{2}[(n + 1)/n]$, calculate $|a_{n+k} - a_n|$ and proceed as in case (a).

(c) $|a_{n+k} - a_n| \leq \dfrac{1}{(n + 2)!} + \dfrac{1}{(n + 3)!} + \cdots + \dfrac{1}{(n + k - 1)!}$, continue

as in the examples in § 2.2.

(d) See exercise (b).

7. Hint: Show that $a_{n+1} - a_n > 0$ and $a_n \leq M$.

9. Hint: To obtain the limit write $a_3 = a_2^{1/2} a_1^{1/2}$, then $a_4 = a_3^{1/2} a_2^{1/2} = a_2^{1/4} a_1^{1/4} a_2^{1/2} = a_2^{(1/2 + 1/2^2)} a_1^{1/4}$, and so on.

11. Hint: Show the existence of the limit, then pass to the limit in the relation.

13. Hint: Take logarithm and use **2.6-3**.

Exercises 2.C

1. $\lim\limits_{n \to \infty} a_n = \lim\limits_{n \to \infty} h \sum\limits_{\mu=1}^{n} \dfrac{1}{(1 + \mu h)^2} = \displaystyle\int_0^1 \dfrac{dx}{(1 + x)^2} = \dfrac{1}{2} \quad \left(h = \dfrac{1}{n} \right).$

3. $\lim\limits_{n \to \infty} a_n = \lim\limits_{n \to \infty} h \sum\limits_{\mu=1}^{n} \sec^2 \left(\dfrac{\pi}{4} \mu h \right) = \displaystyle\int_0^1 \sec^2 \left(\dfrac{\pi}{4} x \right) dx = \dfrac{4}{\pi} \quad \left(h = \dfrac{1}{n} \right).$

5. $\log_e (1 + p)$. Hint: Use Example 20, § 2.8.

7. $\lim\limits_{n \to \infty} a_n = \lim\limits_{n \to \infty} h \sum\limits_{\mu=1}^{n} \dfrac{1}{1 + (\mu h)^2} = \displaystyle\int_0^1 \dfrac{dx}{1 + x^2} = \dfrac{\pi}{4} \quad \left(h = \dfrac{1}{n} \right).$

9. $\frac{1}{2}$. Hint: Use method of Example 3, § 2.8.

11. $\log_e (1 + p)$. Hint: Use method of Example 20, § 2.8.

Exercises 3.A

1. $S_n = \dfrac{1}{2} \sum\limits_{k=1}^{n} \left(\dfrac{1}{k} - \dfrac{1}{k + 2} \right) = \dfrac{1}{2} \left(1 + \dfrac{1}{2} - \dfrac{1}{n + 1} - \dfrac{1}{n + 2} \right) \to \dfrac{3}{4}$;

3. $S_n = \sum\limits_{k=1}^{n} \left(\dfrac{1}{k^2} - \dfrac{1}{(k + 1)^2} \right) = 1 - \dfrac{1}{(n + 2)^2} \to 1$.

5. $S_n = \dfrac{1}{2} \sum\limits_{k=1}^{n} \left[\dfrac{1}{k(k + 1)} - \dfrac{1}{(k + 1)(k + 2)} \right] = \dfrac{1}{2} \left(\dfrac{1}{2} - \dfrac{1}{(n + 1)(n + 2)} \right) \to \dfrac{1}{4}$;

7. no limit ; 9. $\dfrac{1}{5}$; 11. $\sum\limits_{n=1}^{\infty} \dfrac{1}{(2n - 1)(2n + 1)} = \dfrac{1}{2}$;

13. $\sum\limits_{n=1}^{\infty} \dfrac{2n - 1}{(n^2 + 1)(n^2 - 2n + 2)} = 1$;

15. $\log 2 + \sum\limits_{n=1}^{\infty} \left[\log \left(1 + \dfrac{1}{n + 1} \right) - \log \left(1 + \dfrac{1}{n} \right) \right]$;   17. div. ;   19. div. ;

21. $\sum\limits_{n=1}^{\infty} a_n < \sum\limits_{n=1}^{\infty} \dfrac{1}{2^{n-1}} = 2$;   23. $\sum\limits_{n=1}^{\infty} a_n < \sum\limits_{n=1}^{\infty} \dfrac{1}{2^{n-1}} = 2$;   25. $\sum\limits_{n=2}^{\infty} a_n < \sum\limits_{n=1}^{\infty} \dfrac{1}{n^2}$,

conv. ;   27. $\sum\limits_{n=1}^{\infty} a_n < \sum\limits_{n=1}^{\infty} \dfrac{1}{n^2}$, conv.;   29. conv.;   31. div.;   33. conv.;

35. conv.;   37. conv.;   39. conv.;   41. conv.;   43. conv.;   45. div.;

47. div.;   49. con.;   51. conv.;   53. div.;   55. $S \approx \sum\limits_{k=1}^{9} \dfrac{1}{k^4} + \dfrac{1}{3} \dfrac{1}{10^3}$

$= 1.0823...$;   57. 15 terms; error $< f(n + 1) = \dfrac{1}{(n + 1)|\log (n + 1)|^2} < 10^{-2}$

for $n \geq 15$;   59. div.;   61. conv.;   63. div.;   65. conv.;   67. conv.; 69. conv.;   71. div.;   73. conv.;   75. conv.;   77. conv.;   79. conv.; 81. conv.;   83. div.;   85. conv.;   87. conv. if $\beta - \alpha > 1$ and div. if $\beta - \alpha \leq 1$.   89. Hint: $(d - \varepsilon)/n < a_n < (d + \varepsilon)/n$.   91. Hint: Use Cauchy-Schwarz inequality.   93. Hint: Use $(pq)^{1/2} \leq \frac{1}{2}(p + q)$.   95. Hint: Use Cauchy-Schwarz inequality.   97. Hint: Use $\lim_{n\to\infty} (b_1 + b_2 + \cdots + b_n)/n = \lim_{n\to\infty} b_n$.

Exercises 4.A

1. conv.;   3. conv.;   5. conv.;   7. conv.;   9. conv.;   11. conv.;   13. conv.;   15. $S \approx \dfrac{1}{2!} - \dfrac{1}{3!} + \dfrac{1}{4!} - \dfrac{1}{5!} + \dfrac{1}{6!} - \dfrac{1}{7!}$;   17. $S \approx \sum_{n=1}^{11} \dfrac{1}{(2n-1)^3}$; 19. abs. conv.;   21. abs. conv.;   23. abs. conv.;   25. cond. conv.; 31. $S_n = \sum_{k=1}^{n} (-1)^{k-1}\left(\dfrac{1}{k} + \dfrac{1}{k+1}\right) = 1 - \dfrac{(-1)^n}{n+1} \to 1$.   35. Hint: First by method of Example 15 show that $\cos x + \cos 2x + \cdots + \cos nx = [\sin(nx/2)\cos(n+1)(x/2)]/\sin x/2$ is bounded if $|\sin x/2| \geq \delta > 0$, and then apply Dirichlet's test.

Exercises 5.A

1. $f(x) = 1$, $|x| < 1$
     $= \frac{1}{2}$, $|x| = 1$
     $= 0$, $|x| > 1$.

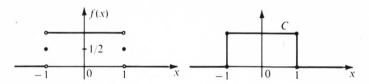

C is not the graph of $f(x)$.

3. $f(x) = 1$, $x \neq 0$, $|x| \leq 1$
     $= 0$, $x = 0$.

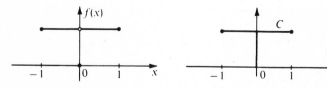

C is not the graph of $f(x)$.

5. $f(x) = 1$, $0 \le x \le b$.

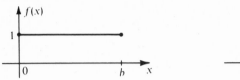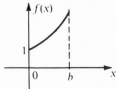

C is the graph of $f(x)$.

7. Note that $f_n(x) = \left(1 + \dfrac{x}{n}\right)^n = \left[\left(1 + \dfrac{1}{m}\right)^m\right]^x$, $m = \dfrac{n}{x}$, for a fixed x is a monotonically increasing sequence bounded by e^x (see 1.2). $f(x) = e^x$, $0 \le x \le b$. The graphs of $f(x)$ and C coincide.

9. $f(x) = x$, $x \ne 0$; $f(x) = 1$, $x = 0$, $\{f(x)\}$ is not uniformly convergent on $T = [0, 1]$. However, on $T' = [a, 1]$, $a > 0$ it converges uniformly.

$$\int_0^1 f_n(x)\,dx = \frac{1}{2} - \frac{1}{n} + \frac{\log(n+1)}{n} \text{ and } \lim_{n \to \infty} \int_0^1 f_n(x)\,dx = \frac{1}{2} = \int_0^1 f(x)\,dx,$$

$$\lim_{n \to \infty} f_n'(x) = \lim_{n \to \infty}\left[1 - \frac{n+1}{(nx+1)^2}\right] = 1, \quad x \ne 0,$$

$$= -\infty, \quad x = 0,$$

$\lim_{n \to \infty} f_n'(x) \ne f'(x)$ on T but $\lim_{n \to \infty} f_n'(x) = f'(x)$ on T'.

11. $f(x) = 0$ on $T = [0, 1]$, since $f_n(0) = f(1) = 0$, $\lim_{n \to \infty} f_n(x) = 0$ on $0 < x < 1$.

For $x = 1/n$ [or for $x = 1/(2n+1)^{1/2}$ for which $f_n(x)$ has a maximum] the inequality $|0 - nx(1 - x^2)^n| = [1 - (1/n^2)]^n < \varepsilon$ does not hold for all $n > n_0$ if $\varepsilon < 1$. This proves that the sequence does not converge uniformly on T.

$$\int_0^1 f_n(x) = \frac{n}{2(n+1)} \to \frac{1}{2} \ne \int_0^1 f(x)\,dx = 0, \quad f'(x) = 0 \ne \lim_{n \to \infty} f_n'(x) \text{ on } T.$$

13. Note that $f_n[(2n)^{-1/2}] = (2ne)^{-1/2}$ is the maximum of $f_n(x)$ on T. Since $f(x) = 0$, $|0 - f_n(x)| \le (2ne)^{-1/2} < \varepsilon$ for $n > n_0$, and $\{f_n(x)\}$ converges uniformly. Consequently

$$\int_0^x f(t)\,dt = 0 = \lim_{n \to \infty} \int_0^x f_n(t)\,dt, \quad f_n'(x) = 1, \quad x = 0,$$

$$= 0, \quad x \ne 0, \quad \lim_{n \to \infty} f_n'(x) \ne f'(x) \text{ on } T.$$

15. Since the series as well as the term by term differentiated series converge uniformly, differentiation and integration are permissible.

17. Since the series converges uniformly, it may be integrated termwise. It is not differentiable, since the differentiated series diverges.

19. The series does not converge uniformly on $T = (-1, 1)$ and it is not integrable and differentiable on T.

21. At the points $x = 2k\pi$ ($k = 0, \pm 1, \pm 2, \ldots$) the series diverges. It

is not differentiable on T. However, on $\varepsilon \leq x \leq 2\pi - \varepsilon$

$$\lim_{\varepsilon \to 0+} \int_\varepsilon^x f(x)\, dx = \sum_{n=1}^\infty \lim_{\varepsilon \to 0+} \int_\varepsilon^x \frac{\cos nx}{n^\alpha} = \sum_{n=1}^\infty \frac{\sin nx}{n^{\alpha+1}}$$

holds, that is, $f(x)$ is integrable by definition of improper integrals (see Chapter 8).

23. The series and the termwise differentiated series $-\sum_{n=1}^\infty (\log n)/n^x$ converge uniformly on any interval $1 < a \leq x$. However, on $T = (1, \infty)$ both series are not uniformly convergent. The series is not integrable and not differentiable on T.

Exercises 6.A

1. $r = 1$, $(-1, 1)$;   3. $r = 1$, $[-1, 1)$;   5. $r = \frac{1}{2}$, $(-\frac{1}{2}, \frac{1}{2})$;   7. $r = \infty$, $(-\infty, \infty)$;   9. $r = 1$, $[-1, 1)$;   11. $r = 4$, $(-4, 4)$;   13. $r = 1$, $(-1, 1)$; 15. $r = 1$, $(-1, 1)$;   17. $r = 1$, $[-1, 1)$;   19. $r = 1$, $[-1, 1]$.

Exercises 6.B

1. (a) $x^6 = [3 + (x - 3)]^6 = 3^6 + \binom{6}{1}3^5(x - 3) + \binom{6}{2}3^4(x - 3)^2 + \cdots + (x - 3)^6$.

(b) $x^6 = [-3 + (x + 3)]^6 = (-3)^6 + \binom{6}{1}(-3)^5(x + 3) + \binom{6}{2}(-3)^4(x + 3)^2 + \cdots + (x + 3)^6$.

(c) x^6.

(d) a) $R_3(x) = [(x - 3)^4/4!]f^{(4)}(\rho) = 15(x - 3)^4\rho^2$, $3 \leq \rho \leq x$.

b) $R_3(x) = [(x + 3)^4/4!]f^{(4)}(\rho) = 15(x + 3)^4\rho^2$, $-3 \leq \rho \leq x$.

$R_7(x) = 0$ in cases a) and b).

3. $e^x = e^a\left(1 + \dfrac{x - a}{1!} + \dfrac{(x - a)^2}{2!} + \cdots + \dfrac{(x - a)^n}{n!} + \cdots\right)$,

$R_n(x) = \dfrac{(x - a)^{n+1}}{(n + 1)!}e^\rho$, $a \leq \rho \leq x$.

5. (a) $|R_n(x)| = \left|\dfrac{x^{n+1}}{(n + 1)!}\sin\left[\rho + (n + 1)\dfrac{\pi}{2}\right]\right| \leq \dfrac{1}{(n + 1)!} < 10^{-6}$ for $n \geq 9$.

$\sin x \approx x - \dfrac{x^3}{3!} + \dfrac{x^5}{5!} - \dfrac{x^7}{7!} + \dfrac{x^9}{9!}$.

(b) $|R_n(x)| = \dfrac{x^{n+1}}{(x + 1)(1 + \rho)^{n+1}} \leq \dfrac{1}{(n + 1)2^{n+1}} < 10^{-6}$ for $n \geq 12$.

$\log(1 + x) \approx x - \dfrac{1}{2}x^2 + \dfrac{1}{3}x^3 - \cdots - \dfrac{x^{12}}{12}$.

7. $(e^x)^{1/2} = 1 + \dfrac{x}{2} + \dfrac{1}{2!}\left(\dfrac{x}{2}\right)^2 + \cdots + \dfrac{1}{n!}\left(\dfrac{x}{2}\right)^n + \cdots$, $(-\infty, \infty)$.

9. $(1 - x^4)^{1/2} = 1 + \dfrac{1}{2}(-x^4) + \dbinom{1/2}{2}(-x^4)^2 + \cdots + \dbinom{1/2}{2}(-x^4)^n + \cdots$,

$[-1, 1]$ (Raabe's test).

11. $\dfrac{x}{(x^2 - 1)(x + 2)} = \dfrac{1}{6}\,\dfrac{1}{x - 1} + \dfrac{1}{2}\,\dfrac{1}{x + 1} - \dfrac{2}{3}\,\dfrac{1}{x + 2} = -\dfrac{1}{6}\displaystyle\sum_{n=0}^{\infty} x^n$

$\qquad\qquad + \dfrac{1}{2}\displaystyle\sum_{n=0}^{\infty}(-1)^n x^n - \dfrac{1}{3}\displaystyle\sum_{n=0}^{\infty}(-1)^n\left(\dfrac{x}{2}\right)^n$

$\qquad\qquad = \displaystyle\sum_{n=0}^{\infty}\left[-\dfrac{1}{6} + \dfrac{1}{2}(-1)^n - \dfrac{1}{3}\dfrac{(-1)^n}{2^n}\right]x^n$.

13. $\sin^2 x = \dfrac{1}{2}(1 - \cos 2x) = \dfrac{1}{2} - \dfrac{1}{2}\cos 2x = \dfrac{1}{2} - \dfrac{1}{2}\displaystyle\sum_{n=0}^{\infty}(-1)^n\dfrac{(2x)^{2n}}{(2n)!}$.

15. Hint: Multiply the series of $\arctan x$ (Chapter 6, Example 13) and the series of $\log(1 + x)$ (Chapter 6, Example 9).

17. **5.7-5** does not apply to the rearranged series, since it is not a power series. (The powers of x in a power series are steadily increasing!)

Exercises 7.A

1. (a) neither;   (b) even;   (c) even;   (d) odd;   (e) even;   (f) odd;
   (g) even;   (h) even.

3. even;   5. odd;   7. neither.

9. $x = 2\left(\sin x - \dfrac{\sin 2x}{2} + \dfrac{\sin 3x}{3} - \cdots - (-1)^{n-1}\dfrac{\sin nx}{n} + \cdots\right)$.

11. $\dfrac{1}{2}\pi - x = \dfrac{1}{2}\pi - 2\left(\sin x - \dfrac{\sin 2x}{2} + \dfrac{\sin 3x}{3} - \cdots + (-1)^{n-1}\dfrac{\sin nx}{n}\right)$.

Note how Exercise 11 follows from 9.

Exercises 7.B

1. $\alpha_0 = 0$, $\alpha_\mu = 0$, $\beta_{2\mu} = 0$, $\beta_{2\mu-1} = \dfrac{4}{\pi}\,\dfrac{1}{2\mu - 1}$, $\mu = 1, 2, 3, \ldots$.

3. $a_\mu = \dfrac{2}{\pi}\displaystyle\int_0^\pi \sin \mu x\, dx$; $a_1 = \dfrac{4}{\pi}$, $a_2 = 0$, $a_3 = \dfrac{4\pi}{3}$.

5. Note that if $F(x)$ is integrable, so is $F(x)\cos(x/2)$ and $F(x)\sin(x/2)$. By Corollary 2 of **7.2-1**.

$$\lim_{n\to\infty}\int_{-\pi}^{\pi} F(x)\sin\left(n + \dfrac{1}{2}\right)x\, dx = \lim_{n\to\infty}\int_{-\pi}^{\pi} F(x)\cos\dfrac{x}{2}\sin nx\, dx$$

$$+ \lim_{n\to\infty}\int_{-\pi}^{\pi} F(x)\sin\dfrac{x}{2}\cos nx\, dx$$

$$= 0 + 0 = 0 .$$

APPENDIX: ANSWERS AND HINTS TO ODD-NUMBERED EXERCISES

Exercises 7.C

1. Hint: Multiply $f(x) = \frac{1}{2}a_0 + \sum_{n=1}^{\infty}\left[a_n\cos\frac{n\pi x}{l} + b_n\sin\frac{n\pi x}{l}\right]$ by $f(x)$ and integrate from $-l$ to l.

3. $x^2 = \frac{1}{3} - \frac{4}{\pi^2}\left[\cos\pi x - \frac{1}{2^2}\cos 2\pi x + \frac{1}{3^2}\cos 3\pi x + \cdots + \frac{(-1)^{n-1}}{n^2}\cos n\pi x + \cdots\right]$.

5. Define $f[(3k-1)\pi] = \pi^2$, $k = \pm 1, \pm 2, \cdots$. Then

$$f(x) = x + x^2 = \frac{\pi^2}{3} + 4\sum_{n=1}^{\infty}(-1)^n\frac{\cos nx}{n^2} + 2\sum_{n=1}^{\infty}(-1)^{n-1}\frac{\sin nx}{n}$$

for $x = \pi$ yields

$$\pi^2 = \frac{\pi^2}{3} + 4\sum_{n=1}^{\infty}\frac{1}{n^2}, \quad \text{whence} \quad \frac{\pi^2}{6} = \sum_{n=1}^{\infty}\frac{1}{n^2}.$$

Exercises 7.D

1. $\sum_{n=1}^{\infty}\frac{1}{n^6} = \frac{\pi^6}{945}$.

3. Termwise integration of the given series yields $\sum_{n=1}^{\infty}\frac{\sin nx}{n\log(1+n)}$, which does not converge absolutely and uniformly for all x. Consequently, by **7.6-1** the trigonometric series is not a Fourier series.

Exercises 7.E

1. Note that $f(x)$ is an even function. Then by §7.8 $f(x) = \frac{1}{\pi}\int_0^{\infty}A(s)\cos sx\,ds$, where $A(s) = 2\int_0^{\infty}f(t)\cos st\,dt = \frac{2(1-\cos s)}{s^2}$, Thus

$$f(x) = 1 - |x| = \frac{2}{\pi}\int_0^{\infty}\frac{1-\cos s}{s^2}\cos sx\,ds,$$

whence

$$\int_0^{\infty}\frac{1-\cos s}{s^2}\cos sx\,ds = \frac{\pi}{2}(1-|x|), \quad |x| \le 1,$$
$$= 0, \quad |x| > 1.$$

3. Hint: Use $f(x) = \frac{1}{\pi}\int_0^{\infty}[A(s)\cos sx + B(s)\sin sx]\,ds$, where

$$A(s) = \int_{-\infty}^{\infty}f(t)\cos st\,dt, \quad B(s) = \int_{-\infty}^{\infty}f(t)\sin st\,dt$$

(see §7.8).

5. $f(x) = \frac{2}{\pi}\int_0^{\infty}\frac{2\cos s - \cos 2s - 1}{s^2}\cos xs\,ds$.

205

Exercises 8.A

1. $f(x)$ is discontinuous at $x = 0$ and the integral does not exist.

3. $\lim\limits_{b \to \infty} \int_0^b \dfrac{dx}{(x^2 + 1)(x^2 + 4)} = \lim\limits_{b \to \infty} \left[\dfrac{1}{3} \arctan b - \dfrac{1}{6} \arctan \dfrac{b}{2} \right] = \dfrac{\pi}{12}$.

5. $\displaystyle\int_{-\infty}^{\infty} \dfrac{x^4 dx}{(x^2 + 1)^2(x^2 + 4)} = 2 \int_0^{\infty} \dfrac{x^4 dx}{(x^2 + 1)^2(x^2 + 4)} = 2 \lim\limits_{b \to \infty} \int_0^b \dfrac{x^4 dx}{(x^2 + 1)^2(x^2 + 4)}$

$\qquad\qquad = 2 \lim\limits_{b \to \infty} \left[\dfrac{1}{6} \dfrac{b}{b^2 + 1} - \dfrac{11}{18} \arctan b + \dfrac{8}{9} \arctan \dfrac{b}{2} \right]$

$\qquad\qquad = \dfrac{5\pi}{18}$.

7. $\lim\limits_{c \to \infty} \displaystyle\int_0^c e^{-ax} \cos bx \, dx = \lim\limits_{c \to \infty} \left[\dfrac{e^{-ac}}{a^2 + b^2}(-a \cos bc + b \sin bc) + \dfrac{a}{a^2 + b^2} \right] = \dfrac{a}{a^2 + b^2}$.

9. Put $e^{x/3} = t$,

$\qquad \displaystyle\int_{-\infty}^{\infty} \dfrac{e^{x/3}}{1 + e^x} dx = \int_0^{\infty} \dfrac{dt}{1 + t^3} = \lim\limits_{b \to \infty} \int_0^b \dfrac{dt}{1 + t^3}$

$\qquad\qquad = \lim\limits_{b \to \infty} \left[\log \dfrac{1 + t}{(1 + t + t^2)^{1/2}} + 3^{1/2} \arctan \dfrac{2t - 1}{3^{1/2}} \right]_0^b = \dfrac{2\pi}{3^{1/2}}$.

11. $\lim\limits_{b \to \infty} \displaystyle\int_2^b \dfrac{dx}{x(\log x)^k} = \lim\limits_{b \to \infty} \dfrac{(\log x)^{1-k}}{1 - k}$, $\quad k \neq 1]_2^b = \dfrac{(\log 2)^{1-k}}{k - 1}$, $\quad k > 1$,

$\qquad\qquad = \lim\limits_{b \to \infty} \log (\log x)$, $\quad k = 1]_2^b = \infty$, $\quad k \leq 1$.

13. Since $\lim\limits_{x \to \infty} x^2 f(x) = \frac{1}{2}$, the integral converges by the Corollary of **8.3-3**.

15. Since $\lim\limits_{x \to \infty} x^{3/2} f(x) = 1$, the integral converges by the Corollary of **8.3-3**.

17. Since $\lim\limits_{x \to \infty} x^{2-p} f(x) = 1$, the integral converges by the Corollary of **8.3-3**

for $0 < p < 1$.

19. Since $\lim\limits_{x \to \infty} x^2 f(x) = 0$, the integral converges by the Corollary of **8.3-3**.

Exercises 8.B

1. Hint: The proof follows the lines of Example 3.

3. cond. conv.;   5. cond. conv.;   7. cond. conv.;   9. cond. conv.;

11. abs. conv.

Exercises 8.C

1. div., since $\lim\limits_{\varepsilon \to 0+} \int_\varepsilon^{\pi/2} \cot x \, dx = \lim\limits_{\varepsilon \to 0+} [\log \sin x]_\varepsilon^{\pi/2} = -\infty$.

3. conv., since $\lim\limits_{\varepsilon \to 0+} \int_\varepsilon^1 \log x \, dx = \lim\limits_{\varepsilon \to 0+} [x(\log x - 1)]_\varepsilon^1 = -1$.

5. conv., since $\lim\limits_{\varepsilon \to 0+} \displaystyle\int_\varepsilon^1 x^3 \log x \, dx = \lim\limits_{\varepsilon \to 0+} \left[\dfrac{x^4}{4}\left(\log x - \dfrac{1}{4}\right) \right]_\varepsilon^1 = -\dfrac{1}{16}$.

7. conv., since $\int_0^1 \log \left(\dfrac{1}{1-x} \right) dx = \int_1^\infty \dfrac{\log t}{t^2} \, dt = \lim_{b \to \infty} \left[-\dfrac{1}{t} (\log t + 1) \right]_1^b = 1.$

Exercises 8.D

1. $\lim_{\varepsilon \to 0+} \int_\varepsilon^1 \dfrac{\log x}{x^{1/2}} \, dx = \lim_{\varepsilon \to 0+} [2(x)^{1/2} (\log x - 2)]_\varepsilon^1 = -4,$ or by Corollary of

   8.6-2 the integral converges, since $\lim_{x \to 0+} f(x) x^{3/4} = 0.$

3. conv., since $\int_0^1 \dfrac{\cos (1/x)}{x} \, dx = \int_1^\infty \dfrac{\cos t \, dt}{x} \ \left(t = \dfrac{1}{x} \right)$ converges by Corol-

   lary of **8.4-1**.

5. conv., since $\lim_{x \to 1-} \dfrac{(1-x)^p \log x}{1+x} = 0, \ 0 < p < 1$ and Corollary of **8.6-2**

   applies.

7. conv., since $\lim_{x \to 0+} x^p (\log \sin x) = 0, \ 0 < p < 1$ and Corollary of **8.6-2** is

   satisfied.

9. conv., since $\int_0^\pi \dfrac{dx}{(\sin x)^p} = \int_0^{\pi/2} \dfrac{dx}{(\sin x)^p} + \int_{\pi/2}^\pi \dfrac{dx}{(\sin x)^p}$ and $\lim_{x \to 0+} \dfrac{x^p}{(\sin x)^p} = 1,$

   $\lim_{x \to \pi} \dfrac{\pi - x}{\sin x} = 1, \ 0 < p < 1,$ thus Corollary of **8.6-2** is satisfied.

Exercises 8.E

1. Hint: See § 8.1 and 8.3.   3. div.

5. conv., since $\displaystyle\int_{-\infty}^\infty \dfrac{x \, dx}{e^x + x^4} = \int_{-\infty}^0 \dfrac{x \, dx}{e^x + x^4} + \int_0^\infty \dfrac{x \, dx}{e^x + x^4} = -\int_0^\infty \dfrac{t \, dt}{e^{-t} + t^4}$

   $+ \displaystyle\int_0^\infty \dfrac{x \, dx}{e^x + x^4} \ (x = -t)$ and $\lim_{t \to \infty} t^2 f(t) = \lim_{x \to \infty} x^2 f(x) = 0.$ Thus Corollary

   of **8.3-3** in satisfied for $p = 2 > 1.$

7. conv.;   9. conv.

11. conv. for $0 < a < 1,$ since $\displaystyle\int_0^\infty \dfrac{x^{a-1}}{1+x} \, dx = \int_0^1 \dfrac{x^{a-1}}{1+x} \, dx + \int_1^\infty \dfrac{x^{a-1}}{1+x} \, dx$

    and the first integral converges by Corollary of **8.6-2** for $a > 0,$ the
    second integral converges by Corollary of **8.3.3** for $a < 1.$

13. conv. for $a < 3,$ since $\int_0^\infty x^a \cos x^4 \, dx = \frac{1}{4} \int_0^\infty t^{(a-3)/4} \cos t \, dt \ (x = t^{1/4})$
    converges for $a < 3$ and diverges for $a \geq 3$ (Corollary of **8.4-1**).

15. conv. for $a \geq 0.$

Exercises 8.F

1. conv. unif., since $M(x) = 2/(1+x^2)$ exists (**8.10-2**).
3. conv. unif., since $M(x) = e^{-0.01x^2}$ exists (**8.10-2**).

5. conv. unif. by **8.10-4** $[f(x, y) = \sin x, \ g(x) = 1/x^y]$.
7. conv. unif. by **8.10-3**, where $M(x) = x^{-0.9}$.
9. conv. unif. by **8.10-4**.
11. conv. unif. by **8.10-4**.
13. conv. unif. by **8.10-4**.

Exercises 8.G

1. Hint: Integrate twice with respect to y under the integral sign from 0 to y.
3. Integration of $\int_0^\infty e^{-ax} \cos yx \, dx$ with respect to y from 0 to y yields

$$\int_0^\infty \frac{e^{-ax} \sin yx}{x} \, dx = \arctan \frac{y}{a} \ .$$

5. Hint: Integrate $\int_0^\infty e^{-x} \sin xy \, dx = y/(1 + y^2)$.

Exercises 8.H

1. $G(y) = \displaystyle\int_0^\infty \frac{1 - e^{-yx^2}}{x^2} \, dx$. $\dfrac{dG}{dy} = \displaystyle\int_0^\infty e^{-yx^2} \, dx = \dfrac{\pi^{1/2}}{2} y^{-1/2}$ (using the familiar probability integral). $G = \pi^{1/2} y^{1/2} + C$. Since $G = 0$ for $y = 0$, $C = 0$.
3. $\frac{1}{2} \log [(1 + b^2)/(1 + a^2)]$.
7. Hint: Show that $F'(\alpha) = -2F(\alpha)$. To determine the integration constant C use $\int_0^\infty e^{-x^2} \, dx = \frac{1}{2}\pi^{1/2}$.

Exercises 8.I

1. Hint: Put $\ln 1/x = t$.
3. (a) $\Gamma\left(\dfrac{3}{2}\right) = \dfrac{1}{2}\Gamma\left(\dfrac{1}{2}\right) = \dfrac{\pi^{1/2}}{2}$;   (b) $\Gamma\left(\dfrac{5}{2}\right) = \dfrac{3}{4}\pi^{1/2}$;   (c) $\displaystyle\int_0^\infty e^{-\alpha t} t^{1/2} \, dt$

$= \alpha^{-3/2}\Gamma\left(\dfrac{3}{2}\right) = \dfrac{\alpha^{-3/2}\pi^{1/2}}{2}$;   (d) $n!$;   (e) $\Gamma\left(n + \dfrac{1}{2}\right) = \dfrac{(2n)!}{4^n n!}\pi^{1/2}$.

7. Hint: Put $2y - 1 = 2n$, $m = 1/2$ in

$$\beta(y, m) = 2 \int_0^{\pi/2} \sin^{2y-1} t \cos^{2m-1} t \, dt = \frac{\Gamma(y)\Gamma(m)}{\Gamma(y + m)} \ .$$

9. Hint: Use Exercises 1 and 3(c).

Exercises 8.J

1. $S \approx S_8 + \dfrac{1}{\log 10} + \dfrac{1}{2}\dfrac{1}{10(\log 10)^2} - \dfrac{1}{12}f'(10) + \dfrac{1}{30}\dfrac{1}{4!}f'''(10) - \dfrac{1}{42}\dfrac{1}{6!}f^{(5)}(10)$,

error $< \dfrac{1}{42}\dfrac{1}{6}f^{(6)} < 10^{-7}$.

3. $S \approx 0.6931472\ldots$, error $< 10^{-7}$.

INDEX